S0-BSE-085

SETON HALL UNIVERSITY
PT1113.F7
The German classics of the ninet   MAIN

3 3073 00314101 5

Samuel B. Eno

VOLUME XVIII

GERHART HAUPTMANN

FERDINAND VON SAAR

DETLEV VON LILIENCRON

PRINCE EMIL VON SCHÖNAICH-CAROLATH

GUSTAV FALKE

ISOLDE KURZ

RICHARD DEHMEL

ARNO HOLZ

OTTO JULIUS BIERBAUM

STEFAN GEORGE

LULU VON STRAUSS UND TORNEY

BÖRRIES VON MÜNCHHAUSEN

RAINER MARIA RILKE

HERMANN HESSE

AGNES MIEGEL

RICARDA HUCH

PERMISSION E.A.SEEMANN, LEIPZIG

THE GERMAN CLASSICS

Masterpieces of German Literature

TRANSLATED INTO ENGLISH

𝔓𝔞𝔱𝔯𝔬𝔫𝔰' 𝔈𝔡𝔦𝔱𝔦𝔬𝔫

IN TWENTY VOLUMES

ILLUSTRATED

THE GERMAN PUBLICATION SOCIETY
NEW YORK

SETON HALL UNIVERSITY
McLAUGHLIN LIBRARY
SO. ORANGE, N. J.

Copyright 1914
by
THE GERMAN PUBLICATION SOCIETY

PT
1113
F7
V. 18
Cp. 2

SETON HALL UNIVERSITY
McLAUGHLIN LIBRARY
SO. ORANGE, N. J.

CONTRIBUTORS AND TRANSLATORS

VOLUME XVIII

Special Writers

LUDWIG LEWISOHN, A.M., Assistant Professor of the German Language and Literature, Ohio State University:
The Life of Gerhart Hauptmann.

PAUL H. GRUMMANN, A.M., Professor of Modern German Literature, University of Nebraska:
The Contemporary German Lyric.

FRIEDRICH SCHOENEMANN, Ph.D., Instructor in German, Harvard University:
Ricarda Huch.

Translators

LUDWIG LEWISOHN, A.M., Assistant Professor of the German Language and Literature, Ohio State University:
Michael Kramer.

CHARLES HENRY MELTZER:
The Sunken Bell.

MARY MORRISON:
The Weavers.

MURIEL ALMON:
The Recollections of Ludolf Ursleu the Younger.

CHARLES WHARTON STORK, Ph.D., Assistant Professor of English, University of Pennsylvania:
Flowrets; The New Railroad; The Goldfinch; The Big Merry-Go-Round; White Lilacs.

MARGARETE MÜNSTERBERG:
Girls Singing; War and Peace; Parting and Return; Oh Germany; A Day Spent; When I Die; Necropolis; Through the Night; From an Oppressed Heart; Wave Dance Song; Many a Night; Like One of These was He; Enough; The Shepherd's Day; The Seafarer; Ballad of the Wall; Fairy Tale; Two Poems to Hans Thoma on His Sixtieth Birthday; Maiden Melancholy; Talk in a Gondola; The Fair Agnete; Midnight, etc.

[v]

CONTENTS OF VOLUME XVIII

ILLUSTRATIONS — VOLUME XVIII

THE LIFE OF GERHART HAUPTMANN

By Ludwig Lewisohn, A.M.

Assistant Professor of the German Language and Literature, Ohio State University

I

FOR a number of years the literary physiognomy of Gerhart Hauptmann was felt, by critics and historians of literature, to be lacking in definiteness of outline. It is even now not uncommon to find Hauptmann described as one still in search of the final medium of self-expression. The rapidity, however, with which literary and philosophical movements follow one another in modern life, should enable us to see the work of Hauptmann in a truer light, an exacter perspective.

The fact is that the drama of Hauptmann, viewed in its totality, is remarkably representative of its epoch in the history of literature and thought. The frequent contrasts in his work between idealism and sheer realism are not due to personal vacillation, but rather to the uncontrollable *Zeitgeist* expressing itself through an exquisitely sensitive organism. Of the two special notes of our time — an exacting consciousness of the actual and a hardy idealism soaring toward the heights of life — many writers sound only one. It is the special praise and achievement of Hauptmann to have united both in his work. He has been vividly alive to the older naturalistic doctrine, announced with such feverish energy by the Goncourts: "The truth, the truth in its nakedness and rawness — that is art." He has not been unaware, on the other hand, of the contrary theory as stated, for instance, by Maeterlinck: "If one desires to produce a lasting and powerful work, it is well to disengage it from the details of reality.'' Or, in other words, Hauptmann's work illustrates an age which has gradually passed from positivism — from the abandoning, in Comte's own words, of '' a vain search after the origin and destination of the universe '' — to a more liberal and mystical philosophy, in the light of which truths of the merely scientific order are seen to be, as Anatole France put it, but precarious and transitory. This is a fairer and exacter interpretation of the creative energy which has given us *The Weavers*, and also *The Sunken Bell* and *The Beaver Coat* as well as *Henry of Aue*.

Hauptmann's interpretation and criticism of life, however, although so constantly shaped by the prevalent intellectual currents of his age, have never been argumentative or direct. In that respect they have differed notably from the interpretation and criticism of other contemporary dramatists. Thus M. Paul Hervieu, for instance, began his career by a brief series of telling arguments against the legal status of woman; he has recently used the stage in defense of the secular institutions of the social order. Brieux has never written a play but to attack some evil, unveil some hypocrisy, or scourge some definite injustice. Shaw has attempted to undermine the emotional bases of our civilization, and Galsworthy is devoting his admirable dramatic gift to the service of various causes. Hauptmann has had the larger, and surely the wiser vision; for all these evils are but accidental and transitory elements in the life of historic man. Man remains. And thus Hauptmann, abandoning more and more the brief social ardor of his youth, has fixed his eye primarily upon humanity amid conditions and conflicts which, however exactly defined in time and space, partake, by their very nature, of the recurrent and the enduring.

This freedom from the heat of any immediate purpose has enabled Hauptmann to attain a higher degree of plasticity in the final aim of every creative artist — the shaping of characters. The men and women of Hervieu and Brieux

Permission Berlin Photo Co., New York

GERHART HAUPTMANN

must, for the play's necessary effectiveness, possess a given set of traits, or, at least, these traits must be emphasized at the expense of their complete selves; or, finally, they must be placed in situations that serve to bring out the expression of the specific energies and passions required by the argument. In other words, the play with a purpose can never divest itself wholly of intrigue in plot, or of artificial emphasis in the drawing of character. Hauptmann has plunged into the fullness of life. His themes have been hunger and love, aspiration and death. Hence his characters are entire men and women, delineated without suppression or undue stress.

To these two facts — Hauptman's sensitiveness to the spiritual temper of his time and his carelessness (since his earliest plays) of its special and hence passing problems — may be set down the solidity and impressiveness of his work. That impressiveness has gradually become apparent far beyond the limits of Germany and may, in the light of the modern growth of critical certainty, be expected to maintain itself. Hence it will be appropriate to seek for the qualities and experiences of Hauptmann's personality in his works, briefly to sketch the movement in the history of German literature from which he proceeds but which he has transcended, and, finally, to attempt to disengage some of his most notable characteristics both as a naturalistic playwright and as a poet.

II

Gerhart Hauptmann is a Silesian both by descent and by his sympathies. His great-grandfather emigrated, as a weaver, from Bohemia to Silesia, and his grandfather also "sat behind the loom." Thus Hauptmann's intense absorption in the fate of the Silesian weavers is almost his birthright. His grandfather, however, returning from the wars of liberation, took up the more lucrative calling of a waiter, and rose, before the end of his life, to be an independent innkeeper. The inn which he owned and which he passed on to his son Robert, was the " Prussian Crown " at Obersalzbrunn, the birthplace of Gerhart Hauptmann. Robert Hauptmann, the poet's father, a man of seriousness and ability, probably described in *Drayman Henschel* as Siebenhaar, married Marie Straehler. Frau Hauptmann belonged to one of the intensely pious families of Silesian Moravians who are almost the only German representatives of Protestantism at its highest emotional pitch. It is not easy to overestimate the influence of his mother and of her affiliations upon Hauptmann. His leaning to a mystical type of Christianity, his sympathy with its representatives, are clearly shown in *Hannele*, in *Rose Bernd*, in *The Fool in Christ*, and in numberless individual characters and passages throughout his works. He is almost alone among modern German authors in his intimate understanding of the religious experiences of the Christian life.

Gerhart Hauptmann, born November 15, 1862, is the youngest child of these parents, whose contrasting characters remind one, in spite of the difference of intellectual and social surroundings, of the characters of Goethe's father and mother. The fact that Gerhart was an unsatisfactory pupil, both in the school of his native village and in the *Realschule* at Breslau, whither he was sent in 1874, is not without significance. The mind of Hauptmann has always been centred upon its intimate aims; even in his boyhood he was difficult to deflect to what seemed alien purposes, and not until many years later did he turn to those interests which are basic to a humanistic education. In 1878 he was removed from school and placed in the household of a maternal uncle, where he was to become a skilled agriculturist. The two years spent here have left indelible traces upon his work. He gained his intimate knowledge of the Silesian countryside as shown in *Before Dawn* and in *Rose Bernd*, and fortified his acquaintance with the spiritual environment from which so many of his characters have come. The girlhood of Helene Krause (*Before Dawn*) and of Kaethe Vockerat (*Lonely Lives*) was passed amid just such influences.

A second stage in the development of the future playwright was reached when, in 1880, he returned to Breslau and was enrolled as a student in the Royal College of Art. He had long taken an interest in sculpture and modeled in a desultory way; this impulse was now to be formed and directed. The academic practice of art, however, failed to content the young student, and a conflict with his teachers ensued; he was rusticated, but readmitted. The impressions of his second Breslau period are set down in two plays, *Colleague Crampton* and *Michael Kramer,* whose protagonists are probably—*mutatis mutandis*—portraits of two professors then active in the Breslau College of Art. Dissatisfaction with the course of instruction was not Hauptmann's only reason for leaving Breslau in 1882. The literary impulse was asserting itself vigorously. Reports reach us of dramas—*Ingeborg* and *Germans and Romans* —and of a romantic epic on Arminius. At all events, in the spring of 1882 Hauptmann joined his favorite brother Carl as a student in the University of Jena.

Here he remained for one year, awakening to all the modern problems and tendencies in the study of nature and society. Social reform and evolutionary monism were then in their heyday and there can be no doubt that the influence of these Jena months had not a little to do with the shaping of the future naturalist. In fact the young artist, setting out during the following spring on a journey to Spain and to Italy, was less impressed by the beauty and the memories of the cities he visited than by the poverty, the vice, and the suffering of the modern Latin populations. In his earliest published work, the Byronic epic *Promethidenlos* (1885), he records the deep and deeply painful impressions which he received in the south of Europe. After a brief stay in Rome he hastened northward.

In this same important year (1883) he was betrothed to Marie Thienemann, one of the five charming daughters of a wealthy merchant. The young women of the Thienemann family were orphans and lived together in a country-house

isolated from the world in what seemed to young Hauptmann an atmosphere of blandness and exquisite peace. His
brothers Carl and Georg had chosen the two older sisters
of his betrothed. Thus Hauptmann lived through the
delightful dream described more than twenty years later
in *The Maidens of the Mount*. But the conflicts of his inner
life made that dream transitory. Not only was he unable
to decide between sculpture and literature as a final aim,
but art itself seemed to him, in an age of so many practical
problems, as possibly a tragic waste. Perhaps to attain
greater spiritual certainty he went once more, in 1884, to
Rome; a severe illness, however, cut short his final experiment as a plastic artist, and, accompanied by his future
wife, he hurried home.

The young couple were married in the spring of 1885.
For a few months Hauptmann entertained the plan of
fitting himself for the stage, but by autumn this plan too
was seen to be impossible and he and his wife took up
their residence in the Berlin suburb of Erkner, a *milieu*
which he has described in its various phases in *The Reconciliation*, *The Beaver Coat* and *The Conflagration*. And
it was here, in his first individual home, that he came into
immediate contact with those new forces in German literature which found their final crystallization in his own work.

III

The decade from 1880 to 1890 is marked in the literary
history of Europe by the transference of naturalistic aims
and methods from the novel to the drama. It opened with
the performance of *Ghosts* (1881) and of Henri Becque's
Les Corbeaux (1882); it closed with that marvelous outburst of naturalistic dramaturgy marked by Tolstoy's
The Might of Darkness (1887), Strindberg's *The Father*
(1887), *Comrades* (1888), *Miss Juliet* (1888), by the found-
ing of the "Théâtre Libre" in Paris (1887), the establish-
ment of the "Freie Buehne" in Berlin (1889), and the first
pronunciamento of the real Hauptmann: his *Before Dawn*

(1889). Now naturalism stood not only for esthetic reform, but for an unmistakable attitude toward man, toward nature, and toward human life. It was the reflection of scientific positivism in literature. It accepted all the implications of positivism and hence wrought a far profounder change in the character and technique of the drama than in those of the novel. For the drama had been hitherto the struggle of free personalities — above all, of responsible personalities. The naturalistic drama rested, by its very assumptions, upon the liberation of the individual will from responsibility — especially from responsibility incurred under some fixed ethical or social law. It saw man oppressed by social institutions, hemmed in by narrow conventions, pursued by the fatality of inherited instincts and evils. Hence it was a drama of moral readjustment. It fixed its vision less upon the evil that men do than upon the evil they endure; it laid greater stress upon being than upon doing. But action is the immemorial basis of all drama; and hence a drama which was static rather than dynamic by its very principles, necessarily sought a new technique. The inevitable truth could not be represented through a technique of exposition, implication, and explication; for life bears but little resemblance to intrigue, and human fortunes are devoid of plot.

It was left for the German drama to develop this new technique. Strindberg alone had approached it; but Strindberg stood apart. The French playwrights had rarely been able to free themselves from the pursuit of a definite thesis and its results upon the structure of the drama. In Germany the new technique appeared suddenly, first in the theories of Arno Holz, next in the work of Holz and Hauptmann, and almost immediately thereafter in the plays of half a dozen notable young dramatists. The way for it had, in a sense, been prepared. Germany was thoroughly discontented with the pale and imitative literary forms that immediately succeeded the Franco-Prussian war. The new empire needed a new literature. Men like Michael Georg Conrad preached pure Zolaism as the salvation of German letters; the young enthusiasts of Berlin who founded the society *Durch* in 1886 insisted upon fidelity to truth and modernity of subject matter; the lyric had already been revolutionized in fact and not only in theory by Detlev von Liliencron. Finally, in 1889, Paul Schlenther and Otto Brahm founded the " Freie Buehne " in direct imitation of the " Théâtre Libre " established by Antoine in Paris two years before. The imitation was very close. Like Antoine they began their series of performances with Ibsen's *Ghosts* and Tolstoy's *Might of Darkness*. In one respect, however, the Germans were more fortunate than their French predecessor. Antoine had done something for Brieux, a little more for François de Curel; Brahm and Schlenther inaugurated the career of Gerhart Hauptmann.

To Hauptmann, living at Erkner since 1885, seeking some form of definite expression, deeply afflicted by the inhumanity of man to man — to Hauptmann had come the varying theories and battle-cries of the day. He yielded to the clamor of the Zolaists and wrote his study *Bahnwaerter Thiel* in 1887. But in literature he had always been drawn primarily to poetry and to the drama. His poetic power, however, had not yet ripened, and the drama was hovering between two worlds — one dead, the other powerless to be born. Kretzer, the German Zolaist, was a frequent guest at Erkner; so were the brothers Hart, critics, poets, and prophets of modernity, Boelsche the essayist, von Hanstein the historian of the movement, and, finally, the East-Prussian, Arno Holz. The latter brought to Hauptmann early in 1889 his sketches and his play *Family Selicke*, in which he had embodied his theory of consistent naturalism — a record of life as pitilessly true as the necessarily selective processes of art will permit. Hauptmann immediately responded to the impulse. Like all the major men of letters, he did not invent the form to which he has given significance and through which he has expressed himself. The almost immediate result of Holz' influence was to liberate Hauptmann's creative force. In October, 1889, *Before*

Dawn was performed under the auspices of the "Freie Buehne."

The technique of the naturalistic drama had been found. Hauptmann extended the form and wrought upon it with extraordinary power and skill. In *The Reconciliation* (1890) and *Lonely Lives* (1891) he returned partly to the methods of Ibsen; but in 1892 he created the naturalistic folk-drama in *The Weavers* and in 1893 the naturalistic comedy in *The Beaver Coat*. The new drama produced notable works in rapid succession—Fulda's *The Slave* (1891), Halbe's *Youth* (1893), Schnitzler's *Flirtation* (1895). But the triumph of naturalism was not undivided. In the very year of *The Weavers,* Ludwig Fulda achieved a great stage success with his romantic comedy in verse, *The Talisman,* and in 1893 Hauptmann himself blended naturalism and poetry in *The Assumption of Hannele.* It is noteworthy that his almost feverish creative activity in the drama now ceased. Two years elapsed before the performance of his historical play *Florian Geyer.* The play failed utterly. It was a blow all the more crushing to Hauptmann since, during these years, he passed through that painful crisis which led to his separation from his first wife. The poet in him welded all the elements of his fate into an imaginative whole which completed his essential development as a man and an artist—*The Sunken Bell.*

IV

What now, briefly, is the technique of the naturalistic drama which Hauptmann has exemplified in a series of plays extending from 1889 to 1912?* In what respect has he so revolutionized the form and content of the modern drama that men as different as John Galsworthy, on the one hand, and the older Henri Lavedan, on the other, are what they are largely through the absorption—conscious or

---

* *Before Dawn, The Reconciliation, Lonely Lives, The Weavers, Colleague Crampton, The Beaver Coat, Drayman Henschel, Michael Kramer, The Conflagration, Rose Bernd, The Rats, Gabriel Schilling's Flight.*

unconscious — of the dramaturgic methods which are, but for the prophetic work of Ibsen, primarily if not exclusively Hauptmann's own?

The technique of the drama of the past, then, rests upon certain conventions of structure. These conventions are summed up as plot, coil, evolution — what you will. They all come to this — that the stuff of life is forced, by a variety of artifices, into the gathering and untying of the traditional dramatic knot. Characters came and went, acted and re-acted, not at the urging of necessity, but in preparation for the climax of the scene, the act, or the play. Polonius had to be hid behind the arras in order to be killed; Desdemona had to lose her kerchief in order to wring Othello's heart, Lady Teazle had to be maneuvred behind the screen in order that she might emerge to confound Joseph and to accept her husband's kindness. These instances illustrate the conventions which Hauptmann was the first dramatist to avoid. His fables represent the stuff of life in its true order and succession both in action and in time. There is no climax unless reality demands one; there is no artificially satisfying conclusion to his plays, since each play represents but a fragmentary vision of the great stream of life which continues to flow.

In addition to avoiding artifices of structure, Hauptmann avoids, so far as possible, artifices of speech. It is difficult for the reader of English to realize this fact, and no trans-lation can convey it adequately. But Hauptmann does not help his characters to an eloquence that is his own. In this respect he has most strikingly followed the Shakespearian warning not to overstep the modesty of nature. His men and women are guiltless of false eloquence, of repartee, of the pat give-and-take of the well-made French play; their words have the simplicity and the savor of real speech. Hence Hauptmann's dramatic interpretation of human character is based upon the authentic material of life itself.

But if these plays are so nearly exact a rendering of the

humble truth, wherein, it may be asked, lies that representative quality, that interpretative power, without which literature ceases to be literature? The answer may be summed up in one of those admirable sayings of Goethe that grow more luminous and inclusive in their wisdom as time goes on:

> Willst du ins Unendliche schreiten,
> Geh nur im Endlichen nach allen Seiten.*

There, surely, is summed up a complete defense of naturalistic art. To observe man and his life relentlessly and to set down the result of such observation with sobriety and yet incisiveness cannot fail leading us in the end to those unescapable world mysteries which rise above the snares of circumstance and are free of the arbitrament of mortality. In other words, the most meaningful interpretation will rest upon a basis of incontestable facts. Pursue these finite facts far enough, as Goethe counsels, and you will fare into the infinite.

Four typical plays, several of which are included in this collection, illustrate all the qualities here set down and satisfy the suggested test. In *The Weavers* we have a complete vision of the soul of man under the stress of want. That vision is fuller and more significant than eloquence or pleading could have made it, and it is built of the humblest materials. In the first act the weavers are depicted in their relations to the manufacturers; in the second the wretchedness of the weavers is illustrated intimately, and the feeble note of their doomed rebellion is struck. The third act shows the public house where the news of the hour flits about, where rebellion is fomented by cheap liquor, and where appear minor but yet sinister factors necessary to the complete portrayal of the fate of the weavers. The masterly fourth act presents the manufacturers and their social views from within — their cravenness, their real difficulties, their genuine inability to free themselves from a con-

---

* If thou wouldst fare into the infinite, follow the finite in all directions.

ventional view of the social order. And, finally, essential
tragedy steps into the fifth act — the cry of Luise's despair,
the soaring and yet destroying faith of old Hilse. It is
made clear that these people bore in their broken hearts
the seed of weakness and inevitable failure. The truth is
there — the humble truth built of the despised details of
man's daily living and suffering. But also the infinite is
there — silently rising and brooding over the fates of
men.

The temper in which Hauptmann wrote *The Beaver Coat*
is harder and dryer; hence the result was, superficially at
least, comedy rather than tragedy. The play is fashioned
with immense economy and concentration of effort. Its
central and recurrent aim is the full portrayal of the protagonist — Mrs. Wolff. There is not a word of comment,
direct or indirect, from any side. Yet, as in the laconic
stories of de Maupassant, a silent implication of intense
ironic force rests over the whole play. Is not Mrs. Wolff
what her world has made her? Could she have turned that
resourcefulness, that intrepidity of hers, into other and
nobler channels? Inevitably scrambling in the mire with
all her kind — who can blame her for wanting to rise?

" If you don't join the scramble — you're lazy: if you do
— you're bad. An' everythin' we does get, we gets out o'
the dirt. . . . An' they, they tells you: Be good, be good!
How? What chance has we got? . . . I wanted to get
on — that's true. An' ain't it natural? We all wants to
get out o' this here mud in which we all fights and scratches
aroun'. . . . Out o' it . . . away from it . . .
higher up if you wants to call it that! "

There is little serenity or beauty in such art. But it has
seen life steadily and seen it whole. Its vision has gone beyond tradition and convention into the heart of man itself.
If that heart is warped, the knowledge of that truth may
help us onward to a clearer path. But this art, at all events,
can create character, and by that unmistakable creative
energy it is justified and assured.

V

But there is the other side to Hauptmann's activity. He has not only, as a naturalistic playwright, created a new technique and a new standard of reality for the drama. He is also a poet. In *The Sunken Bell* and in *Henry of Aue* he has, perhaps alone among contemporary poets, written plays of ideal content and poetic form that are original in manner and conception and powerful on the stage. In a word, he has given new life to the poetic drama; and he has done so, largely, by infusing into it the sobriety, inevitableness, and simplicity which he mastered as a naturalist and in prose.

The Sunken Bell, though raised by its form and method into the realm of the timeless, is the drama of the creative thinker of modern times. The problem of the modern artist is — as Hauptmann has shown in *Lonely Lives* and again, quite recently, in *Gabriel Schilling's Flight* — the conflict between personal and ideal ends. However blended with secondary motives, the kernel of the play is there. The faith by which Heinrich, the bell-founder, lives is the presence of the creative power within him.

> What's germed within me's worthy of the blessing —
> Worthy the ripening.

His one aim is to see that germ ripen, regardless of the world and its rewards, regardless of his personal happiness. To understand the play it is necessary to enter into the overwhelming reality and sincerity of this thought. To the true artist all features and forms of life bring only an added pang of the soul, if this central aim is balked. And it is a perception of this fundamental truth which the homely environment of Heinrich's personal life lacks. His bell falls into the mere. And Magda, his wife, says:

> Pray Heaven that be the worst!
> What matters one bell more or less! If he,
> The Master, be but safe!

The master lives; but he is filled with despair, for it was by no mere chance that his bell was hurled from the heights.

" 'Twas for the valley, not the mountain-top!' "

And to this cry of the artist's despair his wife replies:

"That is not true! Hadst thou but heard, as I,
The Vicar tell the Clerk, in tones that shook:
'How gloriously 'twill sound upon the heights!' "

The opinion of the Vicar and the Clerk are her norm; of the new and unapproached ideal she and her world know nothing. And so Heinrich, driven by his deepest impulse, goes up into the hills and meets a spirit of beauty and refreshment in nature — Rautendelein — who will help him to find his treasures. His heart is not hard. He cannot help Magda, for to her " his wine would be but bitter gall and venom." He stays upon the heights with Rautendelein to build the great work that shall embody his dreams. The ignorant cries of hidebound men serve only to convince him more

"Of the great weight and purpose of his mission."

And yet he fails. It is the tragedy of tragedies. He has left too great a part of himself in his other life.

"Yonder I am at home . . . and yet a stranger —
Here I am strange . . . and yet I am at home."

His children bring their mother's tears up the mountain-side and the sunken bell tolls the destruction of his hopes. He dies — clasping his ideal to his heart; for it is better to die so than to return to the valleys where the ideal is an outcast and a stranger.

In *Henry of Aue* Hauptmann has remolded a legend famous in German literature for nearly a thousand years. The play offers no difficulties to the attentive reader. Hauptmann has humanized the characters of the medieval legend and poem, and has shifted the stress from the miracle which solves the problem of the play to that great change of heart in the protagonist which calls the miracle forth. Henry of Aue, as the pragmatist would put it, helps the universe to show its divinity by breaking away from his personal unhappiness and believing it to be divine. Thus he creates the miracle by which his salvation is brought about.

Something should be said of the form of these two plays. Hauptmann's mastery of lyrical measures is not, perhaps, first-rate, but he has created anew the blank verse of the German drama. That verse has been apt to seem, even at its best, a little heavy, a little stiff — burdened with too great a proportion of end-stopped lines, and lacking flexibility within the verse. In *Henry of Aue,* more especially, however, Hauptmann has written verse in which — as. in Milton or Tennyson — the individual line has ceased to be the rhythmic unit and the essential secret of blank verse — that, namely, of the complete harmony of the verse-paragraph — is found. Even through the medium of translation this may be illustrated from the beginning of Henry's great speech in the second act:

> Life is a brittle vessel, O my friend,
> The Koran saith, and look ye, it is true.
> And I have learned this truth. I would not live
> In a blown egg's void shell. Wouldst thou exalt
> The glory and the grandeur that are man,
> Or call him even in God's image made?
> Scratch him but with a tailor's shears — he bleeds!
> Prick him but gently with a cobbler's awl
> Where the pulse beats, or here, or there, or here,
> And swiftly, irresistibly, will gush
> Even like a liberated fountain, forth
> His pride, his joy, his noble soul and sense,
> Divine illusion, all his love and hate
> And wealth and glory and guerdon of his deed —
> All, all, in brief, that he, blind error's slave,
> Did deem his very own! Be emperor, sultan, pope —
> A naked body huddled in a shroud
> Art thou — today, tomorrow, cold therein and still! *

The writer of these lines and of Luise's outburst in *The Weavers* has little to fear from the future except the inevitable winnowing of his less masterly from the greater remnant of his authentic and enduring work.

---

* The quotations from *The Sunken Bell* are taken from the version by C. H. Meltzer; the quotation from *Henry of Aue* is from my own rendering of that play.— L. L.

GERHART HAUPTMANN

THE WEAVERS

I DEDICATE THIS DRAMA
TO MY FATHER
ROBERT HAUPTMANN

You, dear father, know what feelings lead me
to dedicate this work to you, and I am not called
upon to analyze them here.

Your stories of my grandfather, who in his
young days sat at the loom, a poor weaver like
those here depicted, contained the germ of my
drama. Whether it possesses the vigor of life
or is rotten at the core, it is the best, " so poor
a man as Hamlet is " can offer.

Your

GERHART

[16]

THE WEAVERS*

DRAMATIS PERSONÆ

DREISSIGER, *fustian manufacturer*
MRS. DREISSIGER
PFEIFER, *manager*
NEUMANN, *cashier*
AN APPRENTICE *in* DREISSIGER'S *employment*
JOHN, *coachman*
A MAID
WEINHOLD, *tutor to* DREISSIGER'S *sons*
PASTOR KITTELHAUS
MRS. KITTELHAUS

HEIDE, *Police Superintendent*
KUTSCHE, *policeman*
WELZEL, *publican*
MRS. WELZEL
ANNA WELZEL
WIEGAND, *joiner*
A COMMERCIAL TRAVELER
A PEASANT
A FORESTER
SCHMIDT, *surgeon*
HORNIG, *rag dealer*
WITTIG, *smith*

WEAVERS

BECKER
MORITZ JAEGER
OLD BAUMERT
MOTHER BAUMERT
BERTHA BAUMERT
EMMA BAUMERT
FRITZ, EMMA'S *son (four years old)*
AUGUST BAUMERT
OLD ANSORGE
MRS. HEINRICH
OLD HILSE

MOTHER HILSE
GOTTLIEB HILSE
LUISE, GOTTLIEB'S *wife*
MIELCHEN, *their daughter (six years old)*
REIMANN, *weaver*
HEIBER, *weaver*
A WEAVER'S WIFE
A number of weavers, young and old, of both sexes

The action passes in the Forties, at Kaschbach, Peterswaldau and Langenbielau, in the Eulengebirge.

---

* From *The Dramatic Works of Gerhart Hauptmann*, edited by Ludwig Lewisohn. Permission B. W. Huebsch, New York.

THE WEAVERS (1892)

TRANSLATED BY MARY MORRISON

Assistant Professor of the German Language and Literature, Ohio State University

ACT I

A large whitewashed room on the ground floor of DREISSIGER'S *house at Peterswaldau, where the weavers deliver their finished webs and the fustian is stored. To the left are uncurtained windows, in the back wall there is a glass door, and to the right another glass door, through which weavers, male and female, and children, are passing in and out. All three walls are lined with shelves for the storing of the fustian. Against the right wall stands a long bench, on which a number of weavers have already spread out their cloth. In the order of arrival each presents his piece to be examined by* PFEIFER, DREISSIGER'S *manager, who stands, with compass and magnifying-glass, behind a large table, on which the web to be inspected is laid. When* PFEIFER *has satisfied himself, the weaver lays the fustian on the scale, and an office apprentice tests its weight. The same boy stores the accepted pieces on the shelves.* PFEIFER *calls out the payment due in each case to* NEUMANN, *the cashier, who is seated at a small table.*

It is a sultry day toward the end of May. The clock is on the stroke of twelve. Most of the waiting work-people have the air of standing before the bar of justice, in torturing expectation of a decision that means life or death to them. They are marked, too, by the anxious timidity characteristic of the receiver of charity, who has suffered many humiliations, and, conscious that he is barely tolerated, has acquired the habit of self-effacement. Add to this a rigid expression on every face that tells of constant, fruitless brooding. There is a general resemblance among the men. They have something about them of the dwarf, something of the schoolmaster. The majority are flat-breasted, short-winded, sallow, and poor looking — creatures of the loom, their knees bent with much sitting. At a first glance the women show fewer typical traits. They look over-driven, worried, reckless, whereas the men still make some show of a pitiful self-respect; and their clothes are ragged, while the men's are patched and mended. Some of the young girls are not without a certain charm, consisting in a waxlike pallor, a slender figure, and large, projecting, melancholy eyes.

NEUMANN (*counting out money*). Comes to one and seven-pence halfpenny.

WEAVER'S WIFE (*about thirty, emaciated, takes up the money with trembling fingers*). Thank you, sir.

NEUMANN (*seeing that she does not move on*). Well, something wrong this time, too?

WEAVER'S WIFE (*agitated, imploringly*). Do you think I might have a few pence in advance, sir? I need it that bad.

NEUMANN. And I need a few pounds. If it was only a question of needing it—! [*Already occupied in counting out another weaver's money, gruffly.*] It's Mr. Dreissiger who settles about pay in advance.

WEAVER'S WIFE. Couldn't I speak to Mr. Dreissiger himself, then, sir?

PFEIFER (*now manager, formerly weaver. The type is unmistakable, only he is well fed, well dressed, clean shaven; also takes snuff copiously. He calls out roughly*). Mr. Dreissiger would have enough to do if he had to attend to every trifle himself. That's what we are here for. [*He measures, and then examines through the magnifying-glass.*] Mercy on us! what a draught! [*Puts a thick muffler round his neck.*] Shut the door, whoever comes in.

APPRENTICE (*loudly to* PFEIFER). You might as well talk to stocks and stones.

PFEIFER. That's done!—Weigh! [*The weaver places his web on the scales.*] If you only understood your business a little better! Full of lumps again. I hardly need to look at the cloth to see them. Call yourself a weaver, and "draw as long a bow" as you've done there!

BECKER *has entered. A young, exceptionally powerfully-built weaver; offhand, almost bold in manner.* PFEIFER, NEUMANN, *and the* APPRENTICE *exchange looks of mutual understanding as he comes in.*

BECKER. Devil take it! This is a sweatin' job, and no mistake.

FIRST WEAVER (*in a low voice*).   This blazin' heat means rain.

> [OLD BAUMERT *forces his way in at the glass door on the right, through which the crowd of weavers can be seen, standing shoulder to shoulder, waiting their turn. The old man stumbles forward and lays his bundle on the bench, beside* BECKER'S. *He sits down by it, and wipes the sweat from his face.*]

OLD BAUMERT.   A man has a right to a rest after that.

BECKER.   Rest's better than money.

OLD BAUMERT.   Yes, but we *needs* the money too.   Good mornin' to you, Becker!

BECKER.   Mornin', father Baumert!   Goodness knows how long we'll have to stand here again.

FIRST WEAVER.   That don't matter.   What's to hinder a weaver waitin' for an hour, or for a day?   What else is he there for?

PFEIFER.   Silence there!   We can't hear our own voices.

BECKER (*in a low voice*).   This is one of his bad days.

PFEIFER (*to the weaver standing before him*).   How often have I told you that you must bring cleaner cloth?   What sort of mess is this?   Knots, and straw, and all kinds of dirt.

REIMANN.   It's for want of a new picker, sir.

APPRENTICE (*has weighed the piece*).   Short weight, too.

PFEIFER.   I never saw such weavers.   I hate to give out the yarn to them.   It was another story in my day!   I'd have caught it finely from my master for work like that.   The business was carried on in different style then.   A man had to know his trade—that's the last thing that's thought of nowadays.   Reimann, one shilling.

REIMANN.   But there's always a pound allowed for waste.

PFEIFER.   I've no time.   Next man!   What have you to show?

HEIBER (*lays his web on the table. While* PFEIFER *is examining it, he goes close up to him; eagerly in a low tone*). Beg pardon, Mr. Pfeifer, but I wanted to ask you, sir, if you would perhaps be so very kind an' do me the favor an' not take my advance money off this week's pay.

PFEIFER (*measuring and examining the texture; jeeringly*). Well! What next, I wonder? This looks very much as if half the weft had stuck to the bobbins again.

HEIBER (*continues*). I'll be sure to make it all right next week, sir. But this last week I've had to put in two days' work on the estate. And my missus is ill in bed.

PFEIFER (*giving the web to be weighed*). Another piece of real slop-work. [*Already examining a new web.*] What a selvage! Here it's broad, there it's narrow; here it's drawn in by the weft's goodness knows how tight, and there it's torn out again by the temples. And hardly seventy threads weft to the inch. What's come of the rest? Do you call this honest work? I never saw anything like it.

[HEIBER, *repressing tears, stands humiliated and helpless.*]

BECKER (*in a low voice to* BAUMERT). To please that brute you'd have to pay for extra yarn out o' your own pocket.

WEAVER'S WIFE (*who has remained standing near the cashier's table, from time to time looking round appealingly, takes courage and once more turns imploringly to the cashier*). I don't know what's to come o' me, sir, if you won't give me a little advance this time. O Lord, O Lord!

PFEIFER (*calls across*). It's no good whining, or dragging the Lord's name into the matter. You're not so anxious about Him at other times. You look after your husband and see that he's not to be found so often lounging in the public-house. We can give no pay in advance. We have to account for every penny. It's not our money. People that are industrious, and understand their work, and do it in the fear of God, never need their pay in advance. So now you know.

NEUMANN. If a Bielau weaver got four times as much pay, he would squander it four times over and be in debt into the bargain.

WEAVER'S WIFE (*in a loud voice, as if appealing to the general sense of justice*). No one can't call me idle, but I'm not fit now for what I once was. I've twice had a miscarriage. And as to John, he's but a poor creature. He's been to the shepherd at Zerlau, but he couldn't do him no good, and — you can't do more than you've strength for. We works as hard as ever we can. This many a week I've been at it till far on into the night. An' we'll keep our heads above water right enough if I can just get a bit o' strength into me. But you must have pity on us, Mr. Pfeifer, sir. [*Eagerly, coaxingly.*] You'll please be so very kind as to let me have a few pence on the next job, sir?

PFEIFER (*paying no attention*). Fiedler, one and twopence.

WEAVER'S WIFE. Only a few pence, to buy bread with. We can't get no more credit. We've a lot o' little ones.

NEUMANN (*half aside to the* APPRENTICE, *in a serio-comic tone*). "Every year brings a child to the linen-weaver's wife, heigh-ho, heigh-ho, heigh."

APPRENTICE (*takes up the rhyme, half singing*). "And the little brat it's blind the first weeks of its life, heigh-ho, heigh-ho, heigh."

REIMANN (*not touching the money which the cashier has counted out to him*). We've always got one and fourpence for the web.

PFEIFER (*calls across*). If our terms don't suit you, Reimann, you have only to say so. There's no scarcity of weavers — especially of your sort. For full weight we give full pay.

REIMANN. How anything can be wrong with the weight o' this — !

PFEIFER. You bring a piece of fustian with no faults in it, and there will be no fault in the pay.

REIMANN. It's clean impossible that there's too many knots in this web.

PFEIFER (*examining*). If you want to live well, then be sure you weave well.

HEIBER (*has remained standing near* PFEIFER, *so as to seize on any favorable opportunity. He laughs at* PFEIFER'S *little witticism, then steps forward and again addresses him*). I wanted to ask you, sir, if you would perhaps have the great kindness not to take my advance of sixpence off today's pay? My missus has been bedridden since February. She can't do a hand's turn for me, an' I've to pay a bobbin girl. An' so —

PFEIFER (*takes a pinch of snuff*). Heiber, do you think I have no one to attend to but you? The others must have their turn.

REIMANN. As the warp was given me I took it home and fastened it to the beam. I can't bring back no better yarn than I gets.

PFEIFER. If you're not satisfied, you need come for no more. There are plenty ready to tramp the soles off their shoes to get it.

NEUMANN (*to* REIMANN). Don't you want your money?

REIMANN. I can't bring myself to take such pay.

NEUMANN (*paying no further attention to* REIMANN). Heiber, one shilling. Deduct sixpence for pay in advance. Leaves sixpence.

HEIBER (*goes up to the table, looks at the money, stands shaking his head as if unable to believe his eyes, then slowly takes it up*). Well, I never! — [*Sighing.*] Oh dear, oh dear!

OLD BAUMERT (*looking into* HEIBER'S *face*). Yes, Franz, that's so! There's matter enough for sighing.

HEIBER (*speaking with difficulty*). I've a girl lyin' sick at home too, an' she needs a bottle of medicine.

OLD BAUMERT. What's wrong with her?

HEIBER. Well, you see, she's always been a sickly bit of a thing. I don't know — I needn't mind tellin' you — she brought her trouble with her. It's in her blood, and it breaks out here, there, and everywhere.

OLD BAUMERT. It's always the way. Let folks be poor, and one trouble comes to them on the top of another. There's no help for it and there's no end to it.

HEIBER. What are you carrying' in that cloth, father Baumert?

OLD BAUMERT. We haven't so much as a bite in the house, and so I've had the little dog killed. There's not much on him, for the poor beast was half starved. A nice little dog he was! I couldn't kill him myself. I hadn't the heart to do it.

PFEIFER (*has inspected* BECKER's *web and calls*). Becker, one and threepence.

BECKER. That's what you might give to a beggar; it's not pay.

PFEIFER. Every one who has been attended to must clear out. We haven't room to turn round in.

BECKER (*to those standing near, without lowering his voice*). It's a beggarly pittance, nothing else. A man works his treadle from early morning till late at night, an' when he's bent over his loom for days an' days, tired to death every evening, sick with the dust and the heat, he finds he's made a beggarly one and three-pence!

PFEIFER. No impudence allowed here.

BECKER. If you think I'll hold my tongue for your tellin', you're much mistaken.

PFEIFER (*exclaims*). We'll see about that! [*Rushes to the glass door and calls into the office.*] Mr. Dreissiger, Mr. Dreissiger, will you be good enough to come here?

Enter DREISSIGER. *About forty, full-blooded, asthmatic. Looks severe.*

DREISSIGER. What is it, Pfeifer?

PFEIFER (*spitefully*). Becker says he won't be told to hold his tongue.

DREISSIGER (*draws himself up, throws back his head, stares at* BECKER; *his nostrils tremble*). Oh, indeed!—Becker. [*To* PFEIFER.] Is he the man?

[*The clerks nod.*]

BECKER (*insolently*). Yes, Mr. Dreissiger, yes! [*Pointing to himself.*] This is the man. [*Pointing to* DREISSIGER.] And that's a man too!

DREISSIGER (*angrily*). Fellow, how dare you?

PFEIFER. He's too well off. He'll go dancing on the ice once too often, though.

BECKER (*recklessly*). You shut up, you Jack-in-the-box. Your mother must have gone dancing once too often with Satan to have got such a devil for a son.

DREISSIGER (*now in a violent passion, roars*). Hold your tongue this moment, sir, or —

[*He trembles and takes a few steps forward.*]

BECKER (*holding his ground steadily*). I'm not deaf. My hearing's quite good yet.

DREISSIGER (*controls himself, asks in an apparently cool business tone*). Was this fellow not one of the pack — ?

PFEIFER. He's a Bielau weaver. When there's any mischief going, they're sure to be in it.

DREISSIGER (*trembling*). Well, I give you all warning: if the same thing happens again as last night — a troop of half-drunken cubs marching past my windows singing that low song —

BECKER. Is it " Bloody Justice " you mean?

DREISSIGER. You know well enough what I mean. I tell you that if I hear it again I'll get hold of one of you, and — mind, I'm not joking — before the justice he shall go. And if I can find out who it was that made up that vile doggerel —

BECKER. It's a grand song, that's what it is!

DREISSIGER. Another word and I send for the police on the spot, without more ado. I'll make short work with you young fellows. I've got the better of very different men before now.

BECKER. I believe you there. A real thoroughbred manufacturer will get the better of two or three hundred weavers in the time it takes you to turn round —

swallow 'em up, and not leave as much as a bone. He's got four stomachs like a cow, and teeth like a wolf. That's nothing to him at all!

DREISSIGER (*to his clerks*). That man gets no more work from us.

BECKER. It's all the same to me whether I starve at my loom or by the roadside.

DREISSIGER. Out you go, then, at this moment!

BECKER (*determinedly*). Not without my pay.

DREISSIGER. How much is owing to the fellow, Neumann?

NEUMANN. One and threepence.

DREISSIGER (*takes the money hurriedly out of the cashier's hand, and flings it on the table, so that some of the coins roll off on to the floor*). There you are, then; and now, out of my sight with you!

BECKER. Not without my pay.

DREISSIGER. Don't you see it lying there? If you don't take it and go— It's exactly twelve now. The dyers are coming out for their dinner.

BECKER. I gets my pay into my hand—here—that's where!

　[*Points with the fingers of his right hand at the palm of his left.*]

DREISSIGER (*to the* APPRENTICE). Pick up the money, Tilgner.

　[*The* APPRENTICE *lifts the money and puts it into* BECKER's *hand.*]

BECKER. Everything in proper order.

　[*Deliberately takes an old purse out of his pocket and puts the money into it.*]

DREISSIGER (*as* BECKER *still does not move away*). Well? Do you want me to come and help you?

　[*Signs of agitation are observable among the crowd of weavers. A long, loud sigh is heard, and then a fall. General interest is at once diverted to this new event.*]

DREISSIGER. What's the matter there?

CHORUS OF WEAVERS AND WOMEN. " Some one's fainted."—
" It's a little sickly boy."—" Is it a fit, or what? "

DREISSIGER. What do you say? Fainted?

[*He goes nearer.*]

OLD WEAVER. There he lies, anyway.

[*They make room. A boy of about eight is seen lying on the floor as if dead.*]

DREISSIGER. Does any one know the boy?

OLD WEAVER. He's not from our village.

OLD BAUMERT. He's like one of weaver Heinrich's boys. [*Looks at him more closely.*] Yes, that's Heinrich's little Philip.

DREISSIGER. Where do they live?

OLD BAUMERT. Up near us in Kaschbach, sir. He goes round playin' music in the evenings, and all day he's at the loom. They've nine children an' a tenth a-coming.

CHORUS OF WEAVERS AND WOMEN. " They're terrible put to it."—" The rain comes through their roof."—" The woman hasn't two shirts among the nine."

OLD BAUMERT (*taking the boy by the arm*). Now, then, lad, what's wrong with you? Wake up, lad.

DREISSIGER. Some of you help me, and we'll get him up. It's disgraceful to send a sickly child this distance. Bring some water, Pfeifer.

WOMAN (*helping to lift the boy*). Sure you're not goin' to be foolish and die, lad!

DREISSIGER. Brandy, Pfeifer, brandy will be better.

BECKER (*forgotten by all, has stood looking on. With his hand on the door-latch, he now calls loudly and tauntingly*). Give him something to eat, an' he'll soon be all right. [*Goes out.*]

DREISSIGER. That fellow will come to a bad end.— Take him under the arm, Neumann. Easy now, easy; we'll get him into my room. What?

NEUMANN. He said something, Mr. Dreissiger. His lips are moving.

DREISSIGER. What — what is it, boy?

BOY (*whispers*). I'm h — hungry.

WOMAN. I think he says —

DREISSIGER. We'll find out. Don't stop. Let us get him into my room. He can lie on the sofa there. We'll hear what the doctor says.

>[DREISSIGER, NEUMANN, *and the woman lead the boy into the office. The weavers begin to behave like school-children when their master has left the classroom. They stretch themselves, whisper, move from one foot to the other, and in the course of a few moments are conversing loudly.*]

OLD BAUMERT. I believe as how Becker was right.

CHORUS OF WEAVERS AND WOMEN. "He did say something like that."—"It's nothin' new here to fall down from hunger."—"God knows what's to come of 'em in winter if this cuttin' down o' wages goes on."— "An' this year the potatoes aren't no good at all."— "Things'll get worse and worse till we're all done for together."

OLD BAUMERT. The best thing a man could do would be to put a rope round his neck and hang hisself on his own loom, like weaver Nentwich. [*To another old weaver.*] Here, take a pinch. I was at Neurode yesterday. My brother-in-law, he works in the snuff factory there, and he give me a grain or two. Have you anything good in your kerchief?

OLD WEAVER. Only a little pearl barley. I was coming along behind Ulbrich the miller's cart, and there was a slit in one of the sacks. I can tell you we'll be glad of it.

OLD BAUMERT. There's twenty-two mills in Peterswaldau, but of all they grind, there's never nothin' comes our way.

OLD WEAVER. We must keep up heart. There's always somethin' comes to help us on again.

HEIBER. Yes, when we're hungry, we can pray to all the saints to help us, and if that don't fill our bellies we can put a pebble in our mouths and suck it. Eh, Baumert?

>*Reënter* DREISSIGER, PFEIFER, *and* NEUMANN.

DREISSIGER. It was nothing serious. The boy is all right again. [*Walks about excitedly, panting.*] But all the same it's a disgrace. The child's so weak that a puff of wind would blow him over. How people, how any parents can be so thoughtless is what passes my comprehension. Loading him with two heavy pieces of fustian to carry six good miles! No one would believe it that hadn't seen it. It simply means that I shall have to make a rule that no goods brought by children will be taken over. [*He walks up and down silently for a few moments.*] I sincerely trust such a thing will not occur again.— Who gets all the blame for it? Why, of course the manufacturer. It's entirely our fault. If some poor little fellow sticks in the snow in winter and goes to sleep, a special correspondent arrives posthaste, and in two days we have a blood-curdling story served up in all the papers. Is any blame laid on the father, the parents, that send such a child?—Not a bit of it. How should they be to blame? It's all the manufacturer's fault—he's made the scapegoat. They flatter the weaver, and give the manufacturer nothing but abuse—he's a cruel man, with a heart like a stone, a dangerous fellow, at whose calves every cur of a journalist may take a bite. He lives on the fat of the land, and pays the poor weavers starvation wages. In the flow of his eloquence the writer forgets to mention that such a man has his cares too and his sleepless nights; that he runs risks of which the workman never dreams; that he is often driven distracted by all the calculations he has to make, and all the different things he has to take into account; that he has to struggle for his very life against competition; and that no day passes without some annoyance or some loss. And think of the manufacturer's responsibilities, think of the numbers that depend on him, that look to him for their daily bread. No, No! none of you need wish yourselves in my shoes—you would soon have enough of it.

[*After a moment's reflection.*] You all saw how that fellow, that scoundrel Becker, behaved. Now he'll go and spread about all sorts of tales of my hardheartedness, of how my weavers are turned off for a mere trifle, without a moment's notice. Is that true? Am I so very unmerciful?

CHORUS OF VOICES. No, sir.

DREISSIGER. It doesn't seem to me that I am. And yet these ne'er-do-wells come round singing low songs about us manufacturers — prating about hunger, with enough in their pockets to pay for quarts of bad brandy. If they would like to know what want is, let them go and ask the linen-weavers: they can tell something about it. But you here, you fustian-weavers, have every reason to thank God that things are no worse than they are. And I put it to all the old, industrious weavers present: Is a good workman able to gain a living in my employment, or is he not?

MANY VOICES. Yes, sir; he is, sir.

DREISSIGER. There now! You see! Of course such a fellow as that Becker can't. I advise you to keep these young lads in check. If there's much more of this sort of thing, I'll shut up shop — give up the business altogether, and then you can shift for yourselves, get work where you like — perhaps Mr. Becker will provide it.

FIRST WEAVER'S WIFE (*has come close to* DREISSIGER, *and removes a little dust from his coat with creeping servility*). You've been an' rubbed agin something, sir.

DREISSIGER. Business is as bad as it can be just now, you know that yourselves. Instead of making money, I am losing it every day. If, in spite of this, I take care that my weavers are kept in work, I look for some little gratitude from them. I have thousands of pieces of cloth in stock, and don't know if I'll ever be able to sell them. Well, now, I've heard how many weavers hereabouts are out of work, and — I'll leave Pfeifer to give the particulars — but this much I'll tell you, just to

show you my good will. I can't deal out charity all
round; I'm not rich enough for that; but I can give the
people who are out of work the chance of earning at
any rate a little. It's a great business risk I run by
doing it, but that's my affair. I say to myself: Better
that a man should work for a bite of bread than that
he should starve altogether. Am I not right?

CHORUS OF VOICES. Yes, yes, sir.

DREISSIGER. And therefore I am ready to give employment
to two hundred more weavers. Pfeifer will tell you on
what conditions.   [*He turns to go.*]

FIRST WEAVER'S WIFE (*comes between him and the door,
speaks hurriedly, eagerly, imploringly*). Oh, if you
please, sir, will you let me ask you if you'll be so good —
I've been twice laid up for —

DREISSIGER (*hastily*). Speak to Pfeifer, good woman. I'm
too late as it is.   [*Passes on, leaving her standing.*]

REIMANN (*stops him again. In an injured, complaining
tone*). I have a complaint to make, if you please, sir.
Mr. Pfeifer refuses to — I've always got one and twopence for a web —

DREISSIGER (*interrupts him*). Mr. Pfeifer's my manager.
There he is. Apply to him.

HEIBER (*detaining* DREISSIGER; *hurriedly and confusedly*).
O sir, I wanted to ask if you would p'r'aps, if I might
p'r'aps — if Mr. Pfeifer might — might —

DREISSIGER. What is it you want?

HEIBER. That advance pay I had last time, sir; I thought
p'r'aps you would kindly —

DREISSIGER. I have no idea what you are talking about.

HEIBER. I'm awful hard up, sir, because —

DREISSIGER. These are things Pfeifer must look into — I
really have not the time. Arrange the matter with
Pfeifer. [*He escapes into the office.*]

   [*The supplicants look helplessly at one another, sigh,
      and take their places again among the others.*]

PFEIFER (*resuming his task of inspection*). Well, Annie,
let us see what yours is like.

OLD BAUMERT. How much is we to get for the web, then, Mr. Pfeifer?

PFEIFER. One shilling a web.

OLD BAUMERT. Has it come to that!

[*Excited whispering and murmuring among the weavers.*]

ACT II

A small room in the house of WILHELM ANSORGE, *weaver and cottager in the village of Kaschbach, in the Eulengebirge.*

In this room, which does not measure six feet from the dilapidated wooden floor to the smoke-blackened rafters, sit four people. Two young girls, EMMA *and* BERTHA BAUMERT, *are working at their looms;* MOTHER BAUMERT, *a decrepit old woman, sits on a stool beside the bed, with a winding-wheel in front of her; her idiot son* AUGUST *sits on a footstool, also winding. He is twenty, has a small body and head, and long, spider-like legs and arms.*

Faint, rosy evening light makes its way through two small windows in the right wall, which have their broken panes pasted over with paper or stuffed with straw. It lights up the flaxen hair of the girls, which falls loose on their slender white necks and thin bare shoulders, and their coarse chemises. These, with a short petticoat of the roughest linen, form their whole attire. The warm glow falls on the old woman's face, neck, and breast — a face worn away to a skeleton, with shriveled skin and sunken eyes, red and watery with smoke, dust, and working by lamplight — a long goître neck, wrinkled and sinewy — a hollow breast covered with faded, ragged shawls.

Part of the right wall is also lighted up, with stove, stove-bench, bedstead, and one or two gaudily colored sacred prints. On the stove rail rags are hanging to dry, and behind the stove is a collection of worthless lumber. On the bench stand some old pots and cooking utensils, and potato parings are laid out on it, on paper, to dry. Hanks of yarn and reels hang from the rafters; baskets of bobbins stand beside the looms. In the back wall there is a low door without fastening. Beside it a bundle of willow wands is set up against the wall, and beyond them lie some damaged quarter-bushel baskets.

The room is full of sound — the rhythmic thud of the looms, shaking floor and walls, the click and rattle of the shuttles passing back and forward, and the steady whirr of the winding-wheels, like the hum of gigantic bees.

MOTHER BAUMERT (*in a querulous, feeble voice, as the girls stop weaving and bend over their webs*). Got to make knots again already, have you?

Permission Berlin Photo Co., New York

NICOLA PERSCHEID

GERHART HAUPTMANN

EMMA (*the elder of the two girls, about twenty-two, tying a broken thread*). It's the plagueyest web, this!

BERTHA (*fifteen*). Yes, it's real bad yarn they've given us this time.

EMMA. What can have happened to father? He's been away since nine.

MOTHER BAUMERT. That he has! yes. Where in the wide world c'n he be?

BERTHA. Don't you worry yourself, mother.

MOTHER BAUMERT. I can't help it, Bertha lass.

[EMMA *begins to weave again.*]

BERTHA. Stop a minute, Emma!

EMMA. What is it!

BERTHA. I thought I heard some one.

EMMA. It'll be Ansorge comin' home.

Enter FRITZ, *a little, barefooted, ragged boy of four.*

FRITZ (*whimpering*). I'm hungry, mother.

EMMA. Wait, Fritzel, wait a bit! Gran'father'll be here very soon, an' he's bringin' bread along with him, an' coffee too.

FRITZ. But I'm awful hungry, mother.

EMMA. Be a good boy now, Fritz. Listen to what I'm tellin' you. He'll be here this minute. He's bringin' nice bread an' nice corn-coffee; an' when we stops workin' mother'll take the tater peelin's and carry them to the farmer, and the farmer'll give her a drop o' good buttermilk for her little boy.

FRITZ. Where's grandfather gone?

EMMA. To the manufacturer, Fritz, with a web.

FRITZ. To the manufacturer?

EMMA. Yes, yes, Fritz, down to Dreissiger's at Peterswaldau.

FRITZ. Is it there he gets the bread?

EMMA. Yes; Dreissiger gives him money, and then he buys the bread.

FRITZ. Does he give him a heap of money?

EMMA (*impatiently*). Oh, stop that chatter, boy.
> [*She and* BERTHA *go on weaving for a time, and then both stop again.*]

BERTHA. August, go and ask Ansorge if he'll give us a light.   [AUGUST *goes out accompanied by* FRITZ.]

MOTHER BAUMERT (*overcome by her childish apprehension, whimpers*). Emma! Bertha! where c'n the man be stayin'?

BERTHA. Maybe he looked in to see Hauffe.

MOTHER BAUMERT (*crying*). What if he's sittin' drinkin' in the public-house?

EMMA. Don't cry, mother! You know well enough father's not the man to do that.

MOTHER BAUMERT (*half distracted by a multitude of gloomy forebodings*). What — what — what's to become of us if he don't come home? if he drinks the money, an' don't bring us nothin' at all? There's not so much as a handful o' salt in the house — not a bite o' bread, nor a bit o' wood for the fire.

BERTHA. Wait a bit, mother! It's moonlight just now. We'll take August with us and go into the wood and get some sticks.

MOTHER BAUMERT. Yes, an' be caught by the forester.

ANSORGE, *an old weaver of gigantic stature, who has to bend down to get into the room, puts his head and shoulders in at the door. Long, unkempt hair and beard.*

ANSORGE. What's wanted?

BERTHA. Light, if you please.

ANSORGE (*in a muffled voice, as if speaking in a sick-room*). There's good daylight yet.

MOTHER BAUMERT. Is we to sit in the dark next?

ANSORGE. I've to do the same mayself.   [*Goes out.*]

BERTHA. It's easy to see that he's a miser.

EMMA. Well, there's nothin' for it but to sit an' wait his pleasure.

Enter MRS. HEINRICH, *a woman of thirty, heavy with child; an expression of torturing anxiety and apprehension on her worn face.*

MRS. HEINRICH.   Good evenin' t'you all.

MOTHER BAUMERT.   Well, Jenny, and what's your news?

MRS. HEINRICH (*who limps*).   I've got a piece o' glass into my foot.

BERTHA.   Come an' sit down, then, an' I'll see if I c'n get it out.

> [MRS. HEINRICH *seats herself.*   BERTHA *kneels down in front of her, and examines her foot.*]

MOTHER BAUMERT.   How are ye all at home, Jenny?

MRS. HEINRICH (*breaks out despairingly*).   Things is in a terrible way with us!

> [*She struggles in vain against a rush of tears; then weeps silently.*]

MOTHER BAUMERT.   The best thing as could happen to the likes o' us, Jenny, would be if God had pity on us an' took us away out o' this weary world.

MRS. HEINRICH (*no longer able to control herself, screams, still crying*).   My children's starvin'.   [*Sobs and moans.*]   I don't know what to do no more!   I c'n work till I drops—I'm more dead'n alive—things don't get different!   There's nine hungry mouths to fill!   We got a bit o' bread last night, but it wasn't enough even for the two smallest ones.   Who was I to give it to, eh?   They all cried: Me, me, mother! give it to me!   *   *   *   An' if it's like this while I'm still on my feet, what'll it be when I've to take to bed?   Our few taters was washed away.   We haven't a thing to put in our mouths.

BERTHA (*has removed the bit of glass and washed the wound*).   We'll put a rag round it.   Emma, see if you can find one.

MOTHER BAUMERT.   We're no better off'n you, Jenny.

MRS. HEINRICH.   You has your girls, any way.   You've a husband as c'n work.   Mine was taken with one o' his fits last week again—so bad that I didn't know what to do with him, and was half out o' my mind with fright.

And when he's had a turn like that, he can't stir out o' bed under a week.

MOTHER BAUMERT.   Mine's no better.   He's goin' to pieces, too.   He's breathin's bad now as well as his back.   An' there's not a farthin' nor a farthin's worth in the house. If he don't bring a few pence with him today, I don't know what we're to do.

EMMA.   It's the truth she's tellin' you, Jenny.   We had to let father take the little dog with him today, to have him killed, that we might get a bite into our stomachs again!

MRS. HEINRICH.   Haven't you got as much as a handful o' flour to spare?

MOTHER BAUMERT.   An' that we haven't, Jenny.   There's not as much as a grain o' salt in the house.

MRS. HEINRICH.   Well, then, I don't know — [*Rises, stands still, brooding.*]   I don't know what'll be the end o' this!   It's more'n I c'n bear.   [*Screams in rage and despair.*]   I'd be contented if it was nothin' but pigs' food! — But I can't go home again empty-handed — that I can't.   God forgive me, I see no other way out of it.   [*She limps quickly out.*]

MOTHER BAUMERT (*calls after her in a warning voice*). Jenny, Jenny! don't you be doin' anything foolish, now!

BERTHA.   She'll do herself no harm, mother.   You needn't be afraid.

EMMA.   That's the way she always goes on.

[*Seats herself at the loom and weaves for a few seconds.*]

AUGUST *enters, carrying a tallow candle, and lighting his father,* OLD BAUMERT, *who follows close behind him, staggering under a heavy bundle of yarn.*

MOTHER BAUMERT.   Oh, father, where have you been all this long time?   Where have you been?

OLD BAUMERT. Come now, mother, don't fall on a man like that. Give me time to get my breath first. An' look who I've brought with me.

MORITZ JAEGER comes stooping in at the low door. Reserve soldier, newly discharged. Middle height, rosy-cheeked, military carriage. His cap on the side of his head, hussar fashion, whole clothes and shoes, a clean shirt without collar. Draws himself up and salutes.

JAEGER (*in a hearty voice*). Good-evenin', auntie Baumert!

MOTHER BAUMERT. Well, well now! and to think you've got back! An' you've not forgotten us? Take a chair, then, lad.

EMMA (*wiping a wooden chair with her apron, and pushing it toward* MORITZ). An' so you've come to see what poor folks is like again, Moritz?

JAEGER. I say, Emma, is it true that you've got a boy nearly old enough to be a soldier? Where did you get hold o' him, eh?

[BERTHA, *having taken the small supply of provisions which her father has brought, puts meat into a saucepan, and shoves it into the oven, while* AUGUST *lights the fire.*]

BERTHA. You knew weaver Finger, didn't you?

MOTHER BAUMERT. We had him here in the house with us. He was ready enough to marry her; but he was too far gone in consumption; he was as good as a dead man. It didn't happen for want o' warnin' from me. But do you think she would listen? Not she. Now he's dead an' forgotten long ago, an' she's left with the boy to provide for as best she can. But now tell us how you've been gettin' on, Moritz.

OLD BAUMERT. You've only to look at him, mother, to know that. He's had luck. It'll be about as much as he can do to speak to the likes o' us. He's got clothes like a prince, an' a silver watch, an' thirty shillings in his pocket into the bargain.

JAEGER (*stretching himself consequentially, a knowing smile on his face*). I can't complain. I didn't get on so badly in the regiment.

OLD BAUMERT. He was the major's own servant. Just listen to him — he speaks like a gentleman.

JAEGER. I've got so accustomed to it that I can't help it.

MOTHER BAUMERT. Well, now, to think that such a good-for-nothin' as you was should have come to be a rich man. For there wasn't nothin' to be made of you. You would never sit still to wind more than a hank of yarn at a time, that you wouldn't. Off you went to your tomtit boxes an' your robin redbreast snares — they was all you cared about. Isn't it the truth I'm telling?

JAEGER. Yes, yes, auntie, it's true enough. It wasn't only redbreasts. I went after swallows too.

EMMA. Though we were always tellin' you that swallows was poison.

JAEGER. What did I care? — But how have you all been gettin' on, auntie Baumert?

MOTHER BAUMERT. Oh, badly, lad, badly these last four years. I've had the rheumatics — just look at them hands. An' it's more than likely as I've had a stroke o' some kind too, I'm that helpless. I can hardly move a limb, an' nobody knows the pains I suffers.

OLD BAUMERT. She's in a bad way, she is. She'll not hold out long.

BERTHA. We've to dress her in the mornin' an' undress her at night, an' to feed her like a baby.

MOTHER BAUMERT (*speaking in a complaining, tearful voice*). Not a thing c'n I do for myself. It's far worse than bein' ill. For it's not only a burden to myself I am, but to every one else. Often and often do I pray to God to take me. For oh! mine's a weary life. I don't know — p'r'aps they think — but I'm one that's been a hard worker all my days. An' I've always been able to do my turn too; but now, all at once [*she vainly attempts to rise*] I can't do nothin'. I've a good husband an' good children, but to have to sit here and see them — ! Look at the girls! There's hardly any blood left in them — faces the color of a sheet. But on they must work at these weary looms whether they earn enough to keep theirselves or not. What sort o' life is it they lead? Their feet never off the treadle from year's end to year's end. An' with it all they can't scrape together as much as 'll buy them clothes that they can let theirselves be seen in; never a step can they go to church, to hear a word o' comfort. They're liker scarecrows than young girls of fifteen and twenty.

BERTHA (*at the stove*). It's beginnin' to smoke again!

OLD BAUMERT. There now; look at that smoke. And we can't do nothin' for it. The whole stove's goin' to pieces. We must let it fall, and swallow the soot. We're coughin' already, one worse than the other. We may cough till we choke, or till we cough our lungs up — nobody cares.

JAEGER. But this here is Ansorge's business; he must see to the stove.

BERTHA. He'll see us out o' the house first; he has plenty against us without that.

MOTHER BAUMERT. We've only been in his way this long time past.

OLD BAUMERT. One word of a complaint an' out we go. He's had no rent from us this last half-year.

MOTHER BAUMERT. A well-off man like him needn't be so hard.

OLD BAUMERT. He's no better off than we is, mother. He's hard put to it too, for all he holds his tongue about it.

MOTHER BAUMERT. He's got his house.

OLD BAUMERT. What are you talkin' about, mother? Not one stone in the wall is the man's own.

JAEGER (*has seated himself, and taken a short pipe with gay tassels out of one coat-pocket, and a quart bottle of brandy out of another*). Things can't go on like this.

I'm dumbfoundered when I see the life the people live here. The very dogs in the towns live better.

OLD BAUMERT (*eagerly*). That's what I says! Eh? eh? You know it too! But if you say that here, they'll tell you that it's only bad times.

Enter ANSORGE, an earthenware pan with soup in one hand, in the other a half-finished quarter-bushel basket.

ANSORGE. Glad to see you again, Moritz!

JAEGER. Thank you, father Ansorge — same to you!

ANSORGE (*shoving his pan into the oven*). Why, lad, you look like a duke.

OLD BAUMERT. Show him your watch, Moritz. An' he's got a new suit of clothes, an' thirty shillings cash.

ANSORGE (*shaking his head*). Is that so? Well, well!

EMMA (*puts the potato-parings into a bag*). I must be off; I'll maybe get a drop o' buttermilk for these.

[*Goes out.*]

JAEGER (*the others hanging intently and devoutly on his words*). You know how you all used to be down on me. It was always: Wait, Moritz, till your soldierin' time comes — you'll catch it then. But you see how well I've got on. At the end o' the first half-year I had my good conduct stripes. You've got to be willin' — that's where the secret lies. I brushed the sergeant's boots; I groomed his horse; I fetched his beer. I was as sharp as a needle. Always ready, accoutrements clean and shinin' — first at stables, first at roll-call, first in the saddle. An' when the bugle sounded to the assault — why, then, blood and thunder, and ride to the devil with you!! I was as keen as a pointer. Says I to myself: There's no help for it now, my boy, it's got to be done; and I set my mind to it and did it. Till at last the major said before the whole squadron: There's a hussar now that shows you what a hussar should be!

[*Silence. He lights his pipe.*]

ANSORGE (*shaking his head*). Well, well, well! You had luck with you, Moritz!

 [*Sits down on the floor, with his willow twigs beside him, and continues mending the basket, which he holds between his legs.*]

OLD BAUMERT. Let's hope you've brought some of it to us.— Are we to have a drop to drink your health in?

JAEGER. Of course you are, father Baumert. And when this bottle's done, we'll send for more.

 [*He flings a coin on the table.*]

ANSORGE (*open mouthed with amazement*). Oh my! Oh my! What goings on to be sure! Roast meat frizzlin' in the oven! A bottle o' brandy on the table! [*He drinks out of the bottle.*] Here's to you, Moritz!— Well, well, well!

 [*The bottle circulates freely after this.*]

OLD BAUMERT. If we could any way have a bit o' meat on Sundays and holidays, instead o' never seein' the sight of it from year's end to year's end! Now we'll have to wait till another poor little dog finds its way into the house like this one did four weeks gone by — an' that's not likely to happen soon again.

ANSORGE. Have you killed the little dog?

OLD BAUMERT. We had to do that or starve.

ANSORGE. Well, well! That's so!

MOTHER BAUMERT. A nice, kind little beast he was, too!

JAEGER. Are you as keen as ever on roast dog hereabouts?

OLD BAUMERT. Lord, if we could only get enough of it!

MOTHER BAUMERT. A nice little bit o' meat like that does you a lot o' good.

OLD BAUMERT. Have you lost the taste for it, Moritz? Stay with us a bit, and it'll soon come back to you.

ANSORGE (*sniffing*). Yes, yes! That will be a tasty bite — what a good smell it has!

OLD BAUMERT (*sniffing*). Fine as spice, you might say.

ANSORGE.   Come, then, Moritz, tell us your opinion, you
that's been out and seen the world.   Is things at all
like to improve for us weavers, eh?

JAEGER.   They would need to.

ANSORGE.   We're in an awful state here.   It's not livin' an'
it's not dyin'.   A man fights to the bitter end, but he's
bound to be beat at last — to be left without a roof over
his head, you may say without ground under his feet.
As long as he can work at the loom he can earn some
sort o' poor, miserable livin'.   But it's many a day
since I've been able to get that sort o' job.   Now I tries
to put a bite into my mouth with this here basket-
makin'.   I sits at it late into the night, and by the time
I tumbles into bed I've earned three-half-pence.   I
puts it to you as knows things, if a man can live on that,
when everything's so dear?   Nine shillin' goes in one
lump for house tax, three shillin' for land tax, nine
shillin' for mortgage interest — that makes one pound
one.   I may reckon my year's earnin at just double
that money, and that leaves me twenty-one shillin' for
a whole year's food, an' fire, an' clothes, an' shoes; and
I've got to keep up some sort of a place to live in.   An'
there's odds an' ends.   Is it a wonder if I'm behind-
hand with my interest payments?

OLD BAUMERT.   Some one would need to go to Berlin an'
tell the King how hard put to it we are.

JAEGER.   Little good that would do, father Baumert.
There's been plenty written about it in the newspapers.
But the rich people, they can turn and twist things
round — as cunning as the devil himself.

OLD BAUMERT (*shaking his head*).   To think they've no
more sense than that in Berlin.

ANSORGE.   And is it really true, Moritz?   Is there no law to
help us?   If a man hasn't been able to scrape together
enough to pay his mortgage interest, though he's
worked the very skin off his hands, must his house be
taken from him?   The peasant that's lent the money

on it, he wants his rights — what else can you look for
from him? But what's to be the end of it all, I don't
know.— If I'm put out o' the house — [*In a voice
choked by tears.*] I was born here, and here my father
sat at his loom for more than forty year. Many was
the time he said to mother: Mother, when I'm gone,
keep hold o' the house. I've worked hard for it. Every
nail means a night's weavin', every plank a year's dry
bread. A man would think that —

JAEGER. They're just as like to take the last bite out of
your mouth — that's what they are.

ANSORGE. Well, well, well! I would rather be carried out
than have to walk out now in my old days. Who minds
dyin'? My father, he was glad to die. At the very
end he got frightened, but I crept into bed beside him,
an' he quieted down again. Think of it: I was a lad
of thirteen then. I was tired and fell asleep beside
him — I knew no better — and when I woke he was
quite cold.

MOTHER BAUMERT (*after a pause*). Give Ansorge his soup
out o' the oven, Bertha.

BERTHA. Here, father Ansorge, it'll do you good.

ANSORGE (*eating and shedding tears*). Well, well, well!
 [OLD BAUMERT *has begun to eat the meat out of the
  saucepan.*]

MOTHER BAUMERT. Father, father, can't you have patience
an' let Bertha serve it up properly?

OLD BAUMERT (*chewing*). It's two years now since I took
the sacrament. I went straight after that an' sold my
Sunday coat, an' we bought a good bit o' pork, an'
since then never a mouthful of meat has passed my
lips till tonight.

JAEGER. *We* don't need no meat! The manufacturers eats
it for us. It's the fat o' the land *they* lives on. Whoever don't believe that has only to go down to Bielau
and Peterswaldau. He'll see fine things there — palace
upon palace, with towers and iron railings and plate-

glass windows. Who do they all belong to? Why, of course, the manufacturers! No signs of bad times there! Baked and boiled and fried — horses and carriages and governesses — they've money to pay for all that and goodness knows how much more. They're swelled out to burstin' with pride and good livin'.

ANSORGE. Things was different in my young days. Then the manufacturers let the weaver have his share. Now they keeps everything to theirselves. An' would you like to know what's at the bottom of it all? It's that the fine folks nowadays believes neither in God nor devil. What do they care about commandments or punishments? And so they steals our last scrap o' bread, an' leaves us no chance of earnin' the barest living. For it's their fault. If our manufacturers was good men, there would be no bad times for us.

JAEGER. Listen, then, and I'll read you something that will please you. [*He takes one or two loose papers from his pocket.*] I say, August, run and fetch another quart from the public-house. Eh, boy, do you laugh all day long?

MOTHER BAUMERT. No one knows why, but our August's always happy — grins an' laughs, come what may. Off with you then, quick! [*Exit* AUGUST *with the empty brandy-bottle.*] You've got something good now, eh, father?

OLD BAUMERT (*still chewing; his spirits are rising from the effect of food and drink*). Moritz, you're the very man we want. You can read an' write. You understand the weavin' trade, and you've a heart to feel for the poor weavers' sufferin's. You should stand up for us here.

JAEGER. I'd do that quick enough! There's nothing I'd like better than to give the manufacturers round here a bit of a fright — dogs that they are! I'm an easy-goin' fellow, but let me once get worked up into a real rage, and I'll take Dreissiger in the one hand and Dittrich in the other, and knock their heads together till the sparks fly out o' their eyes. If we could only arrange all to join together, we'd soon give the manufacturers a proper lesson — we wouldn't need no King an' no Government. All we'd have to do would be to say: We wants this and that, and we don't want the other thing. There would be a change of days then. As soon as they see that there's some pluck in us, they'll cave in. I know the rascals; they're a pack o' cowardly hounds.

MOTHER BAUMERT. There's some truth in what you say. I'm not a bad woman. I've always been the one to say as how there must be rich folks as well as poor. But when things come to such a pass as this—

JAEGER. The devil may take them all, for what I care. It would be no more than they deserves.

[OLD BAUMERT *has quietly gone out.*]

BERTHA. Where's father?

MOTHER BAUMERT. I don't know where he can have gone.

BERTHA. Do you think he's not been able to stomach the meat, with not gettin' none for so long?

MOTHER BAUMERT (*in distress, crying*). There now, there! He's not even able to keep it down when he's got it. Up it comes again, the only bite o' good food as he's tasted this many a day.

Reënter OLD BAUMERT, *crying with rage.*

OLD BAUMERT. It's no good! I'm too far gone! Now that I've at last got hold of somethin' with a taste in it, my stomach won't keep it.

[*He sits down on the bench by the stove crying.*]

JAEGER (*with a sudden violent ebullition of rage*). An' yet there's people not far from here, justices they call themselves too, over-fed brutes, that have nothing to do all the year round but invent new ways of wastin' their time. An' these people say that the weavers would be quite well off if only they wasn't so lazy.

ANSORGE. The men as says that are no men at all, they're monsters.

JAEGER. Never mind, father Ansorge; we're makin' the place hot for 'em. Becker and I have been and given Dreissiger a piece of our mind, and before we came away we sang him "Bloody Justice."

ANSORGE. Good Lord! Is that the song?

JAEGER. Yes; I have it here.

ANSORGE. They calls it Dreissiger's song, don't they?

JAEGER. I'll read it to you.

MOTHER BAUMERT. Who wrote it?

JAEGER. That's what nobody knows. Now listen.

> [*He reads, hesitating like a schoolboy, with incorrect accentuation, but unmistakably strong feeling. Despair, suffering, rage, hatred, thirst for revenge, all find utterance.*]

> The justice to us weavers dealt
>   Is bloody, cruel, and hateful;
> Our life's one torture, long drawn out:
>   For lynch law we'd be grateful.

> Stretched on the rack day after day,
>   Hearts sick and bodies aching,
> Our heavy sighs their witness bear
>   To spirit slowly breaking.

> [*The words of the song make a strong impression on* OLD BAUMERT. *Deeply agitated, he struggles against the temptation to interrupt* JAEGER. *At last he can keep quiet no longer.*]

OLD BAUMERT (*to his wife, half laughing, half crying, stammering*). Stretched on the rack day after day. Whoever wrote that, mother, wrote the truth. You can bear witness — eh, how does it go? "Our heavy sighs their witness bear" — What's the rest?

JAEGER. "To spirit slowly breaking."

OLD BAUMERT. You know the way we sigh, mother, day and
night, sleepin' and wakin'.

[ANSORGE *has stopped working, and cowers on the
floor, strongly agitated.* MOTHER BAUMERT *and*
BERTHA *wipe their eyes frequently during the
course of the reading.*]

JAEGER (*continues to read*).

> The Dreissigers true hangmen are,
> Servants no whit behind them;
> Masters and men with one accord
> Set on the poor to grind them.

> You villains all, you brood of hell—

OLD BAUMERT (*trembling with rage, stamping on the floor*).
Yes, brood of hell!!!

JAEGER (*reads*).

> You fiends in fashion human,
> A curse will fall on all like you,
> Who prey on man and woman.

ANSORGE. Yes, yes, a curse upon them!

OLD BAUMERT (*clenching his fist, threateningly*). You prey
on man and woman.

JAEGER (*reads*).

> The suppliant knows he asks in vain,
> Vain every word that's spoken.
> "If not content, then go and starve—
> Our rules cannot be broken."

OLD BAUMERT. What is it? "The suppliant knows he asks
in vain?" Every word of it's true—every word—
as true as the Bible. He knows he asks in vain.

ANSORGE. Yes, yes! It's all no good.

JAEGER (*reads*).

> Then think of all our woe and want,
> O ye who hear this ditty!
> Our struggles vain for daily bread
> Hard hearts would move to pity.

But pity's what *you've* never known,—
You'd take both skin and clothing,
You cannibals, whose cruel deeds
Fill all good men with loathing.

OLD BAUMERT (*jumps up, beside himself with excitement*).
Both skin and clothing. It's true, it's all true! Here
I stands, Robert Baumert, master-weaver of Kaschbach. Who can bring up anything against me? I've
been an honest, hard-workin' man all my life long, an'
look at me now! What have I to show for it? Look
at me! See what they've made of me! Stretched on
the rack day after day. [*He holds out his arms.*] Feel
that! Skin and bone! "You villains all, you brood
of hell!!"
  [*He sinks down on a chair, weeping with rage and
  despair.*]

ANSORGE (*flings his basket from him into a corner, rises, his
whole body trembling with rage, gasps*). An' the
time's come now for a change, I say. We'll stand it
no longer. We'll stand it no longer! Come what may!

ACT III

*The common-room of the principal public-house in Peterswaldau. A large
room with a raftered roof supported by a central wooden pillar, round
which a table runs. In the back wall, a little to the right of the pillar, is
the entrance-door, through the opening of which the spacious lobby or
outer room is seen, with barrels and brewing utensils. To the right of
this door, in the corner, is the bar — a high wooden counter with recep-
tacles for beer-mugs, glasses, etc.; a cupboard with rows of brandy and
liqueur bottles on the wall behind, and between counter and cupboard a
narrow space for the barkeeper. In front of the bar stands a table with
a gay-colored cover, a pretty lamp hanging above it, and several cane
chairs placed around it. Not far off, in the right wall, is a door with
the inscription: Bar Parlor. Nearer the front on the same side an old
eight-day clock stands ticking. At the back, to the left of the entrance-
door, is a table with bottles and glasses, and beyond this, in the corner,
is the great tile-oven. In the left wall there are three small windows.
Below them runs a long bench; and in front of each stands a large
oblong wooden table, with the end towards the wall. There are benches*

*with backs along the sides of these tables, and at the end of each facing
the window stands a wooden chair. The walls are washed blue and
decorated with advertisements, colored prints and oleographs, among
the latter a portrait of Frederick William IV.*

WELZEL, *the publican, a good-natured giant, upwards of fifty, stands behind
the counter, letting beer run from a barrel into a glass.* MRS. WELZEL
*is ironing by the stove. She is a handsome, tidily dressed woman in her
thirty-fifth year.* ANNA WELZEL, *a good-looking girl of seventeen, with
a quantity of beautiful, fair, reddish hair, sits, neatly dressed, with her
embroidery, at the table with the colored cover. She looks up from her
work for a moment and listens, as the sound of a funeral hymn sung by
school-children is heard in the distance.* WIEGAND, *the joiner, in his
working clothes, is sitting at the same table, with a glass of Bavarian
beer before him. His face shows that he understands what the world requires of a man if he is to attain his ends — namely, craftiness, swift-
ness, and relentless pushing forward.* A COMMERCIAL TRAVELER *is
seated at the pillar-table, vigorously masticating a beefsteak. He is of
middle height, stout and thrifty-looking, inclined to jocosity, lively, and
impudent. He is dressed in the fashion of the day, and his portmanteau,
pattern-case, umbrella, overcoat and traveling rug lie on chairs beside him.*

WELZEL (*carrying a glass of beer to the* TRAVELER, but
   addressing WIEGAND). The devil's broke loose in
   Peterswaldau today.

WIEGAND (*in a sharp, shrill voice*). That's because it's
   delivery day at Dreissiger's.

MRS. WELZEL. But they don't generally make such an
   awful row.

WIEGAND. It's may be because of the two hundred new
   weavers that he's going to take on.

MRS. WELZEL (*at her ironing*). Yes, yes, that'll be it. If
   he wants two hundred, six hundred's sure to have come.
   There's no lack of *them.*

WIEGAND. No, they'll last. There's no fear of their dying
   out, let them be ever so badly off. They bring more
   children into the world than we know what to do with.
   [*The strains of the funeral hymn are suddenly heard
   more distinctly.*] There's a funeral today too. Weaver
   Nentwich is dead, you know.

WELZEL. He's been long enough about it. He's been goin'
   about like a livin' ghost this many a long day.

WIEGAND.   You never saw such a little coffin, Welzel; it was
    the tiniest, miserablest little thing I ever glued together.
    And what a corpse!   It didn't weigh ninety pounds.

TRAVELER (*his mouth full*).   What I don't understand's this:
    Take up whatever paper you like and you'll find the
    most heartrending accounts of the destitution among
    the weavers.   You get the impression that three-quar-
    ters of the people in this neighborhood are starving.
    Then you come and see a funeral like what's going on
    just now.   I met it as I came into the village.   Brass
    band, schoolmaster, school children, pastor, and such a
    procession behind them that you would think it was
    the Emperor of China that was getting buried.   If
    the people have money to spend on this sort of thing,
    well—!   [*He takes a drink of beer; puts down the
    glass; suddenly and jocosely.*]   What do you say to it,
    miss?   Don't you agree with me?

    [ANNA *gives an embarrassed laugh, and goes on
    working busily.*]

TRAVELER.   Now, I'll take a bet that these are slippers for
    papa.

WELZEL.   You're wrong, then; I wouldn't put such things
    on my feet.

TRAVELER.   You don't say so!   Now, I would give half of
    what I'm worth if these slippers were for me.

MRS. WELZEL.   Oh, he don't know nothing about such things.

WIEGAND (*has coughed once or twice, moved his chair, and
    prepared himself to speak*).   You were sayin', sir, that
    you wondered to see such a funeral as this.   I tell you,
    and Mrs. Welzel here will bear me out, that it's quite
    a small funeral.

TRAVELER.   But, my good man,—what a monstrous lot of
    money it must cost!   Where does all that come from?

WIEGAND.   If you'll excuse me for saying so, sir, there's a
    deal of foolishness among the poorer working people
    hereabouts.   They have a kind of inordinate idea, if
    I may say so, of the respect an' duty an' honor they're
    bound to show to such as is taken from their midst.

And when it comes to be a case of parents, then there's no bounds whatever to their superstitiousness. The children and the nearest family scrapes together every farthing they can call their own, an' what's still wanting, that they borrow from some rich man. They run themselves into debt over head and ears; they're owing money to the pastor, to the sexton, and to all concerned. Then there's the victuals an' the drink, an' such like. No, sir, I'm far from speaking against dutifulness to parents; but it's too much when it goes the length of the mourners having to bear the weight of it for the rest of their lives.

TRAVELER. But surely the pastor might reason them out of such foolishness.

WIEGAND. Begging your pardon, sir, but I must mention that every little place hereabouts has its church an' its reverend pastor to support. These honorable gentlemen has their advantages from big funerals. The larger the attendance is, the larger the offertory is bound to be. Whoever knows the circumstances connected with the working classes here, sir, will assure you that the pastors are strong against quiet funerals.

Enter HORNIG, *the rag dealer, a little bandy-legged old man, with a strap round his chest.*

HORNIG. Good-mornin', ladies and gentlemen! A glass o' schnapps, if you please, Mr. Welzel. Has the young mistress anything for me today? I've got beautiful ribbons in my cart, Miss Anna, an' tapes, an' garters, an' the very best of pins an' hairpins an' hooks an' eyes. An' all in exchange for a few rags. [*In a changed voice.*] An' out of them rags fine white paper's to be made, for your sweetheart to write you a letter on.

ANNA. Thank you, but I've nothing to do with sweethearts.

MRS. WELZEL (*putting a bolt into her iron*). No, she's not that kind. She'll not hear of marrying.

TRAVELER (*jumps up, affecting delighted surprise, goes forward to* ANNA's *table, and holds out his hand to her across it*). That's sensible, miss. You and I think alike in this matter. Give me your hand on it. We'll both remain single.

ANNA (*blushing scarlet, gives him her hand*). But you are married already!

TRAVELER. Not a bit of it. I only pretend to be. You think so because I wear a ring. I only have it on my finger to protect my charms against shameless attacks. I'm not afraid of you, though. [*He puts the ring into his pocket.*] But tell me, truly, miss, are you quite determined never, never, never to marry?

ANNA (*shakes her head*). Oh, get along with you!

MRS. WELZEL. You may trust her to remain single unless something very extra good turns up.

TRAVELER. And why shouldn't it? I know of a rich Silesian proprietor who married his mother's lady's maid. And there's Dreissiger, the rich manufacturer, his wife is an innkeeper's daughter too, and not half so pretty as you, miss, though she rides in her carriage now, with servants in livery. And why not? [*He marches about, stretching himself, and stamping his feet.*] Let me have a cup of coffee, please.

Enter ANSORGE *and* OLD BAUMERT, *each with a bundle. They seat themselves meekly and silently beside* HORNING, *at the front table to the left.*

WELZEL. How are you, father Ansorge? Glad to see you once again.

HORNIG. Yes, it's not often as you crawl down from that smoky old nest.

ANSORGE (*visibly embarrassed, mumbles*). I've been fetchin' myself a web again.

BAUMERT. He's goin' to work at a shilling the web.

ANSORGE. I wouldn't ha' done it, but there's no more to be made now by basket-weavin'.

WIEGAND. It's always better than nothin'. He does it only to give you employment. I know Dreissiger very well. When I was up there takin' out his double windows last week we were talkin' about it, him and me. It's out of pity that he does it.

ANSORGE. Well, well, well! That may be so.

WELZEL (*setting a glass of schnapps on the table before each of the weavers*). Here you are, then. I say, Ansorge, how long is it since you had a shave? The gentleman over there would like to know.

TRAVELER (*calls across*). Now, Mr. Welzel, you know I didn't say that. I was only struck by the venerable appearance of the master-weaver. It isn't often one sees such a gigantic figure.

ANSORGE (*scratching his head, embarrassed*). Well, well!

TRAVELER. Such specimens of primitive strength are rare nowadays. We're all rubbed smooth by civilization — but I can still take pleasure in nature untampered with! — These bushy eyebrows! That tangled length of beard!

HORNIG. Let me tell you, sir, that them people haven't the money to pay a barber, and as to a razor for themselves, that's altogether beyond them. What grows, grows. They haven't nothing to throw away on their outsides.

TRAVELER. My good friend, you surely don't imagine that I would — [*Aside to* WELZEL.] Do you think I might offer the hairy one a glass of beer?

WELZEL. No, no; you mustn't do that. He wouldn't take it. He's got some queer ideas in that head o' his.

TRAVELER. All right, then, I won't. With your permission, miss. [*He seats himself at* ANNA's *table.*] I declare, miss, that I've not been able to take my eyes off your hair since I came in — such glossy softness, such a splendid quantity! [*Ecstatically kisses his finger-tips.*] And what a color! — like ripe wheat. Come to Berlin with that hair and you'll create no end of a sensation. On my honor, with hair like that you may go to Court. [*Leans back, looking at it.*] Glorious, simply glorious!

WIEGAND. They've given her a fine name because of it.

TRAVELER. And what may that be?

ANNA (*laughing quietly to herself*). Oh, don't listen to that!

HORNIG. The chestnut filly, isn't it?

WELZEL. Come now, we've had enough o' this. I'm not goin' to have the girl's head turned altogether. She's had a-plenty of silly notions put into it already. She'll hear of nothing under a count today, and tomorrow it'll be a prince.

MRS. WELZEL. Don't abuse the girl, father. There's no harm in wantin' to rise in the world. It's as well that people don't all think as you do, or nobody would get on at all. If Dreissiger's grandfather had been of your way of thinkin', they would be poor weavers still. And now they're rollin' in wealth. An' look at old Tromtra. He was nothing but a weaver, too, and now he owns twelve estates, an' he's been made a nobleman into the bargain.

WIEGAND. Yes, Welzel, you must look at the thing fairly. Your wife's in the right this time. I can answer for that. I'd never be where I am, with seven workmen under me, if I had thought like you.

HORNIG. Yes, you understand the way to get on; that your worst enemy must allow. Before the weaver has taken to bed, you're gettin' his coffin ready.

WIEGAND. A man must stick to his business if he's to get on.

HORNIG. No fear of you for that. You know before the doctor when death's on the way to knock at a weaver's door.

WIEGAND (*attempting to laugh, suddenly furious*). And you know better'n the police where the thieves are among the weavers, that keep back two or three bobbins full every week. It's rags you ask for but you don't say No, if there's a little yarn among them.

HORNIG. An' your corn grows in the churchyard. The more that are bedded on the sawdust, the better for you. When you see the rows o' little children's graves, you pats yourself on the belly, and say you: This has been a good year; the little brats have fallen like cock-chafers off the trees. I can allow myself a quart extra in the week again.

WIEGAND. And supposin' this is all true, it still don't make me a receiver of stolen goods.

HORNIG. No; perhaps the worst you do is to send in an account twice to the rich fustian manufacturers, or to help yourself to a plank or two at Dreissiger's when there's building goin' on and the moon happens not to be shinin'.

WIEGAND (*turning his back*). Talk to any one you like, but not to me. [*Then suddenly.*] Hornig the liar!

HORNIG. Wiegand the coffin-jobber!

WIEGAND (*to the rest of the company*). He knows charms for bewitching cattle.

HORNIG. If you don't look out, I'll try one of 'em on you. [WIEGAND *turns pale.*]

MRS. WELZEL (*had gone out; now returns with the TRAV-ELER's coffee; in the act of putting it on the table*). Perhaps you would rather have it in the parlor, sir?

TRAVELER. Most certainly not! [*With a languishing look at* ANNA.] I could sit here till I die.

Enter a YOUNG FORESTER *and a* PEASANT, *the latter carrying a whip. They wish the others " Good Morning," and remain standing at the counter.*

PEASANT. Two brandies, if you please.

WELZEL. Good-morning to you, gentlemen.

> [*He pours out their beverage; the two touch glasses, take a mouthful, and then set the glasses down on the counter.*]

TRAVELER (*to* FORESTER). Come far this morning, sir?

FORESTER. From Steinseiffersdorf — that's a good step.

Two old weavers enter, and seat themselves beside ANSORGE, BAUMERT, *and* HORNIG.

TRAVELER. Excuse me asking, but are you in Count Hochheim's service?

FORESTER. No. I'm in Count Keil's.

TRAVELER. Yes, yes, of course — that was what I meant. One gets confused here among all the counts and barons and other gentlemen. It would take a giant's memory to remember them all. Why do you carry an ax, if I may ask?

FORESTER. I've just taken this one from a man who was stealing wood.

OLD BAUMERT. Yes, their lordships are mighty strict with us about a few sticks for the fire.

TRAVELER. You must allow that if every one were to help himself to what he wanted —

OLD BAUMERT. By your leave, sir, but there's a difference made here as elsewhere between the big an' the little thieves. There's some here as deals in stolen wood wholesale, and grows rich on it. But if a poor weaver —

FIRST OLD WEAVER (*interrupts* BAUMERT). We're forbid to take a single branch; but their lordships, they take the very skin off of us — we've assurance money to pay, an' spinning-money, an' charges in kind — we must go here an' go there, an' do so an' so much field work, all willy-nilly.

ANSORGE. That's just how it is — what the manufacturer leaves us, their lordships takes from us.

SECOND OLD WEAVER (*has taken a seat at the next table*). I've said it to his lordship hisself. By your leave, my lord, says I, it's not possible for me to work on the estate so many days this year. I comes right out with it. For why — my own bit of ground, my lord, it's been next to carried away by the rains. I've to work night and day if I'm to live at all. For oh, what a flood that was! There I stood an' wrung my hands, an' watched the good soil come pourin' down the hill, into the very house! And all that dear, fine seed! I could do nothin' but roar an' cry until I couldn't see out o' my eyes for a week. And then I had to start an' wheel eighty heavy barrow-loads of earth up that hill, till my back was all but broken.

PEASANT (*roughly*). You weavers here make such an awful outcry. As if we hadn't all to put up with what Heaven sends us. An' if you *are* badly off just now, whose fault is it but your own? What did you do when trade was good? Drank an' squandered all you made. If you had saved a bit then, you'd have it to fall back on now when times is bad, and not need to be goin' stealin' yarn and wood.

FIRST YOUNG WEAVER (*standing with several comrades in the lobby or outer room, calls in at the door*). What's a peasant but a peasant, though he lies in bed till nine?

FIRST OLD WEAVER. The peasant an' the count, it's the same story with 'em both. Says the peasant when a weaver wants a house: I'll give you a little bit of a hole to live in, an' you'll pay me so much rent in money, an' the rest of it you'll make up by helpin' me to get in my hay an' my corn — and if that don't please you, why, then you may go elsewhere. He tries another, and to the second he says the same as to the first.

BAUMERT (*angrily*). The weaver's like a bone that every dog takes a gnaw at.

PEASANT (*furious*). You starvin' curs, you're no good for anything. Can you yoke a plough? Can you draw a straight furrow or throw a bundle of sheaves on to a cart. You're fit for nothing but to idle about an' go after the women. A pack of scoundrelly ne'er-do-wells!

[*He has paid and now goes out. The* FORESTER *follows, laughing.* WELZEL, *the joiner, and* MRS. WELZEL *laugh aloud; the* TRAVELER *laughs to himself. Then there is a moment's silence.*]

HORNIG. A peasant like that's as stupid as his own ox. As if I didn't know all about the distress in the villages

round here. Sad sights I've seen! Four and five lyin'
naked on one sack of straw.

TRAVELER (*in a mildly remonstrative tone*). Allow me to
remark, my good man, that there's a great difference
of opinion as to the amount of distress here in the
Eulengebirge. If you can read —

HORNIG. I can read straight off, as well as you. An' I
know what I've seen with my own eyes. It would be
queer if a man that's traveled the country with a pack
on his back these forty years an' more didn't know
something about it. There was the Fullers, now. You
saw the children scrapin' about among the dung-heaps
with the peasants' geese. The people up there died
naked, on the bare stone floors. In their sore need they
ate the stinking weavers' glue. Hunger carried 'em
off by the hundred.

TRAVELER. You must be aware, since you are able to read,
that strict investigation has been made by the Government, and that —

HORNIG. Yes, yes, we all know what that means. They
send a gentleman that knows all about it already better
nor if he had seen it, an' he goes about a bit in the
village where the brook flows broad an' the best houses
is. He don't want to dirty his shinin' boots. Thinks
he to hisself: All the rest 'll be the same as this. An'
so he steps into his carriage, an' drives away home
again, an' then writes to Berlin that there's no distress
in the place at all. If he had but taken the trouble
to go higher up into a village like that, to where the
stream comes in, or across the stream on to the narrow
side — or, better still, if he'd gone up to the little out-
o'-the-way hovels on the hill above, some of 'em that
black an' tumble-down as it would be the waste of a
good match to set fire to 'em — it's another kind o'
report he'd have sent to Berlin. They should ha' come
to me, these government gentlemen that wouldn't
believe there was no distress here. I would ha' shown

'em something.   I'd have opened their eyes for 'em in some of these starvation holes.

[*The strains of the Weavers' Song are heard, sung outside.*]

WELZEL.   There they are, roaring at that devil's song again.

WIEGAND.   They're turning the whole place upside down.

MRS. WELZEL.   You'd think there was something in the air.

JAEGER *and* BECKER *arm in arm, at the head of a troop of young weavers, march noisily through the outer room and enter the bar.*

JAEGER.   Halt!   To your places!

[*The new arrivals sit down at the various tables, and begin to talk to other weavers already seated there.*]

HORNIG (*calls out to* BECKER).   What's up now, Becker, that you've got together a crowd like this?

BECKER (*significantly*).   Who knows but something may be goin' to happen?   Eh, Moritz?

HORNIG.   Come, come, lads.   Don't you be a-gettin' of yourselves into mischief.

BECKER.   Blood's flowed already.   Would you like to see it?

[*He pulls up his sleeve and shows bleeding tattoo-marks on the upper part of his arm.   Many of the other young weavers do the same.*]

BECKER.   We've been at barber Schmidt's gettin' ourselves vaccinated.

HORNIG.   Now the thing's explained.   Little wonder there's such an uproar in the place, with a band of young rapscallions like you paradin' round.

JAEGER (*consequentially, in a loud voice*).   You may bring two quarts at once, Welzel!   I pay.   Perhaps you think I haven't got the needful.   You're wrong, then. If we wanted we could sit an' drink your best brandy an' swill coffee till tomorrow morning with any bagman in the land.

[*Laughter among the young weavers.*]

TRAVELER (*affecting comic surprise*). Is the young gentleman kind enough to take notice of me?

[*Host, hostess, and their daughter,* WIEGAND, *and the* TRAVELER *all laugh.*]

JAEGER. If the cap fits, wear it.

TRAVELER. Your affairs seem to be in a thriving condition. young man, if I may be allowed to say so.

JAEGER. I can't complain. I'm a traveler in made-up goods. I go shares with the manufacturers. The nearer starvation the weaver is, the better I fare. His want butters my bread.

BECKER. Well done, Moritz! You gave it him that time. Here's to you!

[WELZEL *has brought the corn-brandy. On his way back to the counter he stops, turns round slowly, and stands, an embodiment of phlegmatic strength, facing the weavers.*]

WELZEL (*calmly but emphatically*). You let the gentleman alone. He's done you no harm.

YOUNG WEAVERS. And we're doing him no harm.

[MRS. WELZEL *has exchanged a few words with the* TRAVELER. *She takes the cup with the remains of his coffee and carries it into the parlor. The* TRAVELER *follows her amidst the laughter of the weavers.*]

YOUNG WEAVERS (*singing*).

" The Dreissigers the hangmen are,
    Servants no whit behind them."

WELZEL. Hush-sh! Sing that song anywhere else you like, but not in my house.

FIRST OLD WEAVER. He's quite right. Stop that singin,' lads.

BECKER (*roars*). But we must march past Dreissiger's, boys, and let him hear it once more.

WIEGAND. You'd better take care — you may march once **too** often! [*Laughter and cries of Ho, ho!*]

WITTIG has entered; a gray-haired old smith, bare-headed, with leather apron and wooden shoes, sooty from the smithy. He is standing at the counter waiting for his schnapps.

WITTIG. Let 'em go on with their doin's. The dogs as barks most, bites least.

OLD WEAVERS. Wittig, Wittig!

WITTIG. Here he is. What do you want with him?

OLD WEAVERS. "It's Wittig!"—"Wittig, Wittig!"— "Come here, Wittig."—"Sit beside us, Wittig."

WITTIG. Do you think I would sit beside a set of rascals like you?

JAEGER. Come and take a glass with us.

WITTIG. Keep your brandy to yourselves. I pay for my own drink. [*Takes his glass and sits down beside* BAUMERT *and* ANSORGE. *Clapping the latter on the stomach.*] What's the weavers' food so nice? Sauerkraut and roasted lice!

OLD BAUMERT (*drunk with excitement*). But what would you say now if they'd made up their minds as how they would put up with it no longer.

WITTIG (*with pretended astonishment, staring openmouthed at the old weaver*). Heinerle! you don't mean to tell me that that's you? [*Laughs immoderately.*] O Lord, O Lord! I could laugh myself to death. Old Baumert risin' in rebellion! We'll have the tailors at it next, and then there'll be a rebellion among the baa-lambs, and the rats and the mice. Damn it all, but we'll see some sport.

[*He nearly splits with laughter.*]

OLD BAUMERT. You needn't go on like that, Wittig. I'm the same man I've always been. I still say 'twould be better if things could be put right peaceably.

WITTIG. Rot! How could it be done peaceably? Did they do it peaceably in France? Did Robespeer tickle the rich men's palms? No! It was: Away with them, every one! To the gilyoteen with 'em! Allongs onfong!* You've got your work before you. The geese'll not fly ready roasted into your mouths.

OLD BAUMERT. If I could make even half a livin'—

FIRST OLD WEAVER. The water's up to our chins now, Wittig.

SECOND OLD WEAVER. We're afraid to go home. It's all the same whether we works or whether we lies abed; it's starvation both ways.

FIRST OLD WEAVER. A man's like to go mad at home.

OLD ANSORGE. I've come to that pass now that I don't care how things goes.

OLD WEAVERS (*with increasing excitement*). "We've no peace anywhere."—"We've no spirit to work."—"Up with us in Steenkunzendorf you can see a weaver sittin' by the stream washin' hisself the whole day long, naked as God made him. It's driven him clean out of his mind."

THIRD OLD WEAVER (*moved by the spirit, stands up and begins to "speak with tongues," stretching out his hand threateningly*). Judgment is at hand! Have no dealings with the rich and the great! Judgment is at hand! The Lord God of Sabaoth—

[*Some of the weavers laugh. He is pulled down on to his seat.*]

WELZEL. That's a chap that can't stand a single glass— he gets wild at once.

THIRD OLD WEAVER (*jumps up again*). But they—they believe not in God, not in hell, not in heaven. They mock at religion.

FIRST OLD WEAVER. Come, come now, that's enough!

BECKER. You let him do his little bit o' preaching. There's many a one would be the better for takin' it to heart.

VOICES (*in excited confusion*). "Let him alone!"—"Let him speak!"

THIRD OLD WEAVER (*raising his voice*). But hell is opened, saith the Lord; its jaws are gaping wide, to swallow up

---

*Allons enfants (Marseillaise).

THE SILESIAN WEAVERS

THE SILESIAN WEAVERS

From the Painting by Karl Hübner

all those that oppress the afflicted and pervert judgment in the cause of the poor. [*Wild excitement.*]

THIRD OLD WEAVER (*suddenly declaiming, schoolboy
fashion*).

> When one has thought upon it well,
> It's still more difficult to tell
> Why they the linen-weaver's work despise.

BECKER. But we're fustian-weavers, man. [*Laughter.*]

HORNIG. The linen-weavers is ever so much worse off than
you. They're wanderin' about among the hills like
ghosts. You people here have still got the pluck left
in you to kick up a row.

WITTIG. Do you suppose the worst's over here? It won't
be long till the manufacturers drain away that little
bit of strength they still has left in their bodies.

BECKER. You know what he said: It will come to the
weavers workin' for a bite of bread. [*Uproar.*]

SEVERAL OLD AND YOUNG WEAVERS. Who said that?

BECKER. Dreissiger said it.

A YOUNG WEAVER. The damned rascal should be hung up
by the heels.

JAEGER. Look here, Wittig. You've always jawed such a
lot about the French Revolution, and a good deal too
about your own doings. A time may be coming, and
that before long, when every one will have a chance to
show whether he's a braggart or a true man.

WITTIG (*flaring up angrily*). Say another word if you dare!
Has you heard the whistle o' bullets? Has you done
outpost duty in an enemy's country?

JAEGER. You needn't get angry about it. We're comrades.
I meant no harm.

WITTIG. None of your comradeship for me, you impudent
young fool.

Enter KUTSCHE, *the policeman.*

SEVERAL VOICES. Hush — sh! Police!

> [*This calling goes on for some time, till at last there
> is complete silence, amidst which* KUTSCHE *takes
> his place at the central pillar table.*]

KUTSCHE. A small brandy, please.

[*Again complete silence.*]

WITTIG. I suppose you've come to see if we're all behavin' ourselves, Kutsche?

KUTSCHE (*paying no attention to* WITTIG). Good morning, Mr. Wiegand.

WIEGAND (*still in the corner in front of the counter*). Good morning t'you.

KUTSCHE. How's trade?

WIEGAND. Thank you, much as usual.

BECKER. The chief constable's sent him to see if we're spoilin' our stomach on these big wages we're gettin'.

[*Laughter.*]

JAEGER. I say, Welzel, you will tell him how we've been feastin' on roast pork an' sauce an' dumplings and sauerkraut, and now we're sittin' at our champagne wine. [*Laughter.*]

WELZEL. The world's upside down with them today.

KUTSCHE. An' even if you had the champagne wine and the roast meat, you wouldn't be satisfied. I've to get on without champagne wine as well as you.

BECKER (*referring to* KUTSCHE's *nose*). He waters his beet-root with brandy and gin. An' it thrives on it too.

[*Laughter.*]

WITTIG. A p'liceman like that has a hard life. Now it's a starving beggar boy he has to lock up, then it's a pretty weaver girl he has to lead astray; then he has to get roarin' drunk an' beat his wife till she goes screamin' to the neighbors for help; and there's the ridin' about on horseback and the lyin' in bed till nine — nay, faith, but it's no easy job!

KUTSCHE. Jaw away; you'll jaw a rope round your neck in time. It's long been known what sort of a fellow you are. The magistrates knows all about that rebellious tongue o' yours. I know who'll drink wife and child into the poorhouse an' himself into gaol before long, who it is that'll go on agitatin' and agitatin' till he brings down judgment on himself and all concerned.

WITTIG (*laughs bitterly*). It's true enough—no one knows what'll be the end of it. You may be right yet. [*Bursts out in fury.*] But if it does come to that, I know who I've got to thank for it, who it is that's blabbed to the manufacturers an' all the gentlemen round, an' blackened my character to that extent that they never give me a hand's turn of work to do—an' set the peasants an' the millers against me, so that I'm often a whole week without a horse to shoe or a wheel to put a tire on. I know who's done it. I once pulled the damned brute off his horse, because he was givin' a little stupid boy the most awful flogging for stealin' a few unripe pears. But I tell you this, Kutsche, and you know me —if you get me put into prison, you may make your own will. If I hears as much as a whisper of it, I'll take the first thing as comes handy, whether it's a horseshoe or a hammer, a wheel-spoke or a pail; I'll get hold of you if I've to drag you out of bed from beside your wife, and I'll beat in your brains, as sure as my name's Wittig.

[*He has jumped up and is going to rush at* KUTSCHE.]

OLD AND YOUNG WEAVERS (*holding him back*). Wittig, Wittig! Don't lose your head!

KUTSCHE (*has risen involuntarily, his face pale. He backs toward the door while speaking. The nearer the door the higher his courage rises. He speaks the last words on the threshold, and then instantly disappears*). What are you goin' on at me about? I didn't meddle with you. I came to say somethin' to the weavers. My business is with them an' not with you, and I've done nothing to you. But I've this to say to you weavers: The superintendent of police herewith forbids the singing of that song—Dreissiger's song, or whatever it is you calls it. And if the yelling of it on the streets isn't stopped at once, he'll provide you with plenty of time and leisure for goin' on with it in gaol. You may sing there, on bread an' water, to your hearts' content.

[*Goes out.*]

WITTIG (*roars after him*). He's no right to forbid it — not if we was to roar till the windows shook an' they could hear us at Reichenbach — not if we sang till the manufacturers' houses tumbled about their ears an' all the superintendents' helmets danced on the top of their heads. It's nobody's business but our own.

[BECKER *has in the meantime got up, made a signal for singing, and now leads off, the others joining in.*]

> The justice to us weavers dealt
> Is bloody, cruel, and hateful;
> Our life's one torture, long drawn out;
> For lynch law we'd be grateful.

[WELZEL *attempts to quiet them, but they pay no attention to him.* WIEGAND *puts his hands to his ears and rushes off. During the singing of the next stanza the weavers rise and form into procession behind* BECKER *and* WITTIG, *who have given pantomimic signs for a general break-up.*]

> Stretched on the rack, day after day,
> Hearts sick and bodies aching,
> Our heavy sighs their witness bear
> To spirit slowly breaking.

[*Most of the weavers sing the following stanza out on the street, only a few young fellows, who are paying, being still in the bar. At the conclusion of the stanza no one is left in the room except* WELZEL *and his wife and daughter,* HORNIG, *and* OLD BAUMERT.]

> You villains all, you brood of hell,
> You fiends in fashion human,
> A curse will fall on all like you,
> Who prey on man and woman.

WELZEL (*phlegmatically collecting the glasses*). Their backs are up today, an' no mistake.

HORNIG (*to* OLD BAUMERT, *who is preparing to go*). What in the name of Heaven are they up to, Baumert?

BAUMERT. They're goin' to Dreissiger's to make him add something on to the pay.

WELZEL. And are you joining in these foolish goings on?

OLD BAUMERT. I've no choice, Welzel. The young men may an' the old men must.

[*Goes out rather shamefacedly.*]

HORNIG. It'll not surprise me if this ends badly.

WELZEL. To think that even old fellows like him are goin' right off their heads!

HORNIG. We all set our hearts on something!

ACT IV

Peterswaldau.— Private room of DREISSIGER, *the fustian manufacturer — luxuriously furnished in the chilly taste of the first half of this century. Ceiling, doors, and stove are white, and the wall paper, with its small, straight-lined floral pattern, is dull and cold in tone. The furniture is mahogany, richly carved, and upholstered in red. On the right, between two windows with crimson damask curtains, stands the writing-table, a high bureau with falling flap. Directly opposite to this is the sofa, with the strong-box beside it; in front of the sofa a table, with chairs and easy-chairs arranged about it. Against the back wall is a gun-rack. All three walls are decorated with bad pictures in gilt frames. Above the sofa is a mirror with a heavily gilded rococo frame. On the left an ordinary door leads into the hall. An open folding door at the back shows the drawing-room, over-furnished in the same style of comfortless ostentation. Two ladies,* MRS. DREISSIGER *and* MRS. KITTELHAUS, *the Pastor's wife, are seen in the drawing-room, looking at pictures.* PASTOR KITTELHAUS *is there too, engaged in conversation with* WEINHOLD, *the tutor, a theological graduate.*

KITTELHAUS (*a kindly little elderly man, enters the front room, smoking and chatting familiarly with the tutor, who is also smoking; he looks round and shakes his head in surprise at finding the room empty*). You are young, Mr. Weinhold, which explains everything. At your age we old fellows held — well, I won't say the same opinions — but certainly opinions of the same tendency. And there's something fine about youth —

youth with its grand ideals. But unfortunately, Mr.
Weinhold, they don't last; they are as fleeting as April
sunshine. Wait till you are my age. When a man has
said his say from the pulpit for thirty years — fifty-
two times every year, not including saints' days — he
has inevitably calmed down. Think of me, Mr. Weinhold, when you come to that pass.

WEINHOLD (*nineteen, pale, thin, tall, with lanky fair hair;
restless and nervous in his movements*). With all due
respect, Mr. Kittelhaus, I can't think people have such
different natures.

KITTELHAUS. My dear Mr. Weinhold, however restless-
minded and unsettled a man may be — [*in a tone of
reproof*] — and you are a case in point — however
violently and wantonly he may attack the existing order
of things, he calms down in the end. I grant you, certainly, that among our professional brethren individuals are to be found, who, at a fairly advanced age, still
play youthful pranks. One preaches against the drink
evil and founds temperance societies, another publishes
appeals which undoubtedly read most effectively. But
what good do they do? The distress among the weavers, where it does exist, is in no way lessened — but the
peace of society is undermined. No, no; one feels
inclined in such cases to say: Cobbler, stick to your
last; don't take to caring for the belly, you who have
the care of souls. Preach the pure Word of God, and
leave all else to Him who provides shelter and food
for the birds, and clothes the lilies of the field. But I
should like to know where our good host, Mr. Dreissiger, has suddenly disappeared to.

[MRS. DREISSIGER, *followed by* MRS. KITTELHAUS, *now
comes forward. She is a pretty woman of thirty,
of a healthy, florid type. A certain discrepancy
is noticeable between her deportment and way of
expressing herself and her rich, elegant toilette.*]

MRS. DREISSIGER. That's what I want to know too, Mr. Kittelhaus. But it's what William always does. No sooner does a thing come into his head than off he goes and leaves me in the lurch. I've said enough about it, but it does no good.

KITTELHAUS. It's always the way with business men, my dear Mrs. Dreissiger.

WEINHOLD. I'm almost certain that something has happened downstairs.

DREISSIGER *enters, hot and excited.*

DREISSIGER. Well, Rosa, is coffee served?

MRS. DREISSIGER (*sulkily*). Fancy your needing to run away again!

DREISSIGER (*carelessly*). Ah! these are things you don't understand.

KITTELHAUS. Excuse me — has anything happened to annoy you, Mr. Dreissiger?

DREISSIGER. Never a day passes without that, my dear sir. I am accustomed to it. What about that coffee, Rosa?
[MRS. DREISSIGER *goes ill-humoredly and gives one or two violent tugs at the broad embroidered bell-pull.*]

DREISSIGER. I wish you had been downstairs just now, Mr. Weinhold; you'd have gained a little experience. Besides — but now let us have our game of whist.

KITTELHAUS. By all means, sir. Shake off the dust and burden of the day, Mr. Dreissiger; forget it in our company.

DREISSIGER (*has gone to the window, pushed aside a curtain, and is looking out. Involuntarily*). Vile rabble!! Come here, Rosa! [*She goes to the window.*] Look — that tall red-haired fellow there — !

KITTELHAUS. That's the man they call Red Becker.

DREISSIGER. Is he the man that insulted you the day before yesterday? You remember what you told me — when John was helping you into the carriage?

MRS. DREISSIGER (*pouting, drawls*). I'm sure I don't know.

DREISSIGER. Come now, drop that offended air! I must know. I am thoroughly tired of their impudence. If he's the man, I mean to have him arrested. [*The strains of the Weavers' Song are heard.*] Listen to that! Just listen!

KITTELHAUS (*highly incensed*). Is there to be no end to this nuisance? I must acknowledge now that it is time for the police to interfere. Permit me. [*He goes forward to the window.*] See, see, Mr. Weinhold! These are not only young people. There are numbers of steady-going old weavers among them, men whom I have known for years and looked upon as most deserving and God-fearing. There they are, taking part in this unheard-of mischief, trampling God's law under foot. Do you mean to tell me that you still defend these people?

WEINHOLD. Certainly not, Mr. Kittelhaus. That is, sir— *cum grano salis.* For after all, they are hungry and they are ignorant. They are giving expression to their dissatisfaction in the only way they understand. I don't expect that such people —

MRS. KITTELHAUS (*short, thin, faded, more like an old maid than a married woman*). Mr. Weinhold, Mr. Weinhold, how can you?

DREISSIGER. Mr. Weinhold, I am sorry to be obliged to —! I didn't bring you into my house to give me lectures on philanthropy, and I must request that you will confine yourself to the education of my boys, and leave my other affairs entirely to me — entirely! Do you understand?

WEINHOLD (*stands for a moment rigid and deathly pale, then bows, with a strained smile. In a low voice*). Certainly, of course I understand. I have seen this coming. It is my wish too. [*Goes out.*]

DREISSIGER (*rudely*). As soon as possible then, please. We require the room.

Mrs. Dreissiger. William, William!

Dreissiger. Have you lost your senses, Rosa, that you're taking the part of a man who defends a low, blackguardly libel like that song?

Mrs. Dreissiger. But, William, he didn't defend it.

Dreissiger. Mr. Kittelhaus, did he defend it or did he not?

Kittelhaus. His youth must be his excuse, Mr. Dreissiger.

Mrs. Kittelhaus. I can't understand it. The young man comes of such a good, respectable family. His father held a public appointment for forty years, without a breath on his reputation. His mother was overjoyed at his getting this good situation here. And now he himself shows so little appreciation of it.

Pfeifer (*suddenly opens the door leading from the hall and shouts in*). Mr. Dreissiger, Mr. Dreissiger! they've got him! Will you come, please? They've caught one of 'em.

Dreissiger (*hastily*). Has some one gone for the police?

Pfeifer. The superintendent's on his way upstairs.

Dreissiger (*at the door*). Glad to see you, sir. We want you here.

[Kittelhaus *makes signs to the ladies that it will be better for them to retire. He, his wife, and* Mrs. Dreissiger *disappear into the drawing-room.*]

Dreissiger (*exasperated, to the* Police Superintendent, *who has now entered*). I have at last had one of the ringleaders seized by my dyers. I could stand it no longer — their insolence was beyond all bounds — quite unbearable. I have visitors in my house, and these blackguards dare to —! They insult my wife whenever she shows herself; my boys' lives are not safe. My visitors run the risk of being jostled and cuffed. Is it possible that in a well-ordered community incessant public insult offered to unoffending people like myself and my family should pass unpunished? If so — then — then I must confess that I have other ideas of law and order.

SUPERINTENDENT (*a man of fifty, middle height, corpulent, full-blooded. He wears cavalry uniform with a long sword and spurs*). No, no, Mr. Dreissiger — certainly not! I am entirely at your disposal. Make your mind easy on the subject. Dispose of me as you will. What you have done is quite right. I am delighted that you have had one of the ringleaders arrested. I am very glad indeed that a day of reckoning has come. There are a few disturbers of the peace here whom I have long had my eye on.

DREISSIGER. Yes, one or two raw lads, lazy vagabonds, that shirk every kind of work, and lead a life of low dissipation, hanging about the public-houses until they've sent their last half-penny down their throats. But I'm determined to put a stop to the trade of these professional blackguards once and for all. It's in the public interest to do so, not only my private interest.

SUPERINTENDENT. Of course it is! Most undoubtedly, Mr. Dreissiger! No one can possibly blame you. And everything that lies in my power —

DREISSIGER. The cat-o'-nine tails is what should be taken to the beggarly pack.

SUPERINTENDENT. You're right, quite right. We must institute an example.

KUTSCHE, *the policeman, enters and salutes. The door is open, and the sound of heavy steps stumbling up the stair is heard.*

KUTSCHE. I have to inform you, sir, that we have arrested a man.

DREISSIGER (*to* SUPERINTENDENT). Do you wish to see the fellow?

SUPERINTENDENT. Certainly, most certainly. We must begin by having a look at him at close quarters. Oblige me, Mr. Dreissiger, by not speaking to him at present. I'll see to it that you get complete satisfaction, or my name's not Heide.

DREISSIGER. That's not enough for me, though. He goes before the magistrates. My mind's made up.

*JAEGER is led in by five dyers, who have come straight from their work —
faces, hands, and clothes stained with dye. The prisoner, his cap set
jauntily on the side of his head, presents an appearance of impudent
gaiety; he is excited by the brandy he has just drunk.*

JAEGER. Hounds that you are! — Call yourselves working
men! — Pretend to be comrades! Before I would do
such a thing as lay hands on a mate, I'd see my hand
rot off my arm.

   *[At a sign from the SUPERINTENDENT, KUTSCHE
orders the dyers to let go their victim. JAEGER
straightens himself up, quite free and easy. Both
doors are guarded.]*

SUPERINTENDENT (*shouts to JAEGER*). Off with your cap,
lout! [*JAEGER takes it off, but very slowly, still with
an impudent grin on his face.*] What's your name?

JAEGER. What's yours? I'm not your swineherd.

   [Great excitement is produced by this reply.]

DREISSIGER. This is too much of a good thing.

SUPERINTENDENT (*changes color, is on the point of breaking
out furiously, but controls his rage*). We'll see about
this afterward. — Once more, what's your name? [*Re-
ceiving no answer, furiously.*] If you don't answer at
once, fellow, I'll have you flogged on the spot.

JAEGER (*perfectly cheerful, not showing by so much as the
twitch of an eyelid that he has heard the SUPERIN-
TENDENT'S angry words, calls over the heads of those
around him to a pretty servant girl, who has brought in
the coffee and is standing open-mouthed with astonishment at the unexpected sight*). Hillo, Emmy, do you
belong to this company now? The sooner you find
your way out of it, then, the better. A wind may begin
to blow here, an' blow everything away overnight.

   *[The girl stares at JAEGER, and as soon as she com-
prehends that it is to her he is speaking, blushes
with shame, covers her eyes with her hands, and
rushes out, leaving the coffee things in confusion
on the table. Renewed excitement among those
present.]*

SUPERINTENDENT (*half beside himself, to* DREISSIGER).
Never in all my long service — a case of such shameless
effrontery! [JAEGER *spits on the floor.*]

DREISSIGER. You're not in a stable, fellow! Do you understand?

SUPERINTENDENT. My patience is at an end now. For the
last time: What's your name?

[KITTELHAUS, *who has been peering out at the partly
opened drawing-room door, listening to what has
been going on, can no longer refrain from coming
forward to interfere. He is trembling with excitement.*]

KITTELHAUS. His name is Jaeger, sir. Moritz — is it not?
Moritz Jaeger. [*To* JAEGER.] And, Jaeger, you know
me.

JAEGER (*seriously*). You are Pastor Kittelhaus.

KITTELHAUS. Yes, I am your pastor, Jaeger! It was I who
received you, a babe in swaddling clothes, into the
Church of Christ. From my hands you took for the
first time the body of the Lord. Do you remember that,
and how I toiled and strove to bring God's word home
to your heart? Is this your gratitude?

JAEGER (*like a scolded schoolboy. In a surly voice*). I paid
my half-crown like the rest.

KITTELHAUS. Money! Money! Do you imagine that the
miserable little bit of money —? Such utter nonsense!
I'd much rather you kept your money. Be a good man,
be a Christian! Think of what you promised. Keep
God's law. Money! Money!!

JAEGER. I'm a Quaker now, sir. I don't believe in nothing.

KITTELHAUS. Quaker! What are you talking about? Try
to behave yourself, and don't use words you don't
understand. Quaker, indeed! They are good Christian people, and not heathens like you.

SUPERINTENDENT. Mr. Kittelhaus, I must ask you!— [*He
comes between the Pastor and* JAEGER.] Kutsche! tie
his hands!

[*Wild yelling outside:* "Jaeger, Jaeger! come
out!"]

DREISSIGER (*like the others, slightly startled, goes instinctively to the window*). What's the meaning of this next?

SUPERINTENDENT. Oh, I understand well enough. It means that they want to have the blackguard out among them again. But we're not going to oblige them. Kutsche, you have your orders. He goes to the lock-up.

KUTSCHE (*with the rope in his hand, hesitating*). By your leave, sir, but it'll not be an easy job. There's a confounded big crowd out there — a pack of raging devils. They've got Becker with them, and the smith —

KITTELHAUS. Allow me one more word! So as not to rouse still worse feeling, would it not be better if we tried to arrange things peaceably? Perhaps Jaeger will give his word to go with us quietly, or . . .

SUPERINTENDENT. Quite impossible! Think of my responsibility. I couldn't allow such a thing. Come, Kutsche! lose no more time.

JAEGER (*putting his hands together, and holding them out*). Tight, tight, as tight as ever you can! It's not for long.

[KUTSCHE, *assisted by the workmen, ties his hands.*]

SUPERINTENDENT. Now off with you, march! [*To* DREISSIGER.] If you feel anxious, let six of the weavers go with them. They can walk on each side of him, I'll ride in front, and Kutsche will bring up the rear. Whoever blocks the way will be cut down.

[*Cries from below:* " Cock-a-doodle-doo-oo-oo! Bow, wow, wow! "]

SUPERINTENDENT (*with a threatening gesture in the direction of the window*). You rascals, I'll cock-a-doodle-doo and bow-wow you! Forward! March!

[*He marches out first, with drawn sword; the others, with* JAEGER, *follow.*]

JAEGER (*shouts as he goes*). An' Mrs. Dreissiger there may play the lady as proud as she likes, but for all that she's no better than us. Many a hundred times she's served my father with a halfpenny-worth of schnapps. Left wheel — march! [*Exit laughing.*]

DREISSIGER (*after a pause, with apparent calmness*). Well, Mr. Kittelhaus, shall we have our game now? I think there will be no further interruption. [*He lights a cigar, giving short laughs as he does so; when it is lighted, bursts into a regular fit of laughing.*] I'm beginning now to think the whole thing very funny. That fellow! [*Still laughing nervously.*] It really is too comical! First came the dispute at dinner with Weinhold — five minutes after that he takes leave — off to the other end of the world; then this affair crops up — and now we'll proceed with our whist.

KITTELHAUS. Yes, but — [*Roaring is heard outside.*] Yes, but that's a terrible uproar they're making outside.

DREISSIGER. All we have to do is to go into the other room; it won't disturb us in the least there.

KITTELHAUS (*shaking his head*). I wish I knew what has come over these people. In so far I must agree with Mr. Weinhold, or at least till quite lately I was of his opinion, that the weavers were a patient, humble, easily-led class. Was it not your idea of them, too, Mr. Dreissiger?

DREISSIGER. Most certainly that is what they used to be — patient, easily managed, well-behaved and orderly people. They were that as long as these so-called humanitarians let them alone. But for ever so long now they've had the awful misery of their condition held up to them. Think of all the societies and associations for the alleviation of the distress among the weavers. At last the weaver believes in it himself, and his head's turned. Some of them had better come and turn it back again, for now he's fairly set a-going there's no end to his complaining. This doesn't please him, and that doesn't please him. He must have everything of the best.

[*A loud roar of "Hurrah!" is heard from the crowd.*]

KITTELHAUS. So that with all their humanitarianism they have only succeeded in almost literally turning lambs over night into wolves.

DREISSIGER. I won't say that, sir. When you take time to think of the matter coolly, it's possible that some good may come of it yet. Such occurrences as this will not pass unnoticed by those in authority, and may lead them to see that things can't be allowed to go on as they are doing—that means must be taken to prevent the utter ruin of our home industries.

KITTELHAUS. Possibly. But what is the cause, then, of this terrible falling off of trade?

DREISSIGER. Our best markets have been closed to us by the heavy import duties foreign countries have laid on our goods. At home the competition is a struggle of life and death, for we have no protection, none whatever.

PFEIFER (*staggers in, pale and breathless*). Mr. Dreissiger, Mr. Dreissiger!

DREISSIGER (*in the act of walking into the drawing-room, turns round, annoyed*). Well, Pfeifer, what now?

PFEIFER. Oh sir! Oh, sir!—It's worse than ever!

DREISSIGER. What are they up to next?

KITTELHAUS. You're really alarming us—what is it?

PFEIFER (*still confused*). I never saw the like. Good Lord—the superintendent himself! They'll catch it for this yet.

DREISSIGER. What's the matter with you, in the devil's name? Is any one's neck broken?

PFEIFER (*almost crying with fear, screams*). They've set Moritz Jaeger free—they've thrashed the superintendent and driven him away—they've thrashed the policeman and sent him off too—without his helmet—his sword broken! Oh dear, oh dear!

DREISSIGER. I think you've gone crazy, Pfeifer.

KITTLEHAUS. This is actual riot.

SETON HALL UNIVERSITY
Mc LAUGHLIN LIBRARY
SO. ORANGE, N. J.

PFEIFER (*sitting on a chair, his whole body trembling*). It's turning serious, Mr. Dreissiger! Mr. Dreissiger, it's serious now!

DREISSIGER. Well, if that's all the police —

PFEIFER. Mr. Dreissiger, it's serious now!

DREISSIGER. Damn it all, Pfeifer, will you hold your tongue?

MRS. DREISSIGER (*coming out of the drawing-room with* MRS. KITTELHAUS). This is really too bad, William. Our whole pleasant evening's being spoiled. Here's Mrs. Kittelhaus saying that she'd better go home.

KITTELHAUS. You mustn't take it amiss, dear Mrs. Dreissiger, but perhaps, under the circumstances, it *would* be better —

MRS. DREISSIGER. But, William, why in the world don't you go out and put a stop to it?

DREISSIGER. You go and see if you can do it. Try! Go and speak to them! [*Standing in front of the pastor, abruptly.*] Am I such a tyrant? Am I a cruel master?

Enter JOHN *the coachman.*

JOHN. If you please, m'm, I've put to the horses. Mr. Weinhold's put Georgie and Charlie into the carriage. If it comes to the worst, we're ready to be off.

MRS. DREISSIGER. If what comes to the worst?

JOHN. I'm sure I don't know, m'm. But I'm thinkin' this way: The crowd's gettin' bigger and bigger, an' they've sent the superintendent an' the p'liceman to the right-about.

PFEIFER. It's gettin' serious now, Mr. Dreissiger! It's serious!

MRS. DREISSIGER (*with increasing alarm*). What's going to happen? — What do the people want? — They're never going to attack us, John?

JOHN. There's some rascally hounds among 'em, ma'am.

PFEIFER. It's serious now! serious!

SETON HALL UNIVERSITY
McLAUGHLIN LIBRARY
SO. ORANGE, N. J.

DREISSIGER. Hold your tongue, fool!—Are the doors barred?

KITTELHAUS. I ask you as a favor, Mr. Dreissiger—as a favor—I am determined to—I ask you as a favor— [*To* JOHN.] What demands are the people making?

JOHN (*awkwardly*). It's higher wages they're after, the blackguards.

KITTELHAUS. Good, good!—I shall go out and do my duty. I shall speak seriously to these people.

JOHN. Oh, sir, please, sir, don't do any such thing. Words is quite useless.

KITTELHAUS. One little favor, Mr. Dreissiger. May I ask you to post men behind the door, and to have it closed at once after me?

MRS. KITTELHAUS. O Joseph, Joseph! you're not really going out?

KITTELHAUS. I am. Indeed I am. I know what I'm doing. Don't be afraid. God will protect me.

[MRS. KITTELHAUS *presses his hand, draws back, and wipes tears from her eyes.*]

KITTELHAUS (*while the dull murmur of a great, excited crowd is heard uninterruptedly outside*). I'll go—I'll go out as if I were simply on my way home. I shall see if my sacred office—if the people have not sufficient respect for me left to—I shall try— [*He takes his hat and stick.*] Forward, then, in God's name!

[*Goes out accompanied by* DREISSIGER, PFEIFER *and* JOHN.]

MRS. KITTELHAUS. Oh, dear Mrs. Dreissiger! [*She bursts into tears and embraces her.*] I do trust nothing will happen to him.

MRS. DREISSIGER (*absently*). I don't know how it is, Mrs. Kittelhaus, but I—I can't tell you how I feel. I didn't think such a thing was possible. It's—it's as if it was a sin to be rich. If I had been told about all this beforehand, Mrs. Kittelhaus, I don't know but what

I would rather have been left in my own humble position.

MRS. KITTELHAUS.   There are troubles and disappointments in every condition of life, Mrs. Dreissiger.

MRS. DREISSIGER.   True, true, I can well believe that.   And suppose we have more than other people — goodness me! we didn't steal it.   It's been honestly got, every penny of it.   It's not possible that the people can be goin' to attack us!   If trade's bad, that's not William's fault, is it?

[*A tumult of roaring is heard outside.   While the two women stand gazing at each other, pale and startled,* DREISSIGER *rushes in.*]

DREISSIGER.   Quick, Rosa — put on something, and get into the carriage.   I'll be after you this moment.

[*He rushes to the strong-box, and takes out papers and various articles of value.*]

Enter JOHN.

JOHN.   We're ready to start.   But come quickly, before they gets round to the back door.

MRS. DREISSIGER (*in a transport of fear, throwing her arms around* JOHN'*s neck*).   John, John, dear, good John! Save us, John.   Save my boys!   Oh, what is to become of us?

DREISSIGER.   Rosa, try to keep your head.   Let John go.

JOHN.   Yes, yes, ma'am!   Don't you be frightened.   Our good horses'll soon leave them all behind; an' whoever doesn't get out of the way'll be driven over.

MRS. KITTELHAUS (*in helpless anxiety*).   But my husband — my husband?   But, Mr. Dreissiger, my husband?

DREISSIGER.   He's in safety now, Mrs. Kittelhaus.   Don't alarm yourself; he's all right.

MRS. KITTELHAUS.   Something dreadful has happened to him.   I know it.   You needn't try to keep it from me.

DREISSIGER.   You mustn't take it to heart — they'll be sorry for it yet.   I know exactly whose fault it was.   Such

an unspeakable, shameful outrage will not go unpunished. A community laying hands on its own pastor
and maltreating him — abominable! Mad dogs they
are — raging brutes — and they'll be treated as such.
[*To his wife who still stands petrified.*] Go, Rosa, go
quickly! [*Heavy blows at the lower door are heard.*]
Don't you hear? They've gone stark mad! [*The clat-
ter of window-panes being smashed on the ground-floor
is heard.*] They've gone crazy. There's nothing for
it but to get away as fast as we can.

[*Cries of* "Pfeifer, come out!"—"We want
Pfeifer!"—"Pfeifer, come out!" *are heard.*]

MRS. DREISSIGER. Pfeifer, Pfeifer, they want Pfeifer!

PFEIFER (*dashes in*). Mr. Dreissiger, there are people at
the back gate already, and the house door won't hold
much longer. The smith's battering at it like a maniac
with a stable pail.

[*The cry sounds louder and clearer:* "Pfeifer!
Pfeifer! Pfeifer! come out!" MRS. DREISSIGER
rushes off as if pursued. MRS. KITTELHAUS *follows.* PFEIFER *listens, and changes color as he
hears what the cry is. A perfect panic of fear
seizes him; he weeps, entreats, whimpers, writhes,
all at the same moment. He overwhelms* DREIS-
SIGER *with childish caresses, strokes his cheeks and
arms, kisses his hands, and at last, like a drowning
man, throws his arms round him and prevents him
moving.*]

PFEIFER. Dear, good, kind Mr. Dreissiger, don't leave me
behind. I've always served you faithfully. I've
always treated the people well. I couldn't give 'em
more wages than the fixed rate. Don't leave me here —
they'll do for me! If they finds me, they'll kill me.
O God! O God! My wife, my children!

DREISSIGER (*making his way out, vainly endeavoring to free
himself from* PFEIFER'S *clutch*). Can't you let me go,
fellow? It'll be all right; it'll be all right.

For a few seconds the room is empty. Windows are shattered in the drawing-room. A loud crash resounds through the house, followed by a roaring "Hurrah!" For an instant there is silence. Then gentle, cautious steps are heard on the stair, then timid, hushed ejaculations: "To the left!"—"Up with you!"—"Hush!"—"Slow, slow!"—"Don't shove like that!"—"It's a wedding we're goin' to!"—"Stop that crowdin'!"—"You go first!"—"No, you go!"

Young weavers and weaver girls appear at the door leading from the hall, not daring to enter, but each trying to shove the other in. In the course of a few moments their timidity is overcome, and the poor, thin, ragged or patched figures, many of them sickly-looking, disperse themselves through DREISSIGER'S room and the drawing-room, first gazing timidly and curiously at everything, then beginning to touch things. Girls sit down on the sofas, whole groups admire themselves in the mirrors, men stand up on chairs, examine the pictures and take them down. There is a steady influx of miserable-looking creatures from the hall.

FIRST OLD WEAVER (*entering*). No, no, this is carryin' it too far. They've started smashin' things downstairs. There's no sense nor reason in that. There'll be a bad end to it. No man in his wits would do that. I'll keep clear of such goings on.

JAEGER, BECKER, WITTIG *carrying a wooden pail*, BAUMERT, *and a number of other old and young weavers, rush in as if in pursuit of something, shouting hoarsely.*

JAEGER. Where has he gone?

BECKER. Where's the cruel brute?

BAUMERT. If we can eat grass he may eat sawdust.

WITTIG. We'll hang him when we catch him.

FIRST YOUNG WEAVER. We'll take him by the legs and fling him out at the window, onto the stones. He'll never get up again.

SECOND YOUNG WEAVER (*enters*). He's off!

ALL. Who?

SECOND YOUNG WEAVER. Dreissiger.

BECKER. Pfeifer too?

VOICES. Let's get hold o' Pfeifer! Look for Pfeifer!

BAUMERT. Yes, yes! Pfeifer! Tell him there's a weaver here for him to starve.   [*Laughter.*]

JAEGER. If we can't lay hands on that brute Dreissiger himself, we'll make him poor!

BAUMERT. As poor as a church mouse; we'll see to that!

[*All, bent on the work of destruction, rush toward the drawing-room door.*]

BECKER (*who is leading, turns round and stops the others*). Halt! Listen to me! This is nothing but a beginnin'. When we're done here, we'll go straight to Bielau, to Dittrich's, where the steam power-looms is. The whole mischief's done by them factories.

OLD ANSORGE (*enters from hall. Takes a few steps, then stops and looks round, scarcely believing his eyes; shakes his head, taps his forehead*). Who am I? Weaver Anton Ansorge. Has he gone mad, Old Ansorge? My head's goin' round like a humming-top, sure enough. What's he doin' here. He'll do whatever he's a mind to. Where is Ansorge? [*He taps his forehead repeatedly.*] Something's wrong! I'm not answerable! I'm off my head! Off with you, off with you, rioters that you are! Heads off, legs off, hands off! If you takes my house, I takes your house. Forward, forward!

[*Goes yelling into the drawing-room, followed by a yelling, laughing mob.*]

ACT V

Langen-Bielau.— OLD WEAVER HILSE'S *workroom. On the left a small window, in front of which stands the loom. On the right a bed, with a table pushed close to it. Stove, with stove-bench, in the right-hand corner. Family worship is going on.* HILSE, *his old, blind, and almost deaf wife, his son* GOTTLIEB, *and* LUISE, GOTTLIEB'S *wife, are sitting at the table, on the bed and wooden stools. A winding-wheel and bobbins on the floor between table and loom. Old spinning, weaving, and winding implements are disposed of on the smoky rafters; hanks of yarn are hanging down. There is much useless lumber in the low, narrow room. The door, which is in the back wall, and leads into the big outer passage, or entry-room of the house, stands open. Through another open door on the opposite side of the passage, a second, in most respects similar weaver's room is seen. The large passage, or entry-room of the house,*

is paved with stone, has damaged plaster, and a tumble-down wooden
stair-case leading to the attics; a washing-tub on a stool is partly visible;
linen of the most miserable description and poor household utensils lie
about untidily. The light falls from the left into all three apartments.
OLD HILSE *is a bearded man of strong build, but bent and wasted with age,*
toil, sickness, and hardship. He is an old soldier, and has lost an arm.
His nose is sharp, his complexion ashen-gray, and he shakes; he is noth-
ing but skin and bone, and has the deep-set, sore weaver's eyes.

OLD HILSE (*stands up, as do his son and daughter-in-law;*
  prays). O Lord, we know not how to be thankful
  enough to Thee, for that Thou hast spared us this night
  again in Thy goodness, an' hast had pity on us, an'
  hast suffered us to take no harm.   Thou art the All-
  merciful, an' we are poor, sinful children of men —
  that bad that we are not worthy to be trampled under
  Thy feet.   Yet Thou art our loving Father, an' Thou
  will look upon us an' accept us for the sake of Thy
  dear Son, our Lord and Savior Jesus Christ.   '' Jesus'
  blood and righteousness, Our covering is and glorious
  dress.''   An' if we're sometimes too sore cast down
  under Thy chastening — when the fire of Thy purifica-
  tion burns too ragin' hot — oh, lay it not to our charge;
  forgive us our sin.   Give us patience, heavenly Father,
  that after all these sufferin's we may be made par-
  takers of Thy eternal blessedness.   Amen.

MOTHER HILSE (*who has been bending forward, trying hard*
  to hear). What a beautiful prayer you do say, father!
  [LUISE *goes off to the wash-tub*, GOTTLIEB *to the room*
    on the other side of the passage.]

OLD HILSE.   Where's the little lass?

LUISE.   She's gone to Peterswaldau, to Dreissiger's.   She
  finished all she had to wind last night.

OLD HILSE (*speaking very loud*).   You'd like the wheel now,
  mother, eh?

MOTHER HILSE.   Yes, father, I'm quite ready.

OLD HILSE (*setting it down before her*).   I wish I could do
  the work for you.

MOTHER HILSE. An' what would be the good o' that, father? There would I be, sittin' not knowin' what to do.

OLD HILSE. I'll give your fingers a wipe, then, so that they'll not grease the yarn.

[*He wipes her hands with a rag.*]

LUISE (*at the tub*). If there's grease on her hands, it's not from what she's eaten.

OLD HILSE. If we've no butter, we can eat dry bread — when we've no bread, we can eat potatoes — when there's no potatoes left, we can eat bran.

LUISE (*saucily*). An' when that's all eaten, we'll do as the Wenglers did — we'll find out where the skinner's buried some stinking old horse, an' we'll dig it up an' live for a week or two on rotten carrion — how nice that'll be!

GOTTLIEB (*from the other room*). There you are, lettin' that tongue of yours run away with you again.

OLD HILSE. You should think twice, lass, before you talk that godless way. [*He goes to his loom, calls.*] Can you give me a hand, Gottlieb? — there's a few threads to pull through.

LUISE (*from her tub*). Gottlieb, you're wanted to help father.

[GOTTLIEB *comes in, and he and his father set themselves to the troublesome task of " drawing and slaying," that is, pulling the strands of the warp through the " heddles " and " reed " of the loom. They have hardly begun to do this when* HORNIG *appears in the outer room.*]

HORNIG (*at the door*). Good luck to your work!

HILSE AND HIS SON. Thank you, Hornig.

OLD HILSE. I say, Hornig, when do you take your sleep? You're on your rounds all day, an' on watch all night.

HORNIG. Sleep's gone from me nowadays.

LUISE. Glad to see you, Hornig!

OLD HILSE. An' what's the news?

HORNIG. It's queer news this mornin'. The weavers at Peterswaldau has taken the law into their own hands, an' chased Dreissiger an' his whole family out of the place.

LUISE (*perceptibly agitated*). Hornig's at his lies again.

HORNIG. No, missus, not this time, not today.— I've some beautiful pinafores in my cart.— No, it's God's truth I'm tellin' you. They've sent him to the right-about. He came down to Reichenbach last night, but, Lord love you! they daren't take him in there, for fear of the weavers — off he had to go again, all the way to Schweidnitz.

OLD HILSE (*has been carefully lifting threads of the web and bringing them to the holes, through which, from the other side,* GOTTLIEB *pushes a wire hook, with which he catches them and draws them through*). It's about time you were stoppin' now, Hornig?

HORNIG. It's as sure as I'm a livin' man. Every child in the place'll soon tell you the same story.

OLD HILSE. Either your wits are a-wool-gatherin' or mine are.

HORNIG. Not mine. What I'm tellin' you's as true as the Bible. I wouldn't believe it myself if I hadn't stood there an' seen it with my own eyes — as I see you now, Gottlieb. They've wrecked his house from the cellar to the roof. The good china came flyin' out at the garret windows, rattlin' down the roof. God only knows how many pieces of fustian are lying soakin' in the river! The water can't get away for them — it's running over the banks, the color of washin'-blue with all the indigo they've poured out at the windows. Clouds of sky-blue dust was flyin' along. Oh, it's a terrible destruction they've worked! And it's not only the house — it's the dye-works too — an' the stores! They've broken the stair rails, they've torn up the fine flooring — smashed the lookin'-glasses — cut an' hacked an' torn an' smashed the sofas an' the chairs.— It's awful — it's worse than war.

OLD HILSE. An' you would have me believe that my fellow weavers did all that?

[*He shakes his head incredulously. Other tenants of the house have collected at the door and are listening eagerly.*]

HORNIG. Who else, I'd like to know? I could put names to every one of 'em. It was me took the sheriff through the house, an' I spoke to a whole lot of 'em, an' they answered me back quite friendly like. They did their business with little noise, but my word! they did it well. The sheriff spoke to 'em, and they answered him mannerly, as they always do. But there wasn't no stoppin' of them. They hacked on at the beautiful furniture as if they was workin' for wages.

OLD HILSE. *You* took the sheriff through the house?

HORNIG. An' what would I be frightened of? Every one knows me. I'm always turnin' up, like a bad penny. But no one has anything agin' me. They're all glad to see me. Yes, I went the rounds with him, as sure as my name's Hornig. An' you may believe me or not as you like, but my heart's sore yet from the sight — an' I could see by the sheriff's face that he felt queer enough too. For why? Not a livin' word did we hear — they was doin' their work and holdin' their tongues. It was a solemn an' a woeful sight to see the poor starvin' creatures for once in a way takin' their revenge.

LUISE (*with irrepressible excitement, trembling, wiping her eyes with her apron*). An' right they are! It's only what should be!

VOICES AMONG THE CROWD AT THE DOOR. "There's some of the same sort here." — "There's one no farther away than across the river." — "He's got four horses in his stable an' six carriages, an' he starves his weavers to keep 'em."

OLD HILSE (*still incredulous*). What was it set them off?

HORNIG. Who knows? who knows? One says this, another says that.

OLD HILSE. What do they say?

HORNIG. The story as most of 'em tells is that it began with Dreissiger sayin' that if the weavers was hungry they might eat grass. But I don't rightly know.

[*Excitement at the door, as one person repeats this to the other, with signs of indignation.*]

OLD HILSE. Well now, Hornig — if you was to say to me: Father Hilse, says you, you'll die tomorrow, I would answer back: That may be — an' why not? You might even go to the length of saying: You'll have a visit tomorrow from the King of Prussia. But to tell me that weavers, men like me an' my son, have done such things as that — never! I'll never in this world believe it.

MIELCHEN (*a pretty girl of seven, with long, loose flaxen hair, carrying a basket on her arm, comes running in, holding out a silver spoon to her mother*). Mammy, mammy! look what I've got! An' you're to buy me a new frock with it.

LUISE. What d'you come tearing in like that for, girl? [*With increased excitement and curiosity.*] An' what's that you've got hold of now? You've been runnin' yourself out o' breath, an' there — if the bobbins aren't in her basket yet? What's all this about?

OLD HILSE. Mielchen, where did that spoon come from?

LUISE. She found it, maybe.

HORNIG. It's worth its seven or eight shillin's at least.

OLD HILSE (*in distressed excitement*). Off with you, lass — out of the house this moment — unless you want a lickin'! Take that spoon back where you got it from. Out you go! Do you want to make thieves of us all, eh? I'll soon drive that out o' you.

[*He looks round for something to beat her with.*]

MIELCHEN (*clinging to her mother's skirts, crying*). No, grandfather, no! don't lick me! We — we *did* find it. All the other bob — bobbin — girls has — has some too.

LUISE (*half frightened, half excited*). I was right, you see. She found it. Where did you find it, Mielchen?

MIELCHEN (*sobbing*). At — at Peterswal — dau. We — we found them in front of — in front of Drei — Dreissiger's house.

OLD HILSE. This is worse an' worse. Get off with you this moment, unless you want me to help you.

MOTHER HILSE. What's all the to-do about?

HORNIG. I'll tell you what, father Hilse. The best way'll be for Gottlieb to put on his coat an' take the spoon to the police-office.

OLD HILSE. Gottlieb, put on your coat.

GOTTLIEB (*pulling it on, eagerly*). Yes, an' I'll go right into the office an' say they're not to blame us for it, for how c'n a child like that understand about it? an' I brought the spoon back at once. Stop your crying now, Mielchen!

[*The crying child is taken into the opposite room by her mother, who shuts her in and comes back.*]

HORNIG. I believe it's worth as much as nine shillin's.

GOTTLIEB. Give us a cloth to wrap it in, Luise, so that it'll take no harm. To think of the thing bein' worth all that money!

[*Tears come into his eyes while he is wrapping up the spoon.*]

LUISE. If it was only ours, we could live on it for many a day.

OLD HILSE. Hurry up, now! Look sharp! As quick as ever you can. A fine state o' matters, this! Get that devil's spoon out o' the house.

[GOTTLIEB *goes off with the spoon.*]

HORNIG. I must be off now too.

[*He goes, is seen talking to the people in the entry-room before he leaves the house.*]

SURGEON SCHMIDT (*a jerky little ball of a man, with a red, knowing face, comes into the entry-room*). Good-morning, all! These are fine goings on! Take care! take care! [*Threatening with his finger.*] You're a sly lot — that's what you are. [*At* HILSE's *door without coming in.*] Morning, father Hilse. [*To a woman*

in the outer room.] And how are the pains, mother?
Better, eh? Well, well. And how's all with you, father
Hilse? [*Enters.*] Why the deuce! what's the matter
with mother?

LUISE. It's the eye veins, sir — they've dried up, so as she
can't see at all now.

SURGEON SCHMIDT. That's from the dust and weaving by
candle-light. Will you tell me what it means that all
Peterswaldau's on the way here? I set off on my
rounds this morning as usual, thinking no harm; but
it wasn't long till I had my eyes opened. Strange
doings these! What in the devil's name has taken
possession of them, Hilse? They're like a pack of
raging wolves. Riot — why, it's revolution! they're
getting refractory — plundering and laying waste right
and left! Mielchen! where's Mielchen? [MIELCHEN,
her face red with crying, is pushed in by her mother.]
Here, Mielchen, put your hand into my coat pocket.
[MIELCHEN *does so.*] The ginger-bread nuts are for
you. Not all at once, though, you baggage! And a
song first! The fox jumped up on a — come, now —
The fox jumped up — on a moonlight — Mind, I've
heard what you did. You called the sparrows on the
churchyard hedge a nasty name, and they're gone and
told the pastor. Did any one ever hear the like? Fifteen hundred of them agog — men, women, and children. [*Distant bells are heard.*] That's at Reichenbach — alarm-bells! Fifteen hundred people! Un-
comfortably like the world coming to an end!

OLD HILSE. An' is it true that they're on their way to
Bielau?

SURGEON SCHMIDT. That's just what I'm telling you. I've
driven through the middle of the whole crowd. What
I'd have liked to do would have been to get down and
give each of them a pill there and then. They were
following on each other's heels like misery itself, and
their singing was more than enough to turn a man's

stomach. I was nearly sick, and Frederick was shaking on the box like an old woman. We had to take a stiff glass at the first opportunity. I wouldn't be a manufacturer, not though I could drive my carriage and pair. [*Distant singing.*] Listen to that! It's for all the world as if they were beating at some broken old boiler. We'll have them here in five minutes, friends. Good-by! Don't you be foolish. The troops will be upon them in no time. Keep your wits about you. The Peterswaldau people have lost theirs. [*Bells ring close at hand.*] Good gracious! There are our bells ringing too! Every one's going mad.

[*He goes upstairs.*]

GOTTLIEB (*comes back. In the entry-room, out of breath*). I've seen 'em, I've seen 'em! [*To a woman.*] They're here auntie, they're here! [*At the door.*] They're here, father, they're here! They've got bean poles, an' ox-goads, an' axes. They're standin' outside the upper Dittrich's kickin' up an awful row. I think he's payin' 'em money. O Lord! whatever's goin' to happen? What a crowd! Oh, you never saw such a crowd! Dash it all — if once they makes a rush, our manufacturers 'll be hard put to it.

OLD HILSE. What have you been runnin' like that for? You'll go racin' till you bring on your old trouble, and then we'll have you on your back again, strugglin' for breath.

GOTTLIEB (*almost joyously excited*). I had to run, or they would ha' caught me an' kept me. They was all roarin' to me to join 'em. Father Baumert was there too, and says he to me: You come an' get your sixpence with the rest — you're a poor starvin' weaver too. An' I was to tell you, father, from him, that you was to come an' help to pay out the manufacturers for their grindin' of us down. [*Passionately.*] Other times is comin', he says. There's goin' to be a change of days for us weavers. An' we're all to come an' help to bring it about. We're to have our half-pound o' meat on Sundays, and now and again on a holiday sausage with our cabbage. Yes, things is to be quite different, by what he tells me.

OLD HILSE (*with repressed indignation*). An' that man calls hisself your godfather! And he bids you take part in such works o' wickedness? Have nothing to do with them, Gottlieb. They've let themselves be tempted by Satan, an' it's his works they're doin'.

LUISE (*no longer able to restrain her passionate excitement, vehemently*). Yes, Gottlieb, get into the chimney corner, an' take a spoon in your hand, an' dish o' skim milk on your knee, an' put on a petticoat an' say your prayers, and then father'll be pleased with you. And *he* sets up to be a man!

[*Laughter from the people in the entry-room.*]

OLD HILSE (*quivering with suppressed rage*). An' you set up to be a good wife, eh? You calls yourself a mother, an' let your evil tongue run away with you like that? You think yourself fit to teach your girl, you that would egg on your husband to crime an' wickedness?

LUISE (*has lost all control of herself*). You an' your piety an' religion — did they serve to keep the life in my poor children? In rags an' dirt they lay, all the four — it didn't as much as keep 'em dry. Yes! I sets up to be a mother, that's what I do — an' if you'd like to know it, that's why I'd send all the manufacturers to hell — because I'm a mother! — Not one of the four could I keep in life! It was cryin' more than breathin' with me from the time each poor little thing came into the world till death took pity on it. The devil a bit you cared! You sat there prayin' and singin', and let me run about till my feet bled, tryin' to get one little drop o' skim milk. How many hundred nights has I lain an' racked my head to think what I could do to cheat the churchyard of my little one? What harm has a baby like that done that it must come to such a miser-

MISERY

From an Etching by Max Klinger

MISERY

From an Etching by Max Klinger

PERMISSION AMSLER & RUTHARDT, BERLIN

able end — eh? An' over there at Dittrich's they're bathed in wine an' washed in milk. No! you may talk as you like, but if they begins here, ten horses won't hold me back. An' what's more — if there's a rush on Dittrich's, you'll see me in the forefront of it — an' pity the man as tries to prevent me — I've stood it long enough, so now you know it.

OLD HILSE. You're a lost soul — there's no help for you.

LUISE (*frenzied*). It's you that there's no help for! Tatter-breeched scarecrows — that's what you are — an' not men at all. Whey-faced gutter-scrappers that take to your heels at the sound of a child's rattle. Fellows that says " thank you " to the man as gives you a hidin'. They've not left that much blood in you as that you can turn red in the face. You should have the whip taken to you, an' a little pluck flogged into your rotten bones.

[*She goes out quickly. Embarrassed pause.*]

MOTHER HILSE. What's the matter with Liesl, father?

OLD HILSE. Nothin', mother! What should be the matter with her?

MOTHER HILSE. Father, is it only me that's thinkin' it, or is the bells ringin'?

OLD HILSE. It'll be a funeral, mother.

MOTHER HILSE. An' I've got to sit waitin' here yet. Why must I be so long a-dyin', father? [*Pause.*]

OLD HILSE (*leaves his work, holds himself up straight; solemnly*). Gottlieb! — you heard all your wife said to us. Look here, Gottlieb! [*He bares his breast.*] Here they cut out a bullet as big as a thimble. The King knows where I lost my arm. It wasn't the mice as ate it. [*He walks up and down.*] Before that wife of yours was ever thought of, I had spilled my blood by the quart for King an' country. So let her call what names she likes — an' welcome! It does me no harm — Frightened? Me frightened? What would I be frightened of, will you tell me that? Of the few

soldiers, maybe, that'll be comin' after the rioters?
Good gracious me! That would be a lot to be frightened at! No, no, lad; I may be a bit stiff in the back,
but there's some strength left in the old bones; I've
got the stuff in me yet to make a stand against a few
rubbishin' bay'nets.— And if it came to the worst!
Willin', willin' would I be to say good-by to this weary
world. Death'd be welcome — welcomer to me today
than tomorrow. For what is it we leave behind? That
old bundle of aches an' pains we call our body, the care
an' the oppression we call by the name o' life. We
may be glad to get away from it! But there's something to come after, Gottlieb!— an' if we've done ourselves out o' that too — why, then it's all over with us!

GOTTLIEB. Who knows what's to come after? Nobody's
seen it.

OLD HILSE. Gottlieb! don't you be throwin' doubts on the
one comfort us poor people have. Why has I sat here
an' worked my treadle like a slave this forty year an'
more — sat still an' looked on at him over yonder livin'
in pride an' wastefulness — why? Because I have
a better hope, something as supports me in all my
troubles. [*Points out at the window.*] You have your
good things in this world — I'll have mine in the next.
That's been my thought. An' I'm that certain of it —
I'd let myself be torn to pieces. Have we not His
promise? There's a Day of Judgment comin'; but
it's not us as are the judges — no: Vengeance is mine,
saith the Lord.

[*A cry of " Weavers, come out! " is heard outside
the window.*]

OLD HILSE. Do what you will for me. [*He seats himself
at his loom.*] I stay here.

GOTTLIEB (*after a short struggle*). I'm going to work too —
come what may.   [*Goes out.*]

[*The Weavers' Song is heard, sung by hundreds of
voices quite close at hand; it sounds like a dull,
monotonous wail.*]

INMATES OF THE HOUSE (*in the entry-room*). " Oh, mercy
on us! there they come swarmin' like ants! " — " Where
can all these weavers be from? " — " Don't shove like
that, I want to see too." — " Look at that great may-
pole of a woman leadin' on in front! " — " Gracious!
they're comin' thicker an' thicker! "

HORNIG (*comes into the entry-room from outside*). There's
a theayter play for you now! That's what you don't
see every day. But you should go up to the other
Dittrich's an' look what they've done there. It's been
no half work. He's got no house now, nor no factory,
nor no wine-cellar, nor nothin'. They're drinkin' out
o' the bottles — not so much as takin' the time to get
out the corks. One, two, three, an' off with the neck,
an' no matter whether they cuts their mouths or not.
There's some of 'em runnin' about bleedin' like stuck
pigs.— Now they're goin' to do for Dittrich here.

[*The singing has stopped.*]

INMATES OF THE HOUSE. There's nothin' so very wicked
like about them.

HORNIG. You wait a bit! you'll soon see! All they're
doin' just now is makin' up their minds where they'll
begin. Look, they're inspectin' the palace from every
side. Do you see that little stout man there, him with
the stable pail? That's the smith from Peterswaldau — an' a dangerous little chap he is. He batters
in the thickest doors as if they were made o' pie-crust.
If a manufacturer was to fall into his hands it would
be all over with him!

HOUSE INMATES. " That was a crack! " — " There went
a stone through the window! " — " There's old Dittrich, shakin' with fright." — " He's hangin' out a
board." — " Hangin' out a board? " — " What's written on it? " — " Can't you read? " — " It'd be a bad
job for me if I couldn't read! " — " Well, read it,
then! " — " ' You — shall have — full — satis-fac-tion!
You — you shall have full satisfaction.' "

HORNIG. He might ha' spared hisself the trouble—*that* won't help him. It's something else they've set their minds on here. It's the factories. They're goin' to smash up the power-looms. For it's them that is ruinin' the hand-loom weaver. Even a blind man might see that. No! the good folks knows what they're after, an' no sheriff an' no p'lice superintendent'll bring them to reason—much less a bit of a board. Him as has seen 'em at work already knows what's comin'.

HOUSE INMATES. " Did any one ever see such a crowd! "— " What can *these* be wantin'? "—[*Hastily.*] " They're crossin' the bridge! "—[*Anxiously.*] " They're never comin' over on this side, are they? "—[*In excitement and terror.*] " It's to us they're comin'! They're comin' to us! They're comin' to fetch the weavers out o' their houses! "

[*General flight. The entry-room is empty. A crowd of dirty, dusty rioters rush in, their faces scarlet with brandy and excitement; tattered, untidy-looking, as if they had been up all night. With the shout:* " Weavers come out! " *they disperse themselves through the house.* BECKER *and several other young weavers, armed with cudgels and poles, come into* OLD HILSE'S *room. When they see the old man at his loom they start, and cool down a little.*]

BECKER. Come, father Hilse, stop that. Leave your work to them as wants to work. There's no need now for you to be doin' yourself harm. You'll be well taken care of.

FIRST YOUNG WEAVER. You'll never need to go hungry to bed again.

SECOND YOUNG WEAVER. The weaver's goin' to have a roof over his head an' a shirt on his back once more.

OLD HILSE. An' what's the devil sendin' you to do now, with your poles an' axes?

BECKER. These are what we're goin' to break on Dittrich's back.

SECOND YOUNG WEAVER. We'll heat 'em red hot an' stick 'em down the manufacturers' throats, so as they'll feel for once what burnin' hunger tastes like.

THIRD YOUNG WEAVER. Come along, father Hilse! We'll give no quarter.

SECOND YOUNG WEAVER. No one had mercy on us — neither God nor man. Now we're standin' up for our rights ourselves.

OLD BAUMERT *enters, somewhat shaky on the legs, a newly killed cock under his arm.*

OLD BAUMERT (*stretching out his arms*). My brothers — we're all brothers! Come to my arms, brothers!
                                                            [*Laughter.*]

OLD HILSE. And that's the state you're in, Willem?

OLD BAUMERT. Gustav, is it you? My poor starvin' friend. Come to my arms, Gustav!

OLD HILSE (*mutters*). Let me alone.

OLD BAUMERT. I'll tell you what, Gustav. It's nothin' but luck that's wanted. You look at me. What do I look like? Luck's what's wanted. Don't I look like a lord? [*Pats his stomach.*] Guess what's in there! There's food fit for a prince in that belly. When luck's with him a man gets roast hare to eat an' champagne wine to drink.—I'll tell you all something: We've made a big mistake—we must help ourselves.

ALL (*speaking together*). We must help ourselves, hurrah!

OLD BAUMERT. As soon as we gets the first good bite inside us we're different men. Damn it all! but you feels the power comin' into you till you're like an ox, an' that wild with strength that you hit out right an' left without as much as takin' time to look. Dash it, but it's grand!

JAEGER (*at the door, armed with an old cavalry sword*). We've made one or two first-rate attacks.

VOL. XVIII—7

BECKER. We knows how to set about it now. One, two, three, an' we're inside the house. Then, at it like lightnin'—bang, crack, shiver! till the sparks are flyin' as if it was a smithy.

FIRST YOUNG WEAVER. It wouldn't be half bad to light a bit o' fire.

SECOND YOUNG WEAVER. Let's march to Reichenbach an' burn the rich folks' houses over their heads!

JAEGER. That would be nothin' but butterin' their bread. Think of all the insurance money they'd get.

[*Laughter.*]

BECKER. No, from here we'll go to Freiburg, to Tromtra's.

JAEGER. What would you say to givin' all them as holds Government appointments a lesson? I've read somewhere as how all our troubles come from them birocrats, as they calls them.

SECOND YOUNG WEAVER. Before long we'll go to Breslau, for more an' more'll be joinin' us.

OLD BAUMERT (*to* HILSE). Won't you take a drop, Gustav?

OLD HILSE. I never touches it.

OLD BAUMERT. That was in the old world; we're in a new world today, Gustav.

FIRST YOUNG WEAVER. Christmas comes but once a year.

[*Laughter.*]

OLD HILSE (*impatiently*). What is it you want in my house, you limbs of Satan?

OLD BAUMERT (*a little intimidated, coaxingly*). I was bringin' you a chicken, Gustav. I thought it would make a drop o' soup for mother.

OLD HILSE (*embarrassed, almost friendly*). Well, you can tell mother yourself.

MOTHER HILSE (*who has been making efforts to hear, her hand at her ear, motions them off*). Let me alone. I don't want no chicken soup.

OLD HILSE. That's right, mother. An' I want none, an' least of all that sort. An' let me say this much to you, Baumert: The devil stands on his head for joy when he hears the old ones jabberin' and talkin' as if they was infants. An' to you all I say — to every one of you: Me and you, we've got nothing to do with each other. It's not with my will that you're here. In law an' justice you've no right to be in my house.

A VOICE. Him that's not with us is against us.

JAEGER (*roughly and threateningly*). You're on the wrong track, old chap. I'd have you remember that we're not thieves.

A VOICE. We're hungry men, that's all.

FIRST YOUNG WEAVER. We wants to *live* — that's all. An' so we've cut the rope we was hung up with.

JAEGER. And we was in our right! [*Holding his fist in front of the old man's face.*] Say another word, and I'll give you one between the eyes.

BECKER. Come, now, Jaeger, be quiet. Let the old man alone. — What we say to ourselves, father Hilse, is this: Better dead than begin the old life again.

OLD HILSE. Have I not lived that life for sixty years an' more?

BECKER. That doesn't help us — there's *got* to be a change.

OLD HILSE. On the Judgment Day.

BECKER. What they'll not give us willingly we're goin' to take by force.

OLD HILSE. By force. [*Laughs.*] You may as well go an' dig your graves at once. They'll not be long showin' you where the force lies. Wait a bit, lad!

JAEGER. Is it the soldiers you're meanin'? We've been soldiers too. We'll soon do for a company or two of 'em.

OLD HILSE. With your tongues, maybe. But supposin' you did — for two that you'd beat off, ten'll come back.

VOICES (*call through the window*). The soldiers are comin'! Look out!

[*General, sudden silence. For a moment a faint sound of fifes and drums is heard; in the ensuing silence a short, involuntary exclamation:* "The devil! I'm off!" *followed by general laughter.*]

BECKER. Who was that? Who speaks of runnin' away?

JAEGER.   Which of you is it that's afraid of a few paltry helmets? You have me to command you, and I've been in the trade. I know their tricks.

OLD HILSE.   An' what are you goin' to shoot with? Your sticks, eh?

FIRST YOUNG WEAVER.   Never mind that old chap; he's wrong in the upper story.

SECOND YOUNG WEAVER.   Yes, he's a bit off his head.

GOTTLIEB (*has made his way unnoticed among the rioters; catches hold of the speaker*). Would you give your impudence to an old man like him?

SECOND YOUNG WEAVER.   Let me alone. 'Twasn't anything bad I said.

OLD HILSE (*interfering*). Let him jaw, Gottlieb. What would you be meddlin' with him for? He'll soon see who it is that's been off his head today, him or me.

BECKER.   Are you comin', Gottlieb?

OLD HILSE.   No; he's goin' to do no such thing.

LUISE (*comes into the entry-room, calls*). What are you puttin' off your time with prayin' hypocrites like them for? Come quick to where you're wanted! Quick! Father Baumert, run all you can! The major's speakin' to the crowd from horseback. They're to go home. If you don't hurry up, it'll be all over.

JAEGER (*as he goes out*). That's a brave husband o' yours.

LUISE.   Where is he? I've got no husband!

[*Some of the people in the entry-room sing:*

Once on a time a man so small,
      Heigh-ho, heigh!
Set his heart on a wife so tall,
      Heigh diddle-di-dum-di!*]

WITTIG, THE SMITH (*comes downstairs, still carrying the stable pail; stops on his way through the entry-room*). Come on! all of you that is not cowardly scoundrels! — hurrah!

[*He dashes out, followed by* LUISE, JAEGER, *and others, all shouting* "Hurrah!"]

BECKER. Good-by, then, father Hilse; we'll see each other again.   [*Is going.*]

OLD HILSE. I doubt that. I've not five years to live, and that'll be the soonest you'll get out.

BECKER (*stops, not understanding*). Out o' what, father Hilse?

OLD HILSE. Out o' prison — where else?

BECKER (*laughs wildly*). Do you think I'd mind that? There's bread to be had there, anyhow!   [*Goes out.*]

OLD BAUMERT (*has been cowering on a low stool, painfully beating his brains; he now gets up*). It's true, Gustav, as I've had a drop too much. But for all that I knows what I'm about. You think one way in this here matter; I think another. I say Becker's right: even if it ends in chains an' ropes — we'll be better off in prison than at home. You're cared for there, an' you don't need to starve. I wouldn't have joined 'em, Gustav, if I could ha' let it be; but once in a lifetime a man's got to show what he feels. [*Goes slowly toward the door.*] Good-by, Gustav. If anything happens, mind you put in a word for me in your prayers.

[*Goes out. The rioters are now all gone. The entry-room gradually fills again with curious onlookers from the different rooms of the house. OLD HILSE knots at his web. GOTTLIEB has taken an ax from behind the stove and is unconsciously feeling its edge. He and the old man are silently agitated. The hum and roar of a great crowd penetrate into the room.*]

MOTHER HILSE. The very boards is shakin', father — what's goin' on? What's goin' to happen to us?
    [*Pause.*]

OLD HILSE. Gottlieb!

GOTTLIEB. What is it?

OLD HILSE. Let that ax alone.

GOTTLIEB. Who's to split the wood, then?
    [*He leans the ax against the stove. Pause.*]

MOTHER HILSE. Gottlieb, you listen to what father says to you.

> [*Some one sings outside the window:*
> Our little man does all that he can,
>   Heigh-ho, heigh!
> At home he cleans the pots an' the pan,
>   Heigh-diddle-di-dum-di!   [*Passes on.*]

GOTTLIEB (*jumps up, shakes his clenched fist at the window*). Beast! Don't drive me crazy!

> [*A volley of musketry is heard.*]

MOTHER HILSE (*starts and trembles*). Good Lord! is that thunder again?

OLD HILSE (*instinctively folding his hands*). Oh, our Father in heaven! defend the poor weavers, protect my poor brothers.   [*A short pause ensues.*]

OLD HILSE (*to himself, painfully agitated*). There's blood flowin' now.

GOTTLIEB (*had started up and grasped the ax when the shooting was heard; deathly pale, almost beside himself with excitement*). An' am I to lie to heel like a dog still?

A GIRL (*calls from the entry-room*). Father Hilse, father Hilse! get away from the window. A bullet's just flown in at ours upstairs.   [*Disappears.*]

MIELCHEN (*puts her head in at the window, laughing*). Gran'father, gran'father, they've shot with their guns. Two or three's been knocked down, an' one of 'em's turnin' round and round like a top, an' one's twistin' hisself like a sparrow when its head's bein' pulled off. An' oh, if you saw all the blood that came pourin'— !
> [*Disappears.*]

A WEAVER'S WIFE. Yes, there's two or three'll never get up again.

AN OLD WEAVER (*in the entry-room*). Look out! They're goin' to make a rush on the soldiers.

A Second Weaver (*wildly*). Look, look, look at the women! skirts up, an' spittin' in the soldiers' faces already!

A Weaver's Wife (*calls in*). Gottlieb, look at your wife. She's more pluck in her than you. She's jumpin' about in front o' the bay'nets as if she was dancin' to music.

> [*Four men carry a wounded rioter through the entry-room. Silence, which is broken by some one saying in a distinct voice, "It's weaver Ulbrich." Once more silence for a few seconds, when the same voice is heard again: "It's all over with him; he's got a bullet in his ear." The men are heard climbing the wooden stair. Sudden shouting outside: "Hurrah, hurrah!"*]

Voices in the Entry-room. "Where did they get the stones from?"—"Yes, it's time you were off!"—"From the new road."—"Ta-ta, soldiers!"—"It's rainin' paving-stones."

> [*Shrieks of terror and loud roaring outside, taken up by those in the entry-room. There is a cry of fear, and the house door is shut with a bang.*]

Voices in the Entry-room. "They're loadin' again."—"They'll fire another volley this minute."—"Father Hilse, get away from that window."

Gottlieb (*clutches the ax*). What! is we mad dogs? Is we to eat powder an' shot now instead o' bread? [*Hesitating an instant: To the old man*]. Would you have me sit here an' see my wife shot? Never! [*As he rushes out.*] Look out! I'm coming!

Old Hilse. Gottlieb, Gottlieb!

Mother Hilse. Where's Gottlieb gone?

Old Hilse. He's gone to the devil.

Voices from the Entry-room. Go away from the window, father Hilse.

OLD HILSE. Not I! Not if you all goes crazy together!
[*To* MOTHER HILSE, *with rapt excitement.*] My heavenly
Father has placed me here. Isn't that so, mother?
Here we'll sit, an' do our bounden duty — ay, though
the snow was to go on fire.

> [*He begins to weave. Rattle of another volley.* OLD
> HILSE, *mortally wounded, starts to his feet and then
> falls forward over the loom. At the same moment
> loud shouting of "Hurrah!" is heard. The peo-
> ple who till now have been standing in the entry-
> room dash out, joining in the cry. The old woman
> repeatedly asks:* "Father, father, what's wrong
> with you?" *The continued shouting dies away
> gradually in the distance.* MIELCHEN *comes rush-
> ing in.*]

MIELCHEN. Gran'father, gran'father, they're drivin' the
soldiers out o' the village; they've got into Dittrich's
house, an' they're doin' what they did at Dreissiger's.
Gran'father! [*The child grows frightened, notices
that something has happened, puts her finger in her
mouth, and goes up cautiously to the dead man.*]
Gran'father!

MOTHER HILSE. Come now, father, can't you say something?
You're frightenin' me.

THE SUNKEN BELL*

DRAMATIS PERSONÆ

HEINRICH, *a bell-founder*
MAGDA, *his wife*
TWO CHILDREN, *boys, aged five and nine*
THE VICAR
THE SCHOOLMASTER
THE BARBER

OLD WITTIKIN
RAUTENDELEIN, *an elfin creature*
THE NICKELMANN, *an elemental spirit*
THE WOOD-SPRITE
FOUR ELVES
TROLDS AND DWARFS
VILLAGERS

The scenes are laid in the mountains and in a village below.

---

* From *The Dramatic Works of Gerhart Hauptmann*, edited by Ludwig Lewisohn. Permission, Doubleday, Page & Company, New York.

THE SUNKEN BELL (1897)

By GERHART HAUPTMANN

TRANSLATED BY CHARLES HENRY MELTZER

ACT I

A fir-clad glade in the mountains. To the left, in the background, beneath
an overhanging rock, a hut. An old well to the right in the foreground.
RAUTENDELEIN *is seated on the edge of the well, combing her thick golden*
locks and addressing a bee which she is trying to drive away. In one
hand she has a mirror.

RAUTENDELEIN. Thou buzzing, golden wight — whence
    com'st thou here?
Thou sipper of sweets, thou little wax-maker!
Nay! Tease me not, thou sun-born good-for-
    naught!
Dost hear? . . . Begone! . . . 'Tis time I combed
    my hair
With Granny's golden comb. Should I delay,
She'll scold me when she comes. Begone, I say!
What? . . . Loit'ring still? . . . Away — away
    with thee!
Am I a rose bush? . . . Are my lips a rose?
Off to the wood with thee, beyond the brook!
There, there, my pretty bee, bloom cowslips fair,
And crocuses, and violets — thou canst suck
Thy fill of them. Dost think I jest? No. No.
Quick! Get thee home. Thou'rt not in favor
    here.
Thou knowest Granny's cast a spell on thee
For furnishing the Church with altar-lights.
Come! Must I speak again? Go not too far!

Hey! . . . Chimney! Puff some smoke across
    the glade,
To drive away this naughty, wilful bee.
Ho! Gander! Hither! Hither! . . . Hurry!
    Hurry!
Away! Away! [*Bee flies off.*] . . . At last! . . .
    [RAUTENDELEIN *combs her hair quietly for a
    moment or two. Then, leaning over the
    well, she calls down.*]
                                    Hey! Nickelmann!
                                        [*Pause.*]
He does not hear me. Well — I'll sing to myself.

Where do I come from? . . . Whither go?
Tell me — I long to know!
Did I grow as the birds of the woodland gay?
Am I a fay?
Who asks the sweet flower
That blooms in the dell,
And brightens the bower,
Its tale to tell?
Yet, oft, as I sit by my well, alone,
I sigh for the mother I ne'er have known.
But my weird I must dree —
And I'm fair to see —
A golden-haired maid of the forest free!
                        [*Pause. She calls.*]
Hey! Nickelmann! Come up! 'Tis lonely here.
Granny's gone gathering fir-apples. I'm dull!
Wilt keep me company and tell me tales?
Why then, tonight, perhaps, as a reward . . .
I'll creep into some farmer's yard and steal
A big, black cock for thee! . . . Ah, here he
    comes
The silver bubbles to the surface mount!
If he should bob up now, the glass he'd break,
That such bright answer to my nod doth make.
            [*Admiring her reflection in the well.*]

Godden' to thee, my sweet maid o' the well!
Thy name? . . . Rautendelein? . . . Indeed!
I see —
Thou 'rt jealous of my beauty. Look at me.
For I, not thou, Rautendelein should be.
What didst thou answer? Didst thou dare to
    point
Thy finger at thy soft twin-breasts? . . . Nay,
    nay —
I'm fairer; fair as Freya. Not for naught
My hair was spun out of the sunbeams red,
To shine, in golden glory, even as the sun
Shines up at us, at noon, from out a lake.
Aha! Thou spread'st thy tresses, like a net,
All fiery-scarlet, set to catch the fishes!
Thou poor, vain, foolish trull . . . There! Catch
    this stone.
    [*Throwing pebble down the well and disturb-
    ing the reflection.*]
Thy hour is ended. Now — I'm fair alone!
                (*Calling.*)
Ho! Nickelmann! Come — help me pass the
    time!
    [THE NICKELMANN, *a water-spirit, half
    emerges from the well, and flops over the
    edge. He is streaming with water. Weeds
    cling to his head. He snorts like a seal,
    and his eyes blink as if the day-light hurt
    them.*]
He's here! . . . Ha! Ha! Ha! Ha! How dread-
    fully plain
He is! . . . Didst thou not hear me call! Dear,
    dear —
It makes one's flesh creep but to know him near!
NICKELMANN (*croaking*).
    Brekekekex!

RAUTEND. (*mocking*). Brekekekex! Ay, ay —
    It smells of springtide.   Well, is that so strange?
    Why — every lizard, mole, and worm, and
       mouse —
    The veriest water-rat — had scented that.
    The quail, the hare, the trout, the fly, the weeds,
    Had told thee Spring was here.
NICKELM. (*touchily*).   Brekekekex!
    Be not too nosey-wise.   Dost understand?
    Thou ape, thou midge, thou tomtit, irk me not!
    I say, beware! . . . So, Quorax! Quack! Quack!
       Quack!
RAUTEND.   If Master Uncle's cross today,
    I'll leave him all alone to play.
    And I'll go dance a ring-a-round.
    Partners a-plenty, I'll be bound,
    For pretty maidens may be found.
                (*Calling.*)
    Heigh-a-aye!
VOICE OF WOOD-SPRITE (*heard without*).
    Heigh-a-o!
RAUTEND.   My merry faun, come — dance with me, I pray!

Enter the WOOD-SPRITE, *skipping comically across the glade.*

W.-SPRITE. Nay, I'm no dancer; but I know a leap
    Would make the mountain-goat with envy weep.
    If that won't do for thee, I know a game
    Will please thee more, my nixey.   Fly with me;
    I'll show thee in the woods a willow tree
    All hollowed out with age, where never came
    The sound of babbling brook, nor crow of cock.
    There, in the shadow of some friendly rock,
    I'll cut for thee, my own, the wondrous pipe
    All maids must dance to.
RAUTEND. (*eluding him*).   Thanks, I'm not yet ripe
    For such as thou! An' thou must play thy pranks.
    Go — woo thy wood-wench.   She may like thy
       shanks!

Or — go to thy dear partner, who — they say —
Another baby bears thee every day;
Except on Sundays, when, at early morn,
Three dirty little brats to thee are born!
Ha! Ha! Ha!
> [*She runs off into the hut, laughing.* The
> Wood-Sprite *vainly pursues her and re-*
> *turns disconsolate.*]

NICKELM.   Brekekekex! How mad the baggage seems!
The lightning blast thee!

W.-SPRITE (*sitting*).   Ay! . . . I'd love to tame her.
> [*He produces a short pipe and lights it by*
> *striking a match on his hoof.*]

NICKELM.   And how go things at home?

W.-SPRITE.   So so. So so.
It's warmer here than on the hills. You're snug.
Up yonder the wind shrieks and howls all day;
The swollen clouds drift damp about the peaks,
And burst at last, like sponges, when they're
        squeezed.
A foul time we have of it!

NICKELM.   And is that all?

W.-SPRITE. No . . . Yesterday I cut
My first spring salad. It grew near my hut.
This morning, early, I went out,
And, roaming carelessly about,
Through brush and brier,
Then climbing higher,
At last I reached the topmost wood.
There I espied a hateful brood
Of mortals, who did sweat and stew,
And dig the earth, and marble hew.
A curse upon their church and creed —
Their chapels, and their clanging bells * —

---

* The sprites and dwarfs hated bells, especially church bells, as disturbers
of their ancient privacy.

NICKELM.   Their bread they mix with cummin-seed! *

W.-SPRITE.   They plague us in our woods and wells.
           But vain is all our wrath and woe.
           Beside the deep abyss 'twill grow
           With tower and spire, and, overhead,
           The cross that you and I do dread.
           Ay! . . . The noisy monster was all but hung
           In the lofty steeple, and soon had rung.
           But I was alert!   We shall never hear
           That bell!   It is drownèd in the mere!
                          (*Changing tone.*)
           By cock and pie!
           A devil of a joke! . . . I stood on the brink
           Of the cliff, chewing sorrel, to help me think,
           As I rested against a stump of birch,
           'Mid the mountain grasses, I watched the church.
           When, all of a sudden, I saw the wing
           Of a blood-red butterfly, trying to cling
           To a stone.   And I marked how it dipped, and
              tipped,
           As if from a blossom the sweet it sipped.
           I called.   It fluttered, to left and to right,
           Until on my hand I felt it light.
           I knew the elf.   It was faint with fright.
           We babbled o' this,
           And we babbled o' that,
           Of the frogs that had spawned
           Ere the day had dawned,—
           We babbled and gabbled, a-much, I wis:
           Then it broke
           Into tears! . . .
           I calmed its fears.
           And again it spoke.

              " Oh, they're cracking their whips,
                And they gee! and they whoa!

_____
* Cummin-seed was obnoxious to the sprites.

As they drag it aloft
From the dale below.
'Tis some terrible tub, that has lost its lid,
All of iron!   Will nobody rid
Our woods of the horrible thing?   'Twould make
The bravest moss-mannikin shudder and quake.
They swear they will hang it, these foolish
    people,
High up in the heart of the new church steeple,
And they'll hammer, and bang, at its sides all
    day
To frighten good spirits of earth away!''

I hummed, and I hawed, and I said, ho, ho!
As the butterfly fell to the earth: while I
Stole off in pursuit of a herd near by.
I guzzled my fill of good milk, I trow!
Three udders ran dry.   They will seek in vain
So much as a drop of it more to drain.
Then, making my way to a swirling stream,
I hid in the brush, as a sturdy team
Came snorting, and panting, along the road —
Eight nags, tugging hard at their heavy load.
We will bide our time, quoth I — and lay
Quite still in the grass, till the mighty dray
Rumbled by: — when, stealing from hedge to
    hedge,
And hopping and skipping from rock to rock,
I followed the fools.   They had reached the edge
Of the cliff when there came — a block!
With flanks all a-quiver, and hocks a-thrill,
They hauled and they lugged at the dray until,
Worn out by the struggle to move the bell,
They had to lie down for a moment.   Well —
Quoth I to myself, the Faun will play
Them a trick that will spare them more work
    today.

One clutch at the wheel — I had loosened a
    spoke —
A wrench, and a blow, and the wood-work broke.
A wobble, a crack, and the hateful bell
Rolled over — and into the gulf it fell!
And oh, how it sounded,
And clanged, as it bounded,
From crag to crag, on its downward way:
Till at last in the welcoming splash and the
    spray
Of the lake it was lost — for aye!

    [*During* THE WOOD-SPRITE's *speech night has
    drawn near. It is now dusk. Several times,
    toward the end of the narrative, faint cries
    for help have been heard, coming from the
    wood. Enter from back,* HEINRICH. *As he
    approaches the hut,* THE WOOD-SPRITE *van-
    ishes in the wood and* THE NICKELMANN
    disappears in the well.* HEINRICH *is about
    thirty years of age. His face is pale and
    careworn.*]

HEINRICH. Good people — open! Quick! I've lost my way!
    Help! Help! I've fallen! . . . I am weak . . .
    I faint!
    Will no one answer? . . . Help! Kind people!
    Help!

    [*He sinks to the ground, unconscious, near
    the hut. The sun has set — dark purple
    clouds hang over the hills. The wind rises.
    Enter from the wood, carrying a basket on
    her back,* OLD WITTIKIN.]

WITTIKIN. Rautendel'! Come and help me with my load!
    I've too much on my shoulders. Come, I say!
    I'm scant o' breath! . . . Where can the girl
    be dawdling?

          [*A bat flies across the glade.*]

Ho! Stop thy gadding, flitter-mouse, and list!
Thou'lt fill thy greedy craw quite soon enough.
Come hither. Fly through yonder hole and see
If she's within. Then send her quick to me!
[*Faint lightning.* WITTIKIN *shakes her fist
at the sky.*]
Ay, ay, I see thee, Father Thor! . . . 'Twill
storm!
But give thy noisy goats not too much rope,
And see thy great red beard gleams not too
bright.
Rautendel'! Hey! Rautendel' . . . Dost not
hear?
[*A squirrel skips across the path.*]
Hey! Squirrel! Thou hast fleet and nimble feet.
Hop thou into the hut, and, shouldst thou meet
Rautendel', send her hither. As a treat,
I'll give thee, for thy pains, a nut to eat!
[WITTIKIN *sees* HEINRICH *and touches him
contemptuously with her foot.*]
What's this? A stranger? Well, well, I declare!
And pray, what brings you here, my man, so
late?
Rautendel'! . . . Hey! Rautendel'! (*To* HEIN-
RICH.) Are you dead?
Plague take you! As if I'd not more'n enough
To worry me — what wi' the Bailiff and the
Priest
Hunting me down like a mad dog. And now
I find a dead man at my door — Rautendel'!
A rare time I'd have of it, I'll be bound,
If they should find this fellow lying here.
They'd burn my house about my ears. (*To*
HEINRICH.) Art dumb?
Ay. Ay.
[RAUTENDELEIN *enters from hut, and looks
out inquiringly.*]

Oho! Thou'rt come at last. Look there!
We have a visitor. And what a one!
He's still enough. Go! Fetch a truss of hay,
And make a litter.

RAUTEND. In the hut?

WITTIKIN (*grumbling*). What next?
Nay, nay. We've no room in the hut for him.

[*Exit into hut.* RAUTENDELEIN *follows her.
She reappears a moment later, with an
armful of hay, and is about to kneel beside
HEINRICH when he recovers consciousness.*]

HEINRICH. Where am I? Maiden—wilt thou answer me?

RAUTEND. Why, in the mountains.

HEINRICH. In the mountains? Ay—
But how . . . and why? What brought me here
tonight?

RAUTEND. Nay, gentle stranger, naught know I of that.
Why fret thyself about such trifles? See—
Here I have brought thee hay. So lay thy head
Down and take all the rest thou need'st.

HEINRICH. Yes! Yes!
'Tis rest I need. Indeed—indeed—thou'rt
right.
But rest will come to me no more, my child!
(*Uneasily.*)
Now . . . tell me . . . what has happened?

RAUTEND. Nay, if I knew . . .

HEINRICH. Meseems . . . methinks . . . and . . . then . . .
all ends in dreams.
Ay, surely, I am dreaming.

RAUTEND. Here is milk.
Thou must drink some of it, for thou art weak.

HEINRICH (*eagerly*).
Thanks, maiden. I will drink. Give me the milk.

[*He drinks from a bowl which she offers him.*]

RAUTEND. (*while he drinks*).
Thou art not used to mountain ways. Thy home
Lies in the vale below, where mortals dwell.

And, like a hunter who once fell from the cliff
While giving chase to some wild mountain fowl,
Thou hast climbed far too high. And yet . . .
    that man
Was not quite fashioned as the man thou art.

HEINRICH (*after drinking and looking ecstatically and
        fixedly at* RAUTENDELEIN).

Speak on! Speak on! Thy drink was very
    sweet.
But sweeter still thy voice . . .
        [*Again becoming anxious.*]
                      She said — a man
Not fashioned like myself. A better man —
And yet he fell! . . . Speak on, my child.

RAUTEND.   Why speak?

What can my words avail! I'll rather go
And fetch thee water from the brook, to wash
The blood and dust from off thy brow . . .

HEINRICH (*pleading and grasping her by the wrist.* RAU-
      TENDELEIN *stands undecided*).   Ah, stay!

And look into mine eyes with thy strange eyes.
For lo, the world, within thine eyes renewed,
So sweetly bedded, draws me back to life!
Stay, child. O stay!

RAUTEND. (*uneasy*).
        Then . . . as thou wilt. And yet . . .

HEINRICH (*fevered and imploring*).

Ah, stay with me! Thou wilt not leave me so?
Thou dost not dream how dear to me thou art.
Oh, wake me not, my child. I'll tell thee all.
I fell . . . Yet — no. Speak thou; for thy dear
    voice
Has Heaven's own music. God did give it thee.
And I will listen. Speak! . . . Wilt thou not
    speak?
Wilt thou not sing to me? Why then . . . I
    must . . .

I fell. I know not how — I've told thee that —
Whether the path gave way beneath my feet;
Whether 'twas willingly I fell, or no —
God wot. Enough. I fell into the gulf.

[*More fevered.*]

And then I clutched at a wild cherry-tree
That grew between the rocks. It broke — and I,
Still clasping a bough tightly, felt a shower
Of pale pink blossoms riot round my head;
Then swift was hurled to the abyss — and died!
And even now I'm dead. It must be so.
Let no one wake me!

RAUTEND. (*uncertainly*).   Yet thou seem'st alive!
HEINRICH. I know — I know — what once I did not know:
That Life is Death, and only Death is Life.

[*Collapsing again.*]

I fell. I lived — and fell. The bell fell, too!
We two — the bell and I. Was I the first —
To slip, and next — the bell? Or — the reverse?
Who seeks to know? And who could prove the
    truth?
And even were it proven, what care I?
Then I was living. Now — ah, now . . . I'm
    dead.

(*Tenderly.*)

Ah, go not yet!

[*Looks at his hand.*]

            My hand! . . . 'Tis white as milk!
My hand! . . . It hangs so heavy! . . . It seems
    dead.
I cannot lift it! . . . Yet — How sweet thou art!
The touch of thy soft hair doth bring relief,
As water of Bethesda! . . . Nay, do not fear!
My hand shall never harm thee — thou art holy!
Where have we met? . . . I surely know thy
    face.
Somewhere, but where, or when, I cannot tell,

I wrought for thee, and strove — in one grand
    Bell,
To wed the silver music of thy voice
With the warm gold of a Sun-holiday.
It should have been a master-work! . . . I failed.
Then wept I tears of blood.

RAUTEND.   Wept tears of blood?
    I cannot follow thee.   What be these tears?

HEINRICH (*trying to raise his head*).

    Thou lovely picture! . . . Help me to sit up.
      [RAUTENDELEIN *stoops and supports his head.*]
    Dost thou bend down to me?   Then, with love's
        arms,
Do thou release me from this cruel Earth,
Whereunto the hour nails me, as to a cross.
Release me! For thou canst. I know thou canst!
And, with thy tender hands, pluck off the thorns
That crown my head. No crown! Love — only
        Love!
      [*His head is slightly raised. He seems ex-
        hausted.*]
                Thanks! Thanks!
      [*Gently and in a lost kind of way as he looks
        at the landscape.*]
Here all is beautiful! The rustling boughs
Have such a strange, full sound. The darkling
      arms
Of the great firs move so mysteriously.
How solemnly their heads sway to and fro!
The very soul of fairy fantasy
Sighs through the wood. It murmurs low, and
      then,
Still gently whisp'ring, stirs the tiny leaves.
Now it goes singing through the green wood-
      grass.
And now, veiled all in misty white, it nears —
It stretches out its long white hand and points

At me! . . . Now closer, it draws! It touches
    my ear . . .
My tongue . . . my eyes! . . . 'Tis gone! Yet
    thou art here!
Thou art my fantasy! . . . Kiss me, sweet
    fantasy!   [*He faints.*]

RAUTEND. (*half to herself*).
    Thy speech is strange. I know not what it means.
                 [*She suddenly resolves to go.*]
    Lie thou, and sleep.

HEINRICH (*dreaming*).   Kiss me, sweet fantasy!
    [RAUTENDELEIN *stops, and gazes at* HEINRICH.
    The darkness deepens. RAUTENDELEIN *sud-*
    denly grows frightened and calls.]

RAUTEND. O grandmother!
WITTIKIN (*from within the hut*). Well, girl?
RAUTEND.   Come here! Come here!
WITTIKIN (*as above*).
    Nay, come thou here, and help me make the fire!
RAUTEND. O Granny!
WITTIKIN.   Hark'ee, wench. Dost hear me? Come.
    'Tis time we fed the goat. And then to milk it!
RAUTEND. Grandmother! Help him! Help him! He is
    dying!
    [*Enter from hut,* WITTIKIN. *She stands on*
    the threshold, holding a milk pail in her left
    hand, and calls to her cat.]
WITTIKIN. Here! Puss, Puss, Puss!
          [*She looks carelessly at* HEINRICH.]
            He hasn't budged, I see.
Well — mortals all must die. No help for it.
What matter? Let him be. He's better so.
Come — pussy! pussy! . . . Here is milk for
    thee —
Why, where is pussy?
            (*Calling.*)
Hurry, hurry, wood-folk, when I call!
Here, I've milk a-plenty for ye all!

Hurry, hurry, hurry, trold and sprite!

[*Enter ten droll little* TROLDS, *male and female.
They bustle about the milk pail.*]

Here is bread — for every one a bite!
Here's enough to drink, and here's to eat:
Food that dukes and earls 'ud count a treat.

(*To the other* TROLDS.)

Thou, go!
Thou art full, I trow.

(*To the other* TROLDS.)

For thee a sop —
And for thee a drop —
Now enough ye've guzzled,
And off ye hop!

[*They riot and shout.*]

I'll have ye muzzled,
Unless ye stop!
Nay, this won't do —
Ye riotous crew!
Enough for today!
Away! Away!

[*The* TROLDS *vanish into the wood. Moonlight.* THE WOOD-SPRITE *appears, seated
on the rocks beyond the hut. Putting his
horny hands to his mouth, he imitates the
echo of a cry for help.*]

W.-SPRITE.   Help! Help!
WITTIKIN.   Why, what's amiss?
DISTANT VOICES (*from the wood*). Heinrich! Heinrich!
W.-SPRITE (*as above*).   Help! Help!
WITTIKIN (*threateningly to* THE WOOD-SPRITE).

Fool, thy knavish antics cease!
Leave our mountain-folk in peace!
Ay, ay. It pleases thee to vent thy spite
On the poor glass-workers! . . . Thou lov'st to
    bite
Stray dogs — to lead lost travelers into fogs,
And see them floundering in the moorland bogs.

W.-Sprite. Granny, never heed my jests.
　　　　　　Soon thou shalt have noble guests!
　　　　　　Who rides on the goose's down?
　　　　　　The barber, light as lather.
　　　　　　Who rides on the goose's crown?
　　　　　　The parson, reverend father —
　　　　　　The teacher, with his cue —
　　　　　　Three screech-owls — all for you!

The Voices (*nearer*).
　　　　　　Heinrich!

W.-Sprite (*as before*).   Help!

Wittikin.　　　　　Now may the lightning strike thee!
　　　　　　Wouldst hang a schoolmaster about my neck,
　　　　　　And eke a parson?
　　　　　　　　　[*Shaking her fist at* The Wood-Sprite.]
　　　　　　　　　Thou shalt smart for this.
　　　　　　I'll send thee swarming gnats, and stinging flies,
　　　　　　To plague thee till thou shalt be so distraught
　　　　　　Thou'lt long to hide thyself.

W.-Sprite (*with malignant glee*).
　　　　　　　　They're coming, Granny!
　　　　　　　　[*He disappears.*]

Wittikin. Well, and what then?   They're no concern o'
　　　　　　mine.
　　　　　　[*To* Rautendelein, *who is gazing fixedly at*
　　　　　　Heinrich.]
　　　　　　Into the hut!   Blow out the light!   To bed!
　　　　　　Quick, wench!

Rautend. (*sullen and defiant*).
　　　　　　　　I won't!

Wittikin.　　　　　What? Disobey me?
Rautend.　　　　　　　　　　　　Yes!
Wittikin. And why?
Rautend.　　　　They'll take him from me.
Wittikin.　　　　　　　Well? What of 't?
Rautend. They must not take him, Granny!

WITTIKIN.   Girl, ha' done!
          And let them deal wi' him as they may list.
          Dust will to dust, and some day he must die.
          So let him die. He'll be the better for 't.
          See how life irks him, how it rends his heart,
          Wi' pain and agony.

HEINRICH (*dreaming*).   The Sun sets fast!

WITTIKIN. He never saw the Sun, girl. Let him be.
          Come. Follow me. Be warned, or thou wilt rue!
               [*Exit into hut. Cries of* " Heinrich! Hein-
               rich! " RAUTENDELEIN *listens for a mo-
               ment. Then she suddenly breaks a flowery
               twig from a bough, and draws a circle with
               it round* HEINRICH *as she speaks the fol-
               lowing lines.*]

RAUTEND.   With the first fresh buds of Spring,
          Lo, I draw the magic ring!
          Safe from every harm and ill,
          Thus thou art. It is my will!
          Thou art thine, and thine, and mine.
          None may cross the mystic line!
          Be thou youth, or man, or maid,
          Here thou surely must be stayed!
               [*She hides behind the trees in shadow. Enter
               one after the other, from the wood,* THE
               VICAR, THE BARBER, *and* THE SCHOOL-
               MASTER.]

VICAR.   I see a light.

SCHOOLM.   And I!

VICAR.   Where are we now?

BARBER.   God only knows. Again I hear that cry
          Of " Help! Help! Help! "

VICAR.   It is the Master's voice!

SCHOOLM.   I heard no cry.

BARBER.   It came from yonder height.

SCHOOLM.   If one fell up to Heaven, that might be,
          But, as a general rule, one tumbles — down:

Permission Amsler & Ruthardt, Berlin   MAX KLINGER

INTERMEZZO I

From cliff to vale, and not from vale to cliff.
The Master lies — I'd stake my soul upon 't —
Full fifty fathoms deeper: not up here.

BARBER.   'Ods bodikins!   Did you not hear him then?
If that was not the voice of Master Heinrich,
May I be set to shave old Rübezahl!
As I'm a living barber, I will swear
I heard a cry.

SCHOOLM.   Where from?
VICAR.   What place is this?
Ere we continue, tell me that, my friends.
My face is bleeding; I can hardly drag
One foot after another.   How they ache!
I'll go no further.

A VOICE.   Help!
VICAR.   Again that voice!
BARBER.   And this time it was close to where we stand!
VICAR (sitting wearily).

I'm racked with pain.   Indeed, my worthy
    friends,
I can no more.   So leave me, in God's name.
In truth, though you should beat me black and
    blue,
You could not make me budge another step.
I am worn out.   Alack, that this glad day
Should end so sadly!   Who had ever thought
Such things could happen!   And the mighty
    bell —
The noblest of the Master's master-works — !
Thy ways, O Lord, indeed pass finding out
And are most wonderful!

BARBER.   Ay, Father, ay.
And do you wish to know what place this be?
Well, I will tell you.   If you'll be advised,
You'll get from hence — and that without delay.
'Twere better far we spent the livelong night
Bare-backed, and in a hornet's nest, than here.

For, by the Lord, we're on the Silver Hill!
Within a hundred steps should stand the house
Of that accursèd witch.   So — let's away!

VICAR.   I cannot budge.

SCHOOLM.   Nay, come, I pray you, come.
Worse things than witches are encountered
    here.
If they were all, I should not turn a hair.
Ah, there's no wilder spot for leagues around —
A paradise of smugglers, thieves, and rogues —
A trysting-place for cut-throat murderers —
So infamous that Peter — he who longed
To know what fear and trembling meant —
    might learn
Both easily — if he but came this way.

BARBER.   Yes.   One and one make two — we all know that.
But that is not the only thing worth knowing.
I hope, my master, you may never learn
What witchcraft means! . . . The hellish sluts
    who lurk,
Like toads in a hole, hatching their evil plots,
May send you illnesses, and plague your ox,
Make blood flow from the udders of your cows
Instead of milk, and rot your sheep with
    worms —
Or curse your children with unwholesome wens,
And horrible ulcers.   All this they can do.

SCHOOLM.   You're wandering, sirs.   The night has turned
    your heads.
While you go babbling here of witches' games,
Your ears grow dull.   Heard you not moans?
    By Heaven!
I see the very man we seek!

VICAR.   See whom?

SCHOOLM.   Why, Master Heinrich.

BARBER.   Oh, he's lost his wits!

VICAR.   'Twas witchcraft.

SCHOOLM.   Nay, then two and two's not four,
But five.   And that's impossible.   Prate not
Of witches.   For, as I do hope for Heaven,
There lies the master bell-founder himself!
Look!   Now the clouds have ceased to hide the
moon.
Look, gentlemen!   Now!   Now!   Well—was
I right?

VICAR.   Indeed you were, my master.

BARBER.   'Tis the bell-founder!
[*All three hurry toward* HEINRICH, *but recoil
on reaching the edge of the magic ring.*]

VICAR.   Oh!

BARBER.   Oh!

SCHOOLM.   Oh! Oh!

RAUTEND. (*becoming visible for a moment among the trees*).
                         Ha! Ha! Ha! Ha! Ha! Ha!
[*She vanishes amid peals of mocking laughter.
A pause.*]

SCHOOLM. (*bewildered*).
             What was it?

BARBER.   Ay.   What was 't?

VICAR.   I heard a laugh!

SCHOOLM.   The bright light dazzled me.   I do believe
It's made a hole in my head as big as my fist.

VICAR.   You heard the laughter?

BARBER.   Ay, and something cracked.

VICAR.   The laughter seemed to come from every pine
That rustles round us in the growing gloom.
There!   Yonder!   Where the horn-owl hoots
and flies!

BARBER.   Didn't I tell you of these devilish folk?
O Lord, O Lord!   I warned you of their spells.
D'ye think we're safe here?   As for me, I
quake—
My flesh creeps.   Curses on the hag, say I!

VICAR (*raising the crucifix which hangs round his neck, and
moving steadfastly toward the hut*).

You may be right.   Yet, though the Devil him-
    self
Dwelt here, I'd still say: Courage! On! Still on!
Against him we will pit God's Holy Word!
Ah! never yet was Satan's craft more clear
Than when he hurled the Master and the bell
To death — God's servant and his instrument —
The bell that, from the edge of the abyss
Had sung the hymn of everlasting Love,
And Peace, and Mercy, through the firmament!
Here stand we as true soldiers of the Lord!
I'll knock!

BARBER.   D — d — don't risk it!

VICAR.   Yes!   I say, I'll knock!
                  [*He knocks at the door of the hut.*]

WITTIKIN (*from within the hut*).
    Who's there?

VICAR.   A Christian!

WITTIKIN.   Christian or no Christian,
    What d'you want?

VICAR.   Open!

WITTIKIN (*appearing in the doorway, carrying a lighted
    lantern*).   Well?   What's your will?

VICAR.   In God's name, woman, whom thou dost not
    know —

WITTIKIN.   Oho!   A pious opening, I declare!

SCHOOLM.   Thou carrion-crow, how durst thou wag thy
    tongue?
The measure's full — thy time is meted out.
Thy evil life and thy accursèd deeds
Have made thee hated through the countryside.
So — an' thou do not now as thou art bid —
Ere dawn the red cock* from thy roof shall
    crow —
Thy den of thieves shall flame and smoke to
    Heaven!

---

* In Germany " der rothe Hahn " is a symbol of incendiarism.

BARBER (*crossing himself repeatedly*).

    Thou wicked cat! I'm not afraid of thee!

    Ay — scowl, and glare, and glower, as thou wilt!

    Though thy red eyes should light upon my corpse,

    They'll find the Cross before them. Do as thou'rt bid!

VICAR.   I charge thee, woman, in God's holy name,

    Have done with all thy devilish juggleries,

    And help this man! Here lies a child of God,

    A Master, gifted with a wondrous art

    That him doth honor, while it puts to shame

    The damnèd companies of air and Hell.

WITTIKIN (*who has been prowling round* HEINRICH *with her lantern*).

    And, what's all that to do wi' me? Enough!

    You're welcome to the creature. Take him hence.

    What harm did I to him? For aught I care,

    He may live on, till he has spent his breath.

    I'll wager that won't be so very long!

    Ye name him " Master," and ye love the sound

    O' the big iron bells the creature makes.

    Ye all are hard o' hearin', or ye'd know

    There's no good in his bells. He knows it, too.

    Ah, I could tell ye, an I would, what's wrong.

    The best and worst o' them ring false. They're cracked.

    There! Take the litter. Bear the man away —

    The " Master," as ye call him! Master Milksop!

        (*To* HEINRICH.)

    Get up! Go home and help the parson preach!

    Go — help the schoolmaster to birch his boys —

    Go — mix the lather in the barber's shop!

      [THE BARBER *and* THE SCHOOLMASTER *lift* HEINRICH *onto the litter.*]

VICAR. Thou wicked, scolding hag! Restrain thy tongue!

Thy way shall lead thee straight to Hell. Begone!

WITTIKIN. Oh, spare your sermons. I ha' heard ye preach.
I know, I know. 'Tis sinful to ha' senses.
The earth's a coffin, and the Heavens above
Are but a coffin-lid. The stars are holes;
The sun's a bigger hole in the blue sky.
The world 'ud come to grief wi'out the priests,
And God Himself ye'd make a bug-a-boo!
The Lord should take a rod to ye — poor fools!
Ay, fools are ye — all, all! and nothing more!
[*She bangs open her door and goes into hut.*]

VICAR. Thou beldame!

BARBER. For Heaven's sake — don't vex her more!
If you should goad her further, we are lost.

[*Exeunt* THE VICAR, THE SCHOOLMASTER, *and* THE BARBER *into the wood, bearing away* HEINRICH *on the litter. The moon shines out, and lights up the peaceful landscape.* FIRST, SECOND, *and* THIRD ELVES *steal out of the wood one after the other and join hands in a dance.*]

1ST ELF (*whispering*).
Sister!

2D ELF (*as above*). Sister!

1ST ELF (*as above*). White and chill
Shines the moon across the hill.
Over bank, and over brae,
Queen she is, and Queen shall stay.

2D ELF. Whence com'st thou?

1ST ELF. From where the light
In the waterfall gleams bright,
Where the glowing flood doth leap,
Roaring, down into the deep.

Then, from out the mirk and mist,
Where the foaming torrent hissed,
Past the dripping rocks and spray,
Up I swiftly made my way.

3D ELF (*joining them*).
Sisters, is it here ye dance?
1ST ELF. Wouldst thou join us? Quick — advance!
2D ELF. And whence com'st thou?
3D ELF. Hark and hist!
Dance, and dance, as ye may list!
'Mid the rocky peaks forlorn
Lies the lake where I was born.
Starry gems are mirrored clear
On the face of that dark mere.
Ere the fickle moon could wane,
Up I swept my silver train.
Where the mountain breezes sigh,
Over cliff and crag came I!

4TH ELF (*entering*).
Sisters!
1ST ELF. Sister! Join the round!
ALL (*together*). Ring-a-ring-a-ring-around!
4TH ELF. From Dame Holle's flowery brae,
Secretly I stole away.
1ST ELF. Wind and wander, in and out!
ALL (*together*). Ring-a-ring-a-round-about!

[*Lightning and distant thunder. Enter suddenly, from the hut,* RAUTENDELEIN. *Clasping her hands behind her head, she watches
the dance from the doorway. The moonlight falls full on her.*]

RAUTEND. Ho, my fairies!
1ST ELF. Hark! A cry!
2D ELF. Owch! My dress is all awry!
RAUTEND. Ho, ye fairies!
3D. ELF. Oh, my gown!
Flit and flutter, up and down.

RAUTEND. (*joining in the dance*).
>Let me join the merry round,
>Ring-a-ring-a-ring-around!
>Silver nixie, sweetest maid,
>See how richly I'm arrayed.
>All of silver, white and rare,
>Granny wove my dress so fair.
>Thou, my fairy brown, I vow,
>Browner far am I than thou.
>And, my golden sister fair,
>I can match thee with my hair,
>Now I toss it high — behold,
>Thou hast surely no such gold.
>Now it tumbles o'er my face:
>Who can rival me in grace?

ALL (*together*). Wind and wander, in and out,
>Ring-a-ring-a-round-about!

RAUTEND. Into the gulf there fell a bell.
>Where is it lying? Will ye tell?

ALL (*together*). Wind and wander, in and out,
>Ring-a-ring-a-round-about!
>Daisy and forget-me-not,
>Fairy footsteps injure not.

>[*Enter* THE WOOD-SPRITE, *skipping. Thunder
>— this time louder. During the following
>speech, a storm rages — thunder and hail.*]

W.-SPRITE. Daisy and forget-me-not
>Crush I in the earth to rot.
>If the moorland's all a-drip
>'Tis because I leap, and skip!
>Now the bull doth seek his mate,
>Bellows at the stable gate.
>And the heifer, sleeping by,
>Lifts her head and lows reply.
>On the stallion's warm brown hide
>Every fly doth seek his bride,
>While the midges dance above,
>Fill the air with life and love.

See!   The ostler woos the maid!
Buss her, fool!   Dost fear the jade?
With the rotting straw for bed,
Soft and tender, lo they wed!
Hul'lo!   Hul'lo!   Heigh-o-hey!
Whisp'ring's over for today.
Done the dancing, hushed and chill,
Lusty life is master still!
Be it early, be it late,
Mews the tom-cat, mews its mate.
Stork, and thrush, and nightingale,
Hart, and hare, and hen, and quail,
Snipe, and hawk, and swan, and duck,
Crane, and pheasant, doe and buck,
Beetle, moth, and mole, and louse,
Toad, and frog, and bat, and mouse,
Bee, and gnat, and moth, and fly —
All must love, and all must die!

> [THE WOOD-SPRITE *snatches up one of the*
> ELVES *and carries her off into the wood.*
> *The three other* ELVES *vanish in different*
> *directions.* RAUTENDELEIN *remains stand-*
> *ing alone and sad, in the middle of the*
> *glade.   The storm gradually dies away.*
> THE NICKELMANN *rises from the well, as*
> *before.*]

NICKELM.   Brekekekex! — Brekekekex!   Hey!   Ho!
Why dost thou stand there?

RAUTEND.   Thou dear water-sprite —
Alas, I am so sad.   So sad am I!

NICKELM. (*mockingly*).
Brekekekex!   And which eye hurts thee, dear?

RAUTEND. (*gaily*).
The left eye.   But, perhaps, thou think'st I jest?

NICKELM.   Ay, surely, surely.

RAUTEND. (*pointing to a tear in her eye*).
Look — what can it be?

NICKELM. What dost thou mean?

RAUTEND. Why — see what's in my eye!

NICKELM. What's in thine eye? Come — let me see it close.

RAUTEND. A warm, wet drop has fallen on my lid.

NICKELM. The deuce it has! Come nearer — let me see.

RAUTEND. (*holding out the tear to him*).
A tiny, pure, warm, glitt'ring drop of dew.
There, only see!

NICKELM. By Heaven! 'Tis beautiful.
How would it please thee an' I took the thing
And set it in a fine, pink shell for thee?

RAUTEND. Why, as thou wilt. I'll lay it on the edge
Of the well. What can it be?

NICKELM. A wondrous gem!
Within that little globe lies all the pain,
And all the joy, the world can ever know.
'Tis called — a tear!

RAUTEND. A tear! . . . I must have wept.
So now at last I've learned what these tears
be . . .
Oh, tell me something!

NICKELM. Come to me, dear child!

RAUTEND. Not I, forsooth. What good were that to me?
The edge of thine old well is wet and rough;
'Tis overrun with spiders, worms and — worse.
They irk me — all of them. And so dost thou.

NICKELM. Brekekekex! I grieve to hear it, dear.

RAUTEND. Another of those drops! How strange!

NICKELM. More rain!
Behold! Now Father Thor is all ablaze.
The lightnings from his beard fall soft, and
blink
Like babies' eyes, setting the misty train
Of rolling clouds aglow with purple flame.
And yonder, near the gray, mark how a flight
Of ravens rushes madly through the night
To keep him company. With every flash

Their wings gleam wetter in the whirling rain.
Hark, child, how thirstily our Mother Earth
Drinks every drop! And how the trees and
    grass,
The flies and worms, grow glad in the quick light!
                        [*Lightning.*]
Quorax! Now in the valley! Master! Hail!
Old Thor is kindling a rare Easter fire.
His hammer flares — twelve thousand miles it
    sweeps!
The church-tower totters — now the belfry
    cracks!
The smoke pours out! . . .

RAUTEND.   Enough! Enough! No more!
Come, tell me something else. I'm tired of Thor.

NICKELM.   Thou saucy sparrow, thou — Brekekekex!
What ails the creature? When it's stroked —
    it pecks.
A pretty way to thank one! When you're done,
You're no bit further than ere you'd begun!
Am I not right? . . . Still pouting, eh? . . .
    Well, well.
What wouldst thou know?

RAUTEND.   Oh, nothing. Do but go!

NICKELM.   Naught thou wouldst know?

RAUTEND.   Naught!

NICKELM. (*imploringly*).   Then, speak thou, I pray.

RAUTEND.   I long to leave you all and go away!
    [*Her eyes fill with tears and she stares into*
        the distance.]

NICKELM. (*with anguish*):
What have I done to thee? Where wouldst
    thou go?
Is it the world of men that thou wouldst know?
I warn thee, maiden. Man's a curious thing,
Who naught but woe to such as thee could bring.

Although, perchance, with ours his fate's en-
   twined,
He is, yet is not quite, of our own kind.
His world is ours — and yet, I say, beware!
Half here, he lives — half, no one could tell
   where!
Half he's our brother; yet, this many a day,
A foe he's been, and lost to us for aye.
Woe, woe to all who our free mountains flee
To join these mortals, hoping bliss to see!
Man's feet are in the Earth. In toil and pain
He lives his fleeting life. And yet — he's vain.
He's like a plant that in a cellar shoots,
And needs must pluck and pluck at its own roots.
So, languishing for light, he rots away,
Nor ever knows the joy of one sun-ray.
The breath of Spring that kisses the green leaf,
To sickly boughs brings death, and not relief.
Pry thou no further, but let Man alone:
Lest thou should hang about thy neck — a stone.
Man will but sadden thee with his gray skies,
And turn thy happy laugh to tears and sighs.
Thou shalt be chained unto an ancient Book.
Accurst — no more upon the Sun thou'lt look!

RAUTEND. Grandmother says thou art a learned seer.
Yet, an' thou wilt but in thy waters peer,
Thou'lt see that never yet a rill did flow
But longed into the world of men to go.

NICKELM. (*angrily*).
Quorax! Brekekekex! Be not so bold.
Hear now the words of one ten centuries old!
Let slavish streams pursue their fated way,
Work, wash, for men, and grind their corn each
   day,
Water their cabbages and garden stuff,
And swallow — Heav'n knows what! And now
   . . . enough!
        (*Warmly and earnestly.*)

But, O my dear Princess Rautendelein,
For thee a King's chamber were none too fine.
I know a rare crown, all of crystal so green,
In a great golden hall, thou shalt wear it, my
    queen.
The floor and the roof are of clear blue stone,
Red coral the coffers and chests I own. . . .

RAUTEND.   And what though thy coffers of coral be
    wrought?
Life lived with the fishes were good for naught.
And though thy King's crown of pure sapphire
    should be,
Thy daughters should prink it alone with thee.
My own golden tresses are far more dear;
Their touch a caress is; my crown is — here!
                        [*She turns to go.*]

NICKELM.   Where art thou going?
RAUTEND. (*airily and indifferently*).   What is that to thee?
NICKELM. (*sorrowfully*).
    Much. Much. Brekekekex!
RAUTEND.   Oh, whither I will,
Go I.
NICKELM.   And whither wouldst go?
RAUTEND.   Away and away!
NICKELM.   Away and away?
RAUTEND. (*flinging her arms aloft*).   To the world — of men!
                   [*She vanishes in the wood.*]
NICKELM. (*terrified*).
    Quorax!
        (*Whimpering.*)
    Quorax!
        (*Softly.*)
    Quorax!
    (*Shaking his head sadly.*)
            Brekekekex!

ACT II

An old-fashioned room in the house of HEINRICH *the bell-founder. A deep recess occupies half the back wall. In the recess is a large open fireplace, with a chimney above it. A copper kettle is suspended above the unlighted fire. The other half of the back wall, set at an angle, is lighted by a large old-fashioned window, with bottle-glass panes. Below this window, a bed. Doors right and left. That on the right leads to the workshop, while that on the left leads to the courtyard. In the foreground, right, a table and chairs placed. On the table: a full jug of milk, mugs, and a loaf of bread. Near the table, a tub. The room is decorated with works by Adam Kraft, Peter Fischer, etc., conspicuous among them a painted wooden image of Christ on the Cross. Seated at the farther side of the table, and, in their Sunday best, the two* CHILDREN *of* HEINRICH *(boys aged respectively five and nine), with their mugs of milk before them.* MAGDA, *their mother, also in her Sunday best, enters from the right, with a bunch of cowslips in her hand.*
Early morning. The light grows brighter as the action progresses.

MAGDA.   See, children, what I've brought you from the fields!
Beyond the garden — a whole patch grew wild.
Now we can make ourselves look fine and gay,
In honor of your father's birthday feast.

1ST CHILD.   Oh, give me some!

2D CHILD.   And me!

MAGDA.   There! Five for each!
And every single one they say's a key*
That opens Heaven. Now drink your milk, my dears,
And eat your bread.   'Tis almost time to start.
The road to church, you know, is long and steep.

NEIGHBOR (*a woman; looking in at the window*).
What! Up already, neighbor?

MAGDA (*at the window*).   Yes, indeed.
I hardly closed my eyes the livelong night.
But, 'twas not care that kept me wide-awake.

_____

* In Germany the cowslip is called "Himmelschlüssel," *i. e.,* "the key of Heaven."

So now I'm just as fresh as if I'd slept
Sound as a dormouse. Why, how bright it is!

NEIGHBOR. Ay. Ay. You're right.

MAGDA.   You'll come with us, I hope?
Now don't say no. You'll find it easy walking
On the road . . . These tiny children's feet
Shall lead the way, and gently mark our steps.
If you must have the truth, I long for wings:
I'm wild today with joy and eagerness!

NEIGHBOR. And has your good-man not been home all night?

MAGDA. What are you dreaming of? I'll be content
If only the big bell is safely hung
In time to ring the people in to mass!
You see — the time was short. They'd none to
    waste.
And as for sleeping — if the Master snatched
So much as one short wink in the wood-grass —
Why, Heaven be praised! But, oh, what does
    it matter?
The work was hard: but great is the reward.
You cannot think how pure, and clear, and true,
The new bell sounds. Just wait until you hear
Its voice ring out today from the church-tower.
'Tis like a prayer, a hymn, a song of praise —
Filling the heart with comfort and with glad-
    ness.

NEIGHBOR. No doubt, ma'am. Yet one thing amazes me.
From my front door, as doubtless you're aware,
The church upon the hill is plainly seen.
Now — I had heard that when the bell was hung
A white flag would be hoisted from the tower.
I've seen no sign of that white flag. Have you?

MAGDA. Oh, look again. It must be there by now.

NEIGHBOR. No, no. It's not.

MAGDA.   Well, even were you right,
It would not frighten me. Did you but know
The fret and toil and pain, by night and day,

It cost the Master to complete his work,
You would not wonder if the final stroke
Should be delayed a bit.   I understand.
By this time, I'll be bound, the flag is there.
Why, yes, I'm sure it is, could we but see 't.

NEIGHBOR.   I can't believe it.   In the village streets
They do say something dreadful has occurred.
Dark omens, boding evil, fill the air.
But now, a farmer saw a naked witch,
Perched on a boar's back, riding through his
        corn.
Lifting a stone, he cast it at the hag —
Straightway his hand dropped — palsied to the
        knuckles!
'Tis said that all the mischievous mountain
        sprites
Are leagued and up in arms against the bell.
How strange you have not heard all this before!
Well — now the Bailiff's gone into the hills,
With half the village at his heels, to see . . .

MAGDA.   The Bailiff?   Merciful God!   What can be
        wrong?

NEIGHBOR.   Why, nothing's certain.   All may yet be well.
There — don't take on so, neighbor.   Come —
        be calm!
It's not so bad as that.   Now don't 'ee fret.
It seems the wagon and the bell broke down . . .
That's all we've heard.

MAGDA.   Pray Heav'n that be the worst!
What matters one bell more or less! . . . If he,
The Master, be but safe — these flowers may
        stay.
Yet — till we know what's happened . . . Here,
        prithee,
Take the two children . . .
            [*She lifts the two* CHILDREN *through the
                window.*]
                                Will you?

NEIGHBOR.   Why, to be sure.

MAGDA.   Thanks.   Take them home with you.   And, as
                   for me,
               Ah, I must go, as fast as go I can,
               To see what may be done — to help.   For I
               Must be with my dear Master — or, I die!
                   [*Exit hurriedly.   The* NEIGHBOR *retires with
                   the* CHILDREN. *Confused noise of voices
                   without.   Then a piercing cry from* MAGDA.]

Enter quickly THE VICAR, *sighing, and wiping the tears from his eyes.   He
looks around the room hastily, and turns down the coverlet of the bed.
Then, hurrying to the door, he meets* THE SCHOOLMASTER *and* THE
BARBER, *carrying* HEINRICH *in on the litter seen in Act One.* HEINRICH
reclines on a rude bed of green branches. MAGDA, *half beside herself
with anguish, follows, supported by a* MAN *and a* WOMAN. *Crowd of*
VILLAGERS *presses in behind* MAGDA. HEINRICH *is laid on his own bed.*

VICAR (*to* MAGDA).
               Bear up, my mistress!   Put your trust in God!
               We laid him on our litter as one dead;
               Yet, on the way, he came to life again,
               And, as the doctor told us, only now,
               Hope's not yet lost.

MAGDA (*moaning*).   Dear God, who speaks of hope?
               A moment since, I was so happy! . . . Now —
               What's come to me?   What's happened?   Won't
                   you speak?
               Where are the children?

VICAR.   Put your trust in God.
               Do but have patience, mistress.   Patience and
                   faith!
               Often — remember — in our direst need
               God's help is nearest.   And, forget not this:
               Should He, of His all-wisdom, have resolved,
               In His own time, to call the Master hence,
               Still there shall be this comfort for your soul —
               Your husband goes from Earth to endless bliss.

MAGDA.   Why do you speak of comfort, reverend sir?
                Do I need comfort?   Nay — he will get well.
                He must get well.

VICAR.   So all of us do hope.
                But . . . should he not . . . God's holy will be
                    done.
                Come now what may, the Master's fight is won.
                To serve the Lord, he fashioned his great bell.
                To serve the Lord, he scaled the mountain-
                    heights —
                Where the malignant powers of Darkness dwell,
                And the Abyss defies the God of Hosts.
                Serving the Lord, at last he was laid low —
                Braving the hellish spirits in his path.
                They feared the gospel that his bell had rung:
                So leagued themselves against him, one and all,
                In devilish brotherhood.   God punish them!

BARBER.   A wonder-working woman lives hard by,
                Who heals, as the Disciples healed of old,
                By prayer and faith.

VICAR.   Let some one search for her:
                And when she's found, return with her at once.

MAGDA.   What's come to him?   Why do you stand and
                    gape?
                Off with you all!   You shall not stare at him
                With your unfeeling eyes.   D'you hear?   Be-
                    gone!
                Cover him — so — with linen, lest your looks
                Should shame the Master.   Now — away with
                    you!
                Get to the juggler's, if you needs must gape.
                Ah, God!   What's happened? . . . Are ye all
                    struck dumb?

SCHOOLM.   Truly, 'tis hard to tell just what took place.
                Whether he tried to stop the bell — or what . . .
                This much is certain: if you could but see
                How deep he fell, you would go down on your
                    knees

And thank the Lord.   For, if your husband lives,
'Tis nothing short of the miraculous!

HEINRICH (*feebly*).
Give me a little water!

MAGDA (*driving out the* VILLAGERS *quickly*).   Out you go!

VICAR.   Go, my good people.   He has need of rest.
[VILLAGERS *withdraw.*]
If I can serve you, mistress, why, you know
Where you may find me.

BARBER.   Yes, and me.

SCHOOLM.   And me.
No.   On reflection, I'll stay here.

MAGDA.   You'll go!

HEINRICH.   Give me some water!
[THE VICAR, SCHOOLMASTER, *and* BARBER *withdraw slowly, talking low, shaking their
heads, and shrugging their shoulders.*]

MAGDA (*hastening to* HEINRICH *with water*).
Heinrich, are you awake?

HEINRICH.   I'm parched.   Give me some water.   Can't you
hear?

MAGDA (*unable to control herself*).
Nay, patience.

HEINRICH.   Magda, all too soon I'll learn
What patience means.   Bear with me yet awhile.
It will not be for long.   [*He drinks.*]
Thanks, Magda.   Thanks.

MAGDA.   Don't speak to me so strangely, Heinrich.
Don't!
I . . . I'm afraid.

HEINRICH (*fevered and angry*).   Thou must not be afraid.
When I am gone, thou'lt have to live alone.

MAGDA.   I cannot . . . no, I will not . . . live without
thee!

HEINRICH.   Thy pain is childish.   Torture me no more!
It is unworthy,—for thou art a mother.
Bethink thee what that word means, and be
brave!

MAGDA.   Ah, do not be so stern and harsh with me!
HEINRICH (*painfully*).
                  The plain truth harsh and stern?   Again I say —
                  Thy place is by the bedside of thy boys.
                  There lies thy joy, thy peace, thy work, thy life.
                  All — all is tucked up in their fair, white sheets.
                  Could it be otherwise, 'twere infamous!
MAGDA (*falling on his neck*).
                  So help me Heav'n, I love thee far, far, more
                  Than our dear children, and myself, and all!
HEINRICH.   Then woe unto ye all, too soon bereaved!
                  And thrice-unhappy I, untimely doomed
                  To snatch the milk and bread from your poor
                      lips!
                  Yet, on my tongue, I feel them turn to poison.
                  That, too, is just! . . . Farewell.   Thee I com-
                      mend
                  To one from whom none living may escape.
                  Many a man has found Death's deepest shadow
                  Prove but a welcome light.   God grant it be!
                                (*Tenderly.*)
                  Give me thy hand.   I've done thee many a
                      wrong
                  By word and deed.   Often I've grieved thy
                      heart,
                  Far, far, too often.   But thou wilt forgive me!
                  I would have spared thee, had I but been free.
                  I know not what compelled me; yet I know
                  I could not choose but stab thee — and myself.
                  Forgive me, Magda!
MAGDA.   I forgive thee?   What?
                  If thou dost love me, Heinrich, be less sad:
                  Or thou wilt bring the tears back.   Rather —
                      scold.
                  Thou knowest well how dear —
HEINRICH (*painfully*).   I do not know!
MAGDA.   Nay, who, but thou, did wake my woman's soul?
                  Till thou didst come, I was a poor, dull clod,

Pining away beneath a cheerless sky.

Thou — thou — didst rescue me and make me
    live,

Fill me with joy, and set my heart in the sun.

And never did I feel thy love more sure

Than when, with thy strong hand, thou'dst
    draw my face

Out of the dark, and turn it toward the light.

And thou wouldst have me pardon thee! For
    what?

Do I not owe thee all I love in life?

HEINRICH. Strangely entangled seems the web of souls.

MAGDA (*stroking his hair tenderly*).

If I have ever been a help to thee —

If I have sometimes cheered thy working
    hours —

If favor in thine eyes I ever found . . .

Bethink thee, Heinrich: I, who would have given

Thee everything — my life — the world itself —

I had but that to pay thee for thy love!

HEINRICH (*uneasily*).

I'm dying. That is best. God means it well.

Should I live on . . . Come nearer, wife, and
    hear me.

'Tis better for us both that I should die.

Thou think'st, because we blossomed out to-
    gether,

I was the sun that caused thy heart to bloom.

But that the eternal Wonder-Worker wrought,

Who, on the wings of His chill winter-storms,

Rides through a million million woodland
    flowers,

Slaying them, as He passes, in their Spring!

'Tis better for us both that I should die.

See: I was cracked and ageing — all misshaped.

If the great Bell-Founder who molded me

Tosses aside His work, I shall not mourn.

When He did hurl me down to the abyss,
After my own poor, faulty handiwork,
I did not murmur: for my work was bad!
Good wife — the bell that sank into the mere
Was not made for the heights — it was not fit
To wake the answering echoes of the peaks!

MAGDA.   I cannot read the meaning of thy words.
A work — so highly prized, so free from flaw,
So clear and true that, when it first rang out
Between the mighty trees from which it hung,
All marveled and exclaimed, as with one voice,
" The Master's bell sings as the Angels sing! "

HEINRICH (*fevered*).
'Twas for the valley, not the mountain-top!

MAGDA.   That is not true!   Hadst thou but heard, as I,
The Vicar tell the Clerk, in tones that shook,
" How gloriously 'twill sound upon the heights! "

HEINRICH.   'Twas for the valley — not the mountain-top!
I only know 't.   The Vicar does not know.
So I must die — I wish to die, my child.
For, look now: should I heal — as men would
   call 't —
Thanks to the art of our good village leech,
I'd be at best a botch, a crippled wretch;
And so the warm and generous draught of life —
Ofttimes I've found it bitter, ofttimes sweet,
But ever it was strong, as I did drink 't —
Would turn to a stale, flat, unsavory brew,
Thin and grown cold and sour.   I'll none of it!
Let him who fancies it enjoy the draught.
Me it would only sicken and repel.
Hush!   Hear me out.   Though thou shouldst
   haply find
A doctor of such skill that he could cure me,
Giving me back my joy — nerving my hand,
Till it could turn to the old, daily task —
Even then, Magda, I were still undone.

MAGDA.   For God's sake, husband, tell me what to think!
What has come over thee — a man so strong,
So blessed, so weighted down with Heaven's
    best gifts;
Respected, loved, of all — of all admired,
A master of thy craft! . . . A hundred bells
Hast thou set ringing, in a hundred towers.
They sing thy praise, with restless industry;
Pouring the deep, glad beauty of thy soul
As from a hundred wine-cups, through the land.
At eve, the purple-red — at dawn, God's gold —
Know thee. Of both thou art become a part.
And thou — rich, rich, beyond thy greatest
    need —
Thou, voicing God — able to give, and give,
Rolling in happiness, where others go
Begging their daily dole of joy or bread —
Thou look'st unthankfully upon thy work!
Then, Heinrich, why must I still bear the life
That thou dost hate so? . . . What is life to me?
What could that be to me which thou dost
    scorn —
Casting it from thee, like a worthless thing!

HEINRICH. Mistake me not. Now thou thyself hast sounded
Deeper and clearer than my loudest bells.
And many a one I've made! . . . I thank thee,
    Magda.
Yet thou shalt understand my thought. Thou
    must.
Listen! . . . The latest of my works had failed.
With anguished heart I followed where they
    climbed,
Shouting and cursing loudly, as the bell
Was dragged toward the peak. And then —
    it fell.
It fell a hundred fathoms deep, ay, more,
Into the mere. There, in the mere, now lies

The last and noblest work my art could mold!
Not all my life, as I have lived it, Magda,
Had fashioned, or could fashion, aught so good.
Now I have thrown it after my bad work.
While I lie drinking the poor dregs of life,
Deep in the waters of the lake it's drowned.
I mourn not for what's lost.   And then — I
    mourn:
Knowing this only — neither bell, nor life,
Shall evermore come back.   Alas! woe's me!
My heart's desire was bound up in the tones —
The buried tones — I never more shall hear.
And now the life to which I clung so tight
Is turned to bitterness, and grief, and rue,
Madness, and gloom, confusion, pain, and gall!
. . . .

Well, let life go!   The service of the valleys
Charms me no longer, and no more their peace
Calms my wild blood.   Since on the peak I stood,
All that I am has longed to rise, and rise,
Cleaving the mists, until it touched the skies!
I would work wonders with the power on high:
And, since I may not work them, being so weak;
Since, even could I, with much straining, rise,
I should but fall again — I choose to die!
Youth — a new youth — I'd need, if I should
    live:
Out of some rare and magic mountain flower
Marvelous juices I should need to press —
Heart-health, and strength, and the mad lust
    of triumph,
Steeling my hand to work none yet have
    dreamed of!

MAGDA.   O Heinrich, Heinrich, did I but know the spot
Where that thou pantest for, the Spring of
    Youth,
Lies hid, how gladly would these feet of mine
Wear themselves out to find it for thee!   Yea,

Even though the waters which restored thy life
Should bring me death!

HEINRICH (*tormented, collapsing and delirious*).

Thou dearest, truest! . . . No, I will not drink!
Keep it! . . . The Spring is full of blood! . . .
    blood! . . . blood!
I will not! . . . No! . . . Leave me . . . and
    . . . let me . . . die!
[*He becomes unconscious. Enter* THE VICAR.]

VICAR. How goes it with the patient, mistress?

MAGDA.   Ill!

Terribly ill! He's sick in every part.
Some strange, mysterious pain's consuming
    him.
I know not what to fear, and what to hope.
[*Hurriedly throwing a scarf over her shoul-
    ders.*]
Did you not speak of a woman who works
    miracles?

VICAR. I did. Indeed, 'tis that has brought me back.
She lives . . . at most a mile away from here . . .
Her name . . . I can't recall it. But she lives,
If I mistake not, in the pinewood . . . Ay . . .
Her name . . .

MAGDA.   Not Wittikin?

VICAR.   How can you ask!
Why, she's a wicked witch, the Devil's dam,
And she must die. By now they're up in arms,
Eager for battle with the pestilent fiend.
With cudgels, torches, stones, they're hurrying
    fast
To make an end of her. For you must know
She's charged with all the evil that afflicts us.
No. I was thinking of . . . Dame Findeklee . . .
A shepherd's widow . . . and a worthy soul . . .
Her husband left her an old recipe
Which, as I am assured by many here,
Has wondrous virtues. Will you go for her?

MAGDA.   Yes, yes, most reverend sir!

VICAR.   You'll go at once?

[*Enter* RAUTENDELEIN, *disguised as a peasant girl, and carrying a basket of berries in her hand.*]

MAGDA (*to* RAUTENDELEIN).

What wouldst thou, child? . . . Who art thou?

VICAR.   Why — 'tis Anna,

Anna — the maiden from the wayside inn.

Nay, 'twould be vain to question her. Alas,

She's dumb. A good girl. Ah, she's brought some berries.

MAGDA.   Come here, my child . . . What was't I wished to say . . .

Ah, yes! This man lies sick. When he awakes

Be near to help him. Dost thou understand me?

Dame Findeklee . . . That was the name, you said? . . .

But, no; I cannot go. It is too far.

If you'll stay here a moment, I am sure,

My neighbor will go for me . . . I'll come back.

And don't forget . . . O God, my heart will break!   [*Exit.*]

VICAR (*to* RAUTENDELEIN).

Stand here, my child; or, if thou wilt, sit down,

Be good and do the very best thou canst.

Make thyself helpful, while they need thy help.

God will reward thee for the work thou doest.

Thou art greatly changed, dear child, since last I saw thee.

But keep thou honest — be a good, true maid —

For the dear Lord has blessed thee with much beauty.

In truth, my dear, now that I look at thee,

Thou art, yet art not, Anna. As a princess,

Stepped from the pages of some fairy book,

Thou seem'st. So quickly changed! Who would
  have thought
It possible! Well, well! . . . Thou'lt keep him
  cool?
He's burning! (*To* HEINRICH.) May God bring
  thee back to health!   *[Exit.]*
[RAUTENDELEIN, *who till now has seemed shy*
    and meek, changes suddenly and bustles
    about the hearth.]

RAUTEND.   Flickering spark in the ash of death,
Glow with life of living breath!
Red, red wind, thy loudest blow!
I, as thou, did lawless grow!
    Simmer, sing, and simmer!
      [The flame leaps up on the hearth.]

.   .   .   .

Kettle swaying left and right—
Copper-lid, thou'rt none too light!
Bubble, bubble, broth and brew,
Turning all things old to new!
    Simmer, sing, and simmer!

.   .   .   .

Green and tender herbs of Spring,
In the healing draught I fling.
Drink it sweet, and drink it hot—
Life and youth are in the pot!
    Simmer, sing, and simmer!

.   .   .   .

And now to scrape the roots and fetch the water.
The cask is empty . . . But we need more light!
    [She throws the window wide open.]
A glorious day! But there'll be wind anon.
A mighty cloud, in shape like some huge fish,
Lies on the hills. Tomorrow it will burst;
And roystering spirits will ride madly down,
Sweeping athwart the pines, to reach the vale.

Cuckoo! Cuckoo! . . . Here, too, the cuckoo calls,

And the swift swallow darts across the sky . . .

[HEINRICH *has opened his eyes, and lies staring at* RAUTENDELEIN.]

But now to scrape my roots, and fetch the water.

I've much to do since I turned waiting-maid.

Thou, thou, dear flame, shalt cheer me at my work.

HEINRICH (*amazed*).

Tell me . . . who art thou?

RAUTEND. (*quickly and unconcernedly*). I? Rautendelein.

HEINRICH. Rautendelein? I never heard that name.

Yet somewhere I have seen thee once before.

Where was it?

RAUTEND. Why, 'twas on the mountain-side.

HEINRICH. True. True. 'Twas there — what time I fevered lay.

I dreamt I saw thee there . . . Again I dream.

At times we dream strange dreams! See.

Here's my house.

There burns the fire upon the well-known hearth.

Here lie I, in my bed, sick unto death.

I push the window back. There flies a swallow.

Yonder the nightingales are all at play.

Sweet scents float in — of jasmine . . . elder-blossom . . .

I see . . . I feel . . . I know . . . the smallest thing—

Even to the pattern of this coverlet . . .

Each thread . . . each tiny knot . . . I could describe—

And yet I'm dreaming.

RAUTEND. Thou art dreaming? Why?

HEINRICH (*in anguish*).

Because . . . I must be dreaming.

RAUTEND. Art thou so sure?

HEINRICH. Yes. No. Yes. No. I'm wandering. Let me
    dream on!
    Thou askest if I am so sure. I know not.
    Ah, be it what it will: or dream, or life —
    It is. I feel it, see it — thou dost live!
    Real or unreal, within me or without,
    Child of my brain, or whatsoe'er thou art,
    Still I do love thee, for thou art thyself.
    So stay with me, sweet spirit. Only stay!

RAUTEND. So long as thou shalt choose.

HEINRICH.   Then . . . I do dream.

RAUTEND. (*familiarly*).
    Take care. Dost see me lift this little foot
    With the rosy heel? Thou dost? Why, that is
    well.
    Now — here's a hazel nut. I take it — so —
    Between my finger and my dainty thumb —
    I set my heel on it. Crack! Now, 'tis broken.
    Was that a dream?

HEINRICH.   That only God can tell.

RAUTEND. Now watch me. See. I'll come quite close to
    thee,
    And sit upon thy bed. So. Here I am! . . .
    Feasting away as merrily as thou wilt . . .
    Hast thou not room enough?

HEINRICH.   I've all I need.
    But tell me whence thou'rt sprung and who has
    sent thee!
    What would'st thou of a broken, suffering man,
    A bundle of sorrow, drawing near the end
    Of his brief pilgrimage . . . ?

RAUTEND.   I like thee.
    Whence I did spring I know not — nor could tell
    Whither I go. But Granny said one day
    She found me lying in the moss and weeds.
    A hind did give me suck. My home's the wood,
    The mountain-side, the crag, the storm-swept
    moor —

Where the wind moans and rages, shrieks and
    groans,
Or purrs and mews, like some wild tiger-cat!
There thou wilt find me, whirling through the
    air;
There I laugh loud and shout for sheer mad joy;
Till faun and nixie, gnome and water-sprite,
Echo my joy and split their sides with laughter.
I'm spiteful when I'm vexed, and scratch and
    bite:
And who should anger me had best beware.
Yet — 'tis no better when I'm left alone:
For good and bad in me's all mood and impulse.
I'm thus, or thus, and change with each new
    whim.
But thee I am fond of . . . Thee I would not
    scratch.
And, if thou wilt, I'll stay.   Yet were it best
Thou camest with me to my mountain home.
Then thou should'st see how faithfully I'd serve
    thee.
I'd show thee diamonds, and rubies rare,
Hid at the bottom of unfathomed deeps.
Emeralds, and topazes, and amethysts —
I'd bring thee all — I'd hang upon thy lids!
Forward, unruly, lazy, I may be;
Spiteful, rebellious, wayward, what thou wilt!
Yet thou shouldst only need to blink thine eye,
And ere thou'dst time to speak, I'd nod thee —
    yes.
And Granny tells me . . .

HEINRICH.   Ah, thou dear, dear child.
Tell me, who is thy Granny?

RAUTEND.   Dost thou not know?

HEINRICH. No.

RAUTEND.   Not know Granny?

Permission Amsler & Ruthardt, Berlin

INTERMEZZO II

MAX KLINGER

HEINRICH.   No, I am a man,
    And blind.
RAUTEND.   Soon thou shalt see! To me is given
    The power to open every eye I kiss
    To the most hidden mysteries of earth
    And air.
HEINRICH.   Then . . . kiss me!
RAUTEND.   Thou'lt keep still?
HEINRICH.   Nay, try me!
RAUTEND. (*kissing his eyes*).
    Ye eyes, be opened!
HEINRICH.   Ah, thou lovely child,
    Sent to enchant me in my dying hour —
    Thou fragrant blossom, plucked by God's own
        hand
    In the forgotten dawn of some dead Spring —
    Thou free, fair bud — ah, were I but that man
    Who, in the morn of life, fared forth so glad —
    How I would press thee to this leaping heart!
    Mine eyes were blinded. Now, they're filled
        with light,
    And, as by instinct, I divine thy world.
    Ay, more and more, as I do drink thee in,
    Thou dear enigma, I am sure I see.
RAUTEND.   Why — look at me, then, till thine eyes are tired.
HEINRICH.   How golden gleams thy hair! How dazzling
        bright! . . .
    With thee for company, thou dearest dream,
    Old Charon's boat becomes a bark for kings,
    That spreads its purple sails to catch the sun
    Lighting it eastward on its stately way.
    Feel'st thou the Western breeze that creeps
        behind us,
    Flecking with foam from tiny waterfalls
    The swelling bosom of the blue South seas,
    And showering diamonds on us? Dost thou
        not feel it?

And we, reclining here on cloth of gold,
In blissful certitude of what must be,
Do scan the distance that divides us twain . . .
Thou knowest well from what! . . . For thou
    hast seen
The fair green island, where the birch bends
    down,
Bathing its branches in the azure flood —
Thou hearest the glad song of all Spring's
    choirs,
Waiting to welcome us . . .

RAUTEND.   Yes! Yes! I hear it!

HEINRICH (*collapsing*).
So be it. I am ready. When I awake,
A voice shall say to me — Come thou with me.
Then fades the light! . . . Here now the air
    grows chill.
The seer dies, as the blind man had died.
But I have seen thee . . . seen . . . thee . . . !

RAUTEND. (*with incantations*).
    Master, sleep is thine!
    When thou wakest, thou art mine.
    Happy dreams shall dull thy pain,
    Help to make thee whole again.
        [*She bustles about by the hearth.*]
    Hidden treasures, now grow bright!
    In the depths ye give no light.
    Glowing hounds in vain do bark,
    Whine and whimper in the dark!
    We, who serve him, glad will be:
    For the Master sets us free!
        [*Addressing* HEINRICH, *and with gestures.*]
    One, two, three. A new man be!
    For the future thou art free!

HEINRICH (*awaking*).
What's happened to me? . . . From what won-
    drous sleep

Am I aroused? . . . What is this glorious sun
That, streaming through the window, gilds my
    hand?
O breath of morning! Heaven, if 'tis thy will —
If 'tis thy strength that rushes through my
    veins —
If, as a token of thy power, I feel
This strange, new, beating heart within my
    breast?
Then, should I rise again — again I'd long
To wander out into the world of life:
And wish, and strive, and hope, and dare, and
    do . . .
And do . . . and do . . . !

    [RAUTENDELEIN *has meanwhile moved to*
    right and stands, leaning against the wall,
    gazing fixedly at HEINRICH. *A dazzling*
    light falls on her face. Enter MAGDA.]

                Ah, Magda. Is it thou?

MAGDA.   Is he awake?
HEINRICH.   Yes, Magda. Is it thou?
MAGDA (*delightedly*).
    How is it with thee?
HEINRICH (*overcome with emotion*).
              Well. Ah, well! I'll live!
I feel it. I shall live . . . Yes! I shall . . .
    live!

    [*As he speaks, he gazes fixedly, not at* MAGDA,
    but at RAUTENDELEIN, *who stands in an*
    elfin attitude, looking toward him, with an
    unnatural light on her face.]

MAGDA (*overjoyed and embracing* HEINRICH, *who seems un-*
    conscious of her presence).
    He lives! He lives! O dearest Heinrich!
    Dearest!

ACT III

A deserted glass-works in the mountains, near the snow fields. To the right an earthenware pipe, through which water from the natural rock runs into a natural stone trough. To the left a smith's forge, with chimney and bellows. Through the open entrance to the glass-works at back, left, is seen a mountain landscape, with peaks, moors, and dense fir-woods. Close to the entrance is a precipitous descending slope. In the roof is an outlet for the smoke. At the right the rock forms a rude, pointed vault.

THE WOOD-SPRITE, *after throwing a stump on a heap of pinewood outside, enters, reluctantly, and looks around.* THE NICKELMANN *rises from the water-trough, remaining immersed up to his breast.*

NICKELM.   Brekekekex!   Come in!

W.-SPRITE.   Ah, there thou art!

NICKELM.   Ay. Plague upon this nasty smoke and soot!

W.-SPRITE. Have they gone out?

NICKELM.   Have who gone out?

W.-SPRITE.   Why — they.

NICKELM.   Yes. I suppose so. Else they would be here.

W.-SPRITE. I've seen old Horny.

NICKELM.   Ugh!

W.-SPRITE.   . . . With saw and ax.

NICKELM.   What did he say?

W.-SPRITE.   He said . . . thou croakedst much.

NICKELM.   Then let the booby keep his ears closed tight.

W.-SPRITE. And then he said . . . thou quackedst dismally.

NICKELM.   I'll wring his neck for him.

W.-SPRITE.   And serve him right!

NICKELM.   More necks than one I'd wring —

W.-SPRITE (*laughing*).   Accursèd wight!
He crowds us from our hills. He hacks and hews,
Digs up our metals, sweats, and smelts, and
   brews.
The earth-man and the water-sprite he takes
To drag his burdens, and, to harness breaks.

Our fairest elf's his sweetheart. As for us,
We must stand by, and watch them — as they buss.
She steals my cherished flowers, my red-brown ores,
My gold, my precious stones, my resinous stores,
She serves him like a slave, by night and day.
'Tis him she kisses — us she keeps at bay.
Naught stands against him. Ancient trees he fells.
The earth quakes at his tread, and all the dells
Ring with the echo of his thunderous blows.
His crimson smithy furnace glows and shines
Into the depths of my most secret mines.
What he is up to, only Satan knows!

NICKELM.   Brekekekex! Hadst thou the creature slain,
A-rotting in the mere long since he had lain —
The maker of the bell, beside the bell.
And so when next I had wished to throw the stones,
The bell had been my box — the dice, his bones!

W.-SPRITE.   By cock and pie! That, truly, had been well.

NICKELM.   But, as it is, he's hale and strong, and works.
Each hammer-stroke my marrow thrills and irks.

(*Whimpering.*)

He makes her rings, and chains, and bracelets rare —
Kisses her neck, her breast, her golden hair.

W.-SPRITE.   Now, by my goaty face, thou must be crazed.
An old chap whine and whimper?   I'm amazed.
He has a fancy for the child?   What then?
'Tis plain she does not love you water-men.
Cheer up! Although she shall not be thy bride,
The sea is deep: the earth is long and wide.
Catch some fair nixie, and your passion slake.

Live like a pacha: riot — be a rake!
Soon thou'lt be cured: and when they hie to bed,
Thou wilt not even turn to wag thy head.

NICKELM. I'll have his blood, I say! . . .

W.-SPRITE.   She dotes on him.
Thou'rt powerless.

NICKELM.   I'll tear him limb from limb!

W.-SPRITE. She will not have thee, and thy rage is vain.
While Granny stands his friend, thy cries of pain
Will all be wasted. Ay, this loving pair
Is closely guarded. Patience! and beware!

NICKELM. Patience? I hate the word!

W.-SPRITE.   Time runs on fast:
And men are men. Their passion is soon past.

RAUTEND. (*heard singing without*).
A beetle sat in a tree!
Zum! Zum!
A coat all black and white had he!
Zum! Zum!   [*She enters.*]
Oho! We've company. Godden, Godden to you.
Hast washed that gold for me, good Nickelmann?
Hast brought the pine-stumps, as I ordered thee,
Dear Goat's Foot? . . . See: I bend beneath
    the weight
Of the rare treasures I have found today.
Oh, I'm no laggard when I set to work!
Here I have diamonds: here, crystals clear.
This little bag is filled with gold-dust. Look!
And here is honeycomb . . . How warm it grows!

NICKELM. Warm days are followed by still warmer nights.

RAUTEND. Maybe. Cold water is thine element:
So get thee whence thou cam'st, and cool thy-
    self.
[THE WOOD-SPRITE *laughs*. THE NICKEL-
    MANN *sinks silently down into his trough
    and disappears.*]
He will not stop until he's angered me.

W.-Sprite (*still laughing*).
      'Ods bobs!

Rautend.   My garter's twisted at the knee.
    It cuts me. Oh!

W.-Sprite.   Shall I untwist it, dear?

Rautend.   A pretty page thou'dst make! . . . No. Go
        away.
    Thou bring'st ill smells with thee . . . and oh,
        the gnats!
    Why, they are swarming round thee now, in
        clouds.

W.-Sprite. I love them better than the butterflies
    That flap their dusty wings about thy face,
    Now hanging on thy lips — now on thy hair,
    Or clinging to thy hip and breast at night.

Rautend. (*laughing*).
    There! That will do. Enough!

W.-Sprite.   A happy thought!
    Give me this cart-wheel! How did it come here?

Rautend. That thou couldst answer best, thou mischiev-
        ous rogue.

W.-Sprite. Had I not broken down the dray, I trow,
    Thy falcon were not now meshed in thy net.
    So give me thanks — and let me take the thing.
    I'll have it tied with ropes, and smeared with
       pitch,
    And when it's lighted, I will roll it down
    The steepest hillside. Ah! That were a joke!

Rautend. Not for the village-folk. Their huts would flame.

W.-Sprite. The flame of sacrifice! The red, red wind!

Rautend. But I'll not hear of it. So — get thee gone!

W.-Sprite. Thou'rt in a hurry? . . . Must I really go?
    Then tell me first — what is the Master doing?

Rautend. He's working a great work!

W.-Sprite.   Ay, yes, no doubt!
    We know how bells are cast: by day
    Ye work — at night, ye kiss and play.

Hill pines for dale, dale pines for hill,
Then, quick, the Master works his will:
A bastard thing, half brute, half God —
The pride of Earth — to Heaven a clod.
Come to the hazelwoods with me!
What he could be to thee, I'll be.
To honor thee shall be my pleasure —
Ape not the Virgin pure, my treasure!

RAUTEND.   Thou beast! Thou rogue! I'll blind thy thank-
less eyes,
Should'st thou not cease that Master to despise
Whose hammer, clanging through the dark,
long night,
Strikes to redeem thee! . . . For, without his
might,
Thou, I, and all of our unhappy race,
Are curst, and kept beyond the pale of grace.
Yet, stay! . . . Be what thou wilt, thy strength
is vain.
Here he, the Master, and his will, must reign!

W.-SPRITE.   What's that to me? . . . My greeting to thy
love.
Some day, thou'lt see, I'll be thy turtle-dove.
                    [*Exit laughing. Short pause.*]

RAUTEND.   What ails me? . . . Here the air seems close
and warm.
I'll hie to some cool grot beside the snow.
The dripping water, green and cold as ice,
Will soon refresh me . . . Today I trod on a
snake,
As it lay sunning itself on a green stone.
It bit at me — up yonder by the falls.
Heigho! How close it is! . . . Steps! . . . Hark!
Who comes?

Enter THE VICAR, *in mountain costume. He pants for breath as he stands
outside the door.*

VICAR.   Ho! Master Barber! Follow me. This way!
The road was rough. But here I stand, at last.

Well, well. I've come to do God's own good
    work.
My pains will be repaid a hundred-fold
If, like the Blessèd Shepherd, I should find
One poor, lost sheep, and bring him safely home.
So, courage! Courage! [*He enters.*] Is there
    no one here?   [*He sees* RAUTENDELEIN.]
Ah, there thou art. I might have known as much!

RAUTEND. (*pale and angry*).
            What do you seek?

VICAR.   That thou shalt quickly learn.
Ay, soon enough, as God shall be my witness.
Give me but time to get my breath again
And dry my face a bit. And now, my child —
I pray thee, tell me — art thou here alone?

RAUTEND. Thou hast no right to question me!

VICAR.   Oho!
A pretty answer, truly. But thou art frank —
Thou showest me thy very self at once.
So much the better. Now my course is plain.
Thou creature! . . .

RAUTEND.   Man, beware!

VICAR (*folding his hands and approaching her*).
                        I fear thee not!
My heart is pure and true. Thou canst not
    harm me.
He who did give my poor old limbs the strength
To brave thee in thy hidden mountain home
Will not forsake me now. Thou devilish thing,
Think not to daunt me with thy scornful
    glance —
Waste thy infernal witchcraft not on me!
Thou — thou hast lured him hither — to thy
    hills!

RAUTEND. Whom?

VICAR. Whom? Why, Master Heinrich. Canst thou
    ask?

With magic spells, and sweet unhallowed
    draughts,
Thou hast witched him, till he obeys thee like
    a dog.
A man so upright, pious to the core;
A father and a husband! Thou great God!
This mountain trull had but to raise her hand
And, in a trice, she had tied him to her skirts,
Dragged him away with her, where'er she
    pleased,
Shaming the honor of all Christendom.

RAUTEND. If I'm a robber, 'twas not thee I robbed!

VICAR. What! 'Tis not me thou hast robbed? Thou
    insolent jade,
Not me alone, not only his wife and the boys—
No—all mankind thou hast cheated of this man!

RAUTEND. (*suddenly transformed and in triumph*).
Ah, look before thee! See who comes this way!
Dost thou not hear the free and even sound
Of his firm footsteps? Shall thy sland'rous
    flouts
Not even now be turned to joyous shouts?
Dost thou not feel my Balder's conqu'ring
    glance
Dart through thy soul, and stir thee, as the
    dance?
The grass his foot treads down is proud and
    glad.
A King draws nigh! Thou, beggarly wretch,
    art sad?
Hail! Hail! O Master, Master! Thee I greet!
[*She runs to meet* HEINRICH, *and throws her-
    self into his arms as he enters.*]

HEINRICH *is attired in a picturesque working costume. In his hand he
holds a hammer. He enters hand in hand with* RAUTENDELEIN, *and
recognizes* THE VICAR.

HEINRICH. Welcome! Thrice welcome, friend!

VICAR.   Now God be praised!
Belovèd Master; is it yourself I see?
You, who but lately came so near to death,
Now stand before me, beaming with rude
    strength,
Straight as a stout young beech, and hale and
    well —
You, who did seem a sickly, tottering man,
Hopeless, and ageing? What has wrought this
    change?
How, in a moment, has the grace of God,
With but a puff of His all-quickening breath,
Helped you to spring from your sick-bed to life,
Ready to dance, as David danced, and sing,
Praising the Lord, your Saviour and your King!

HEINRICH. 'Tis even as you say.

VICAR.   You are a marvel!

HEINRICH. That also is true. In all my frame I feel
Wonders are being worked.
                    (*To* RAUTENDELEIN.)
                              Go thou, my dear.
The Vicar must be thirsty. Bring some wine.

VICAR. I thank you. But — I will not drink today.

HEINRICH. Go. Bring the wine. I'll vouch for it. 'Tis good.
Well — as you please. I pray you, do not stand.
This is my first encounter with a friend
Since I released myself from the distress
And shame that sickness brings. I had not
    hoped
To welcome you, before all others, here —
Within the narrow sphere that bounds my work.
Now am I doubly glad: for now 'tis clear
You have learned what strength, and love, and
    duty mean.
I see you breaking, with one resolute blow,
The murderous chains of worldly interest —
Fleeing mankind, to seek the one true God.

VICAR.   Now, God be thanked! You are the old, true
    Heinrich.
    They lied, who, in the valley, had proclaimed
    You were no more the man that once we knew.

HEINRICH.   That man am I, and yet . . . another man.
    Open the windows — Light and God stream in!

VICAR.   A goodly saying.

HEINRICH.   Ay. The best I know.

VICAR.   I know some better. Yet your saying's good.

HEINRICH.   Then, if you are ready, give me your right hand.
    I swear, by Cock and Swan and Head of Horse,
    With all my soul to serve you as your friend.
    I'll open to you wide the gates of Spring —
    The Spring that fills my heart.

VICAR.   Do as you say.
    'Twill not be the first time. You know me well.

HEINRICH.   I know you. Yes. And though I knew you not,
    Yea, though a vulgar soul your face should hide,
    So boundless is my craving to do good,
    That I— Enough. Gold always will be gold.
    And even on the souls of sycophants
    Good seed's not wasted.

VICAR.   Master, tell me this:
    What was the meaning of your curious oath?

HEINRICH.   By Cock and Swan?

VICAR.   Ay; and by Head of Horse?

HEINRICH.   I know not how the words came to my lips . . .
    Methinks . . . the weathercock on your church
      steeple —
    The horse's head upon your neighbor's roof —
    The swan that soared into the bright blue sky —
    Or . . . something else — was in my mind just
      then.
    What does it matter? . . . Ah, here comes the
      wine.
    Now, in the deepest sense of every word,
    I drink to our good health . . . yours . . . thine
      . . . and mine.

VICAR.   I thank you: and once more I wish good health
            To him who has so wondrously been healed.
HEINRICH (*pacing to and fro*).
            Yes. I am healed — indeed. I feel it here —
            Here, in my breast, that swells as I draw in
            Strength and new rapture with each living
                breath.
            It is as though the very youth of May
            Gladdened my heart and streamed into my being.
            I feel it in my arm — 'tis hard as steel;
            And in my hand, that, as the eagle's claw,
            Clutches at empty air, and shuts again,
            Wild with impatience to achieve great deeds.
            Saw you the sanctuary in my garden?
VICAR.   What do you mean?
HEINRICH.   There! . . . 'Tis another marvel.
            Look!
VICAR.   I see nothing.
HEINRICH.   I mean yonder tree,
            That seems so like a glowing evening-cloud.
            For the god Freyr once rested in its boughs.
            From its green branches, and from round its
                stem,
            Comes the voluptuous hum of countless bees —
            Hark how they buzz and swarm about the flowers
            Eager to sip sweet draughts from every bud!
            I feel that I am like that wondrous tree . . .
            Even as he came down into those boughs,
            So did the god descend into my soul,
            And, in an instant, it was all a-bloom.
            If any bees go thirsting, let them suck!
VICAR.   Go on, go on, my friend. I love to listen.
            You and your blossoming tree indeed may boast.
            Whether your fruit shall ripen, rests with God!
HEINRICH.   Surely, dear friend. Does He not order all?
            He hurled me down the precipice. 'Twas He
            Who raised me up and caused my life to bloom.

He made the fruit, and flowers, and all that
  grows.
Yet — pray that He may bless my new-born
  Summer!
What's germed within me's worthy of the
  blessing —
Worthy of ripening: really and indeed.
It is a work like none I had yet conceived;
A chime, of all the noblest metals wrought,
That, of itself, shall ring and, ringing, live.
If I but put my hand up to my ear,
Straightway I hear it sing. I close my eyes —
Form after form at once grows palpable.
Behold! What now is freely given to me.
Of old — when ye were wont to acclaim me
  " Master " —
In nameless agony, I vainly sought.
I was no Master then, nor was I happy.
Now am I both; I am happy and a Master!

VICAR.   I love to hear men call you by that name.
Yet it seems strange that you yourself should
  do so.
For what church are you making your great
  work?

HEINRICH. For no church.

VICAR.   Then — who ordered it, my friend?

HEINRICH. He who commanded yonder pine to rise
In strength and majesty beside the abyss! . . .
But — seriously: the little church you had built
Lies half in ruins — half it has been burned.
So I must find a new place on the heights:
A new place, for a new, a nobler, temple!

VICAR.   O Master, Master! . . . But, I will not argue.
Perchance we have misunderstood each other.
To put things plainly, what I mean is this:
As your new work must cost so very dear . . .

HEINRICH. Yes. It is costly.
VICAR.   Such a chime as yours . . .
HEINRICH. Oh, call it what you will.
VICAR.   You said — a chime?
HEINRICH. A name I gave to that which none may name,
           Nor can, nor shall baptize, except itself.
VICAR.   And tell me, pray — who pays you for your
           work?
HEINRICH. Who pays me for my work? Oh, Father!
           Father!
           Would you give joy to joy — add gold to gold?
           If I so named it, and the name you love —
           Call my great work — a chime! . . . But 'tis a
           chime
           Such as no minister in the world has seen.
           Loud and majestic is its mighty voice.
           Even as the thunder of a storm it sounds,
           Rolling and crashing o'er the meads in Spring.
           Ay, in the tumult of its trumpet-tones,
           All the church-bells on earth it shall strike dumb.
           All shall be hushed, as through the sky it rings
           The glad new Gospel of the new-born light!

           .   .   .   .

           Eternal Sun!* Thy children, and my children,
           Know thee for Father, and proclaim thy power.
           Thou, aided by the kind and gentle rain,
           Didst raise them from the dust and give them
           health!
           So now — their joy triumphant they shall send
           Singing along thy clear, bright path to Heaven!
           And now, at last, like the gray wilderness
           That thou has warmed, and mantled with thy
           green,
           Me thou hast kindled into sacrifice!

---

* In the German the Sun is feminine. The original passage has consequently been modified.

I offer thee myself, and all I am! . . .
O Day of Light — when, from the marble halls
Of my fair Temple, the first waking peal
Shall shake the skies — when, from the sombre
    clouds
That weighed upon us through the winter night,
Rivers of jewels shall go rushing down
Into a million hands outstretched to clutch!
Then all who drooped, with sudden power in-
    flamed,
Shall bear their treasure homeward to their
    huts,
There to unfurl, at last, the silken banners,
Waiting — so long, so long — to be upraised,
And, pilgrims of the Sun, draw near the Feast!
  .   .   .   .

O, Father, that great Day! . . . You know the
    tale
Of the lost Prodigal? . . . It is the Sun
That bids his poor, lost children to my Feast.
With rustling banners, see the swelling host
Draw nearer, and still nearer to my Temple.
And now the wondrous chime again rings out,
Filling the air with such sweet, passionate sound
As makes each breast to sob with rapturous pain.
It sings a song, long lost and long forgotten,
A song of home — a childlike song of Love,
Born in the waters of some fairy well —
Known to all mortals, and yet heard of none!
And as it rises, softly first, and low,
The nightingale and dove seem singing, too;
And all the ice in every human breast
Is melted, and the hate, and pain, and woe,
Stream out in tears.
  .   .   .   .

Then shall we all draw nearer to the Cross,
And, still in tears, rejoice, until at last
The dead Redeemer, by the Sun set free,
His prisoned limbs shall stir from their long
    sleep,
And, radiant with the joy of endless youth,
Come down, Himself a youth, into the May!

[HEINRICH's *enthusiasm has swelled as he
has spoken the foregoing speech, till at last
it has become ecstatic. He walks to and
fro.* RAUTENDELEIN, *who has been silently
watching him all this time, showing her
love and adoration by the changing expression of her face, now approaches* HEINRICH,
*with tears in her eyes, kneels beside him,
and kisses his hand.* THE VICAR *has listened
to* HEINRICH *with growing pain and horror.
Toward the end of* HEINRICH's *speech he
has contained himself with difficulty. After
a brief pause he answers. At first he
speaks with enforced calm. Gradually, however, his feeling carries him away.*]

VICAR. And now, dear Master, I have heard you out:
Now every syllable those worthy men
Had told me of your state, alas, is proved.
Yea, even to the story of this chime of bells.
I cannot tell you all the pain I feel! . . .
A truce to empty words! If here I stand,
'Tis not because I thirsted for your marvels.
No! 'Tis to help you in your hour of need!

HEINRICH. My need? . . . And so you think I am in need?

VICAR. Man! Man! Bestir yourself. Awake! You
    dream!
A dreadful dream, from which you'll surely wake
To everlasting sorrow. Should I fail
To rouse you, with God's wise and holy words,
You are lost, ay, lost forever, Master Heinrich!

HEINRICH. I do not think so.

VICAR.   What saith the Good Book?*
  "Those whom He would destroy, He first doth
      blind."

HEINRICH. If God so willed it — you'd resist in vain.
  Yet, should I own to blindness,
  Filled as I feel myself with pure, new life,
  Bedded upon a glorious morning cloud,
  Whence with new eyes I drink in all the heavens;
  Why, then, indeed, I should deserve God's curse,
  And endless Darkness.

VICAR.   Master Heinrich — friend,
  I am too humble to keep pace with you.
  A simple man am I — a child of Earth:
  The superhuman lies beyond my grasp.
  But one thing I do know, though you forget,
  That wrong is never right, nor evil, good.

HEINRICH. And Adam did not know so much in Eden!

VICAR. Fine phrases, sounding well, but meaningless.
  They will not serve to cloak your deadly sin.
  It grieves me sore — I would have spared you
      this.
  You have a wife, and children . . .

HEINRICH.   Well — what more?

VICAR. You shun the church, take refuge in the moun-
      tains;
  This many a month you have not seen the home
  Where your poor wife sits sighing, while, each
      day,
  Your children drink their lonely mother's tears!
                                   [*A long pause.*]

HEINRICH (*with emotion*).
  Could I but wipe away those sorrowful tears,
  How gladly would I do it! . . . But I cannot.
  In my dark hours, I've digged into my soul,
  Only to feel, I have no power to dry them.

---

* So it stands in the original.

I, who am now all love, in love renewed,
Out of the overflowing wealth I own,
May not fill up their cup! For, lo, my wine
Would be to them but bitter gall and venom!
Should he whose hand is as the eagle's claw
Stroke a sick child's wet cheek? . . . Here none
     but God
Could help!

VICAR.   For this there is no name but madness,
And wicked madness. Yes. I speak the truth.
Here stand I, Master, overcome with horror
At the relentless cruelty of your heart.
Now Satan, aping God, hath dealt a blow —
Yes, I must speak my mind — a blow so dread
That even he must marvel at his triumph.
That work, Almighty God, whereof he prates —
Do I not know 't? . . . 'Tis the most awful crime
Ever was hatched within a heathen brain!
Far rather would I see the dreadful plagues
Wherewith the Lord once scourged rebellious
     Egypt
Threaten our Christendom, than watch your
     Temple
Rise to the glory of Beelzebub.
Awake! Arise! Come back, my son, to Christ!
It is not yet too late! Cast out this witch!
Renounce this wanton hag — ay, cast her out!
This elf, this sorceress, this cursèd sprite!
Then in a trice, the evil spell shall fade
And vanish into air. You shall be saved!

HEINRICH. What time I fevered lay, a prey to death,
She came, and raised me up, and made me well.

VICAR.   'Twere better you had died — than live like this!

HEINRICH. Why, as to that, think even as you will.
But, as for me — I took life's burden up.
I live anew, and, till death comes, must thank
Her who did give me life.

VICAR.   Now — I have done!
Too deep, yea to the neck, you are sunk in sin!
Your Hell, decked out in beauty as high Heaven,
Shall hold you fast. I will not waste more words.
Yet mark this, Master: witches make good fuel,
Even as heretics, for funeral-pyres.
Vox populi, vox Dei! Your ill deeds,
Heathen, and secret once, are now laid bare.
Horror they wake, and soon there shall come
    hate.
So it may happen that the storm, long-curbed,
All bounds shall overleap, and that the people
Whom you have outraged in their holiest faith,
Shall rise against you in their own defense,
And crush you ruthlessly!   [*Pause.*]

HEINRICH (*calmly*).   And now hear me . . .
I fear you not! . . . Should they who panting lie
Dash from my hand the cup of cooling wine
I bore to them: if they would rather thirst —
Why, then, it is their will — perhaps their fate —
And none may justly charge me with their act.
I am no longer thirsty. I have drunk.
If it is fitting that, of all men, you —
Who have closed your eyes against the truth —
    should be
That man who now assails so hatefully
The blameless cup-bearer, and flings the mud
Of Darkness 'gainst his soul, where all is light:
Yet I am I! . . . What I would work, I know.
And if, ere now, full many a faulty bell
My stroke has shattered, once again will I
Swing my great hammer for a mightier blow,
Dealt at another bell the mob has made —
Fashioned of malice, gall, and all ill things,
Last but not least among them ignorance.

VICAR.   Then, go your way! Farewell. My task is done.
The hemlock of your sin no man may hope
To rid your soul of. May God pity you!

But this remember! There's a word named rue!
And some day, some day, as your dreams you
    dream,
A sudden arrow, shot from out the blue,
Shall pierce your breast! And yet you shall
    not die,
Nor shall you live. In that dread day you'll
    curse
All you now cherish — God, the world, your
    work,
Your wretched self you'll curse. Then . . .
    think of me!

HEINRICH. Had I a fancy to paint phantoms, Vicar,
I'd be more skillful in the art than you.
The things you rave of never shall come true,
And I am guarded well against your arrow.
No more it frets me, nor my heart can shake,
Than that old bell, which in the water rolled —
Where it lies buried now, and hushed — forever!

VICAR. That bell shall toll again! Then think of me!

ACT IV

The glass-works as in Act Three. A rude door has been hewn out of the rocky wall at the right. Through this, access is obtained to a mountain cave. At the left the open forge, with bellows and chimney. The fire is lighted. Near the forge stands an anvil.

HEINRICH, at the anvil, on which he is laying a bar of red-hot iron which he holds tight with his tongs. Near him stand six little DWARFS attired as mountaineers. The FIRST DWARF holds the tongs with HEINRICH; the SECOND DWARF lifts the great forge hammer and brings it down with a ringing blow on the iron. The THIRD DWARF works the bellows. The FOURTH DWARF stands motionless, intently watching the progress of the work. The FIFTH DWARF stands by, waiting. In his hand he holds a club, ready to strike. The SIXTH DWARF sits perched on the stump of a tree. On his head he wears a glittering crown. Here and there lie fragments of forged iron and castings, models and plans.

HEINRICH (*to* SECOND DWARF).
    Strike hard! Strike harder! Till thy arm
    hangs limp.

Thy whimpering does not move me, thou poor
    sluggard—
Shouldst thou relax before the time I set,
I'll singe thy beard for thee in these red flames.
    [SECOND DWARF *throws his hammer down.*]
Oho! 'Tis as I thought. Well, wait, thou imp!
And thou shalt see I mean what I have threat-
    en'd!
    [SECOND DWARF *struggles and screams as*
    HEINRICH *holds him over the fire.* THIRD
    DWARF *goes to work more busily than ever*
    at the bellows.]

1ST DWARF (*with the tongs*).
    I can't hold on. My hand is stiff, great Master!
HEINRICH. I'm coming.   [*He turns to* SECOND DWARF.]
    Well, dost thou feel stronger now?
    [SECOND DWARF *nods reassuringly, and ham-*
    mers away for dear life.]
HEINRICH. By Cock and Swan! I'll have no mercy on you!
    [*He clutches the tongs again.*]
No blacksmith living could a horseshoe shape
An he should stand on trifles with such rogues.
No sooner have they struck the first good stroke
When off they'd go, and leave the rest to chance.
And as for counting on them for the zeal
That spurs an honest workman to attempt
Ten thousand miracles — why, 'twould be mad.
To work! To work! Hot iron bends — not cold!
    (*To* FIRST DWARF.)
What art thou at?
1ST DWARF (*busily trying to mold the red-hot iron with his*
    hand).   I'm molding it with my hand.
HEINRICH. Thou reckless fool. What? Hast thou lost thy
    wits?
Wouldst thou reduce thy clumsy paw to ashes?

Thou wretched dwarf, if thou shouldst fail me
    now,
What power had I? . . . Without thy helping
    art,
How could I hope to see my cherished work
Rise from the summit of my temple towers
Into the free and sunlit air of heaven?

1st Dwarf. The iron is well forged. The hand is whole —
Deadened and numbed a little: that is all.

Heinrich. Off to the well with thee! the Nickelmann
Will cool thy fingers with his water-weeds.
                (*To the* Second Dwarf.)
Now take the rest thou'st earned, thou lazy imp,
And make the most of it. I'll comfort seek
In the reward that comes of honest effort.
    [*He picks up the newly forged iron, sits, and
        examines it.*]
Ah, here's rare work for you! The kindly
    powers
Have crowned our labor with this good result.
I am content. Methinks I have cause to be,
Since, out of shapelessness, a shape has grown,
And, out of chaos, this rare masterpiece:
Nicely proportioned — here . . . above . . .
    below . . .
Just what was needed to complete the work.
    [*The* Fourth Dwarf *clambers onto a stool
        and whispers in* Heinrich's *ear.*]
What art thou muttering, imp? Disturb me not,
Lest I should tie thy hands and feet together,
And clap a gag into thy chattering throat!
                [Dwarf *retreats in alarm.*]
What's out of joint in the great scheme? What's
    wrong?
What irks thee? Speak when thou art ques-
    tioned, dwarf!

Never as now was I so filled with joy;
Never were heart and hand more surely one.
What art thou grumbling at?   Am I not Master?
Wouldst thou, poor hireling, dare to vie with me?
Well — out with it!   Thy meaning — Speak!
  Be plain!
  [DWARF *returns and whispers*. HEINRICH
    *turns pale, sighs, rises, and angrily lays
    the iron on the anvil.*]
Then may the Devil end this work himself!
I'll grow potatoes, and plant cabbages.
I'll eat and drink and sleep, and then — I'll die!
  [FIFTH DWARF *approaches the anvil.*]
Thou, fellow, do not dare to lay thy hand on 't!
Ay, burst with fury, an thou wilt.   I care not.
And let thy hair stand straight on end — thy
    glance
Dart death.   Thou rogue!   Who yields but once
    to thee,
Or fails to hold thee tightly in his clutch,
Might just as well bow down and be thy slave,
And wait till, with thy club, thou end his pain!
  [FIFTH DWARF *angrily shatters the iron on
    the anvil;* HEINRICH *grinds his teeth with
    rage.*]
Well, well!   Run riot!   No more work tonight.
A truce to duty.   Get ye hence, ye dwarfs!
Should morning, as I hope, put fresh, new life
Into this frame of mine — I'll call ye back.
Go! — Work unbidden would avail me naught.
    (*To* THIRD DWARF.)
Come — drop thy bellows, dwarf.   With all thy
    might,
Thou'dst hardly heat me a new iron tonight.
Away!   Away!
  [*All the* DWARFS, *with the exception of the
    one with the crown, vanish through the
    door, right.*]

And thou, crowned King, who only once shalt
    speak—
Why dost thou linger? Get thee gone, I say.
Thou wilt not speak today, nor yet tomorrow:
Heaven only knows if thou wilt ever speak!
My work! . . . My work! When will it end!
    . . . I'm tired!
I love thee not, sad twilight hour, that liest
Pressed 'twixt the dying day and growing night,
Thou wringest from my nerveless hand the
    hammer,
Yet bring'st me not the sleep, the dreamless
    sleep,
That gives men rest. A heart athirst for work
Knows it must wait, and wait in idleness:
And so—in pain—it waits . . . for the new
    day.
The sun, wrapped round in purple, slowly sinks
Into the depths . . . and leaves us here alone.
While we, who are used to light, look helpless on,
And, stripped of everything, must yield to night.
Rags are the coverlets that cloak our sleep.
At noon we're kings . . . at dusk we're only
    beggars.
    [*He throws himself on a couch and lies
    dreaming, with wide-open eyes. A white
    mist comes in through the open door. When
    it disappears,* THE NICKELMANN *is discov-
    ered leaning over the edge of the water-
    trough.*]

NICKELM. Quorax! . . . Brekekekex! . . . So there he lies—
This Master Earth-Worm—in his mossgrown
    house.
He's deaf and blind, while crookback imps do
    creep
Like the gray mists upon the mountain-side.

Now they uplift their shadowy hands, and
    threaten!
Now they go wringing them, as though in pain!
He sleeps! He does not heed the moaning pines;
The low, malignant piping of the elves
That makes the oldest fir-trees quake and thrill,
And, like a hen that flaps her foolish wings,
Beat their own boughs against their quivering
    flanks . . . !
Now, he grows chiller, as the winter-gray
Searches the marrow in his bones. And still,
Even in sleep, he toils!
Give over, fool! Thou canst not fight with God!
'Twas God that raised thee up, to prove thy
    strength;
And now, since thou art weak, He casts thee
    down!
    [HEINRICH *tosses about and moans in his
    sleep.*]
Vain is thy sacrifice. For Sin is Sin.
Thou hast not wrung from God the right to
    change
Evil to good — or wages give to guilt.
Thou'rt foul with stains. Thy garments reek
    with blood.
Now, call thou ne'er so loud, the gentle hand
That might have washed thee clean, thou'lt
    never see!
Black spirits gather in the hills and dales.
Soon in thine anguished ear the sound shall ring
Of the wild huntsmen and the baying hounds!
They know what game they hunt! . . . And
    now, behold!
The giant builders of the air upraise
Castles of cloud, with monstrous walls and
    towers.

Frowning and grim, they move against thy heights,

Eager to crush thy work, and thee, and all!

HEINRICH. Rautendelein! Help! The nightmare! Oh, I choke!

NICKELM. She hears thee — and she comes — but brings no help!

Though she were Freya, and though thou wert Balder —

Though sun-tipped shafts did fill thy radiant quiver,

And ev'ry shaft that thou shouldst point went home —

Thou must be vanquished. Hear me!

A sunken bell in the deep mere lies,

Under the rocks and the rolling:

And it longs to rise —

In the sunlight again to be tolling!

The fishes swim in, and the fishes swim out,

As the old bell tosses, and rolls about.

It shudders and sways as they come and go,

And weeping is heard, and the sound of woe.

A muffled moan, and a throb of pain,

Answer the swirling flood —

For the mouth of the bell is choked with blood!

Woe, woe, to thee, man, when it tolls again!

Bim! . . . Boom!

The Lord save thee from thy doom!

Bim! . . . Boom!

Hark to the knell!

Death is the burden of that lost bell!

Bim! . . . Boom!

The Lord save thee from thy doom!

[THE NICKELMANN *sinks into the well.*]

HEINRICH.   Help! Help! A nightmare chokes me! Help!
Help! Help!   [*He awakes.*]
Where am I? . . . Am I living?
[*He rubs his eyes and looks round him.*]
No one here?

RAUTEND. (*entering*).
I'm here! Did'st call?

HEINRICH.   Yes! Come! Come here to me.
Lay thy dear hand upon my forehead — so,
And let me stroke thy hair . . . and feel thy
heart.
Come. Nearer. In thy train thou bring'st the
scent
Of the fresh woods and rosemary. Ah, kiss me!
Kiss me!

RAUTEND.   What ails thee, dearest?

HEINRICH.   Nothing, nothing!
Give me a coverlet . . . I lay here chilled . . .
Too tired to work . . . My heart grew faint . . .
And then
Dark powers of evil seemed to enter in . . .
Laid hold of me, possessed me, plagued me sore,
And tried to throttle me . . . But now I'm well.
Have thou no fear, child. I'm myself again!
Now let them come!

RAUTEND.   Who?

HEINRICH.   Why, my foes.

RAUTEND.   What foes?

HEINRICH.   My nameless enemies — ay, one and all!
I stand upon my feet, as once I stood,
Ready to brave them, though they filled my sleep
With crawling, creeping, cowardly terrors full!

RAUTEND.   Thou'rt fevered, Heinrich!

HEINRICH.   Ay, 'tis chill tonight.
No matter. Put thy arms around me. So.

RAUTEND.   Thou, dearest, dearest!

HEINRICH.   Tell me this, my child.
Dost trust in me?

RAUTEND.   Thou Balder! Hero! God!
I press my lips against the fair white brow
That overhangs the clear blue of thine eyes.

                                   [Pause.]

HEINRICH. So — I am all thou say'st? . . . I am thy Balder?
Make me believe it — make me know it, child!
Give my faint soul the rapturous joy it needs,
To nerve it to its task. For, as the hand,
Toiling with tong and hammer, on and on,
To hew the marble and to guide the chisel,
Now bungles here, now there, yet may not halt,
And nothing, small or great, dare leave to chance,
So do we ofttimes lose our passionate faith,
Feel the heart tighten, and the eyes grow dim,
Till, in the daily round of drudging work,
The clear projection of the soul doth vanish.
For, to preserve that Heaven-sent gift is hard.
No clamp have we, no chain, to hold it fast.
'Tis as the aura that surrounds a sun,
Impalpable. That being lost, all's lost.
Defrauded now we stand, and tempted sore
To shirk the anguish that foreruns fruition.
What, in conception, seemed all ecstasy,
Now turns to sorrow. But — enough of this.
Still straight and steady doth the smoke ascend
From my poor human sacrifice to Heaven.
Should now a Hand on high reject my gift,
Why, it may do so. Then the priestly robe
Falls from my shoulder — by no act of mine;
While I, who erst upon the heights was set,
Must look my last on Horeb, and be dumb!
But now bring torches! Lights! And show
    thine art
Enchantress! Fill the winecup! We will drink!

Ay, like the common herd of mortal men,
With resolute hands our fleeting joy we'll grip!
Our unsought leisure we will fill with life,
Not waste it, as the herd, in indolence.
We will have music!

RAUTEND.   O'er the hills I flew:
Now, as a cobweb, on the breezes drifting,
Now frolicking as a bee, or butterfly,
And darting hungrily from flower to flower.
From each and all, from every shrub and plant,
Each catch-fly, harebell, and forget-me-not,
I dragged the promise, and I forced the oath,
That bound them never to do harm to thee.
And so — the blackest elf, most bitter foe
To thee, so good and white, should vainly seek
To cut thy death-arrow!*

HEINRICH.   What is this arrow?
I know the spirit! . . . Yes, I know 't! . . .
There came
A spirit to me once, in priestly garb,
Who, threat'ning, raised his hand, the while he
raved
Of some such arrow that should pierce my heart.
Who'll speed the arrow from his bow, I say?
Who — who will dare?

RAUTEND.   Why, no one, dearest. No one.
Thou'rt proof against all ill, I say — thou'rt
proof.
And now, blink but thine eye, or only nod,
And gentle strains shall upward float, as mist,
Hem thee about, and, with a wall of music,
Guard thee from call of man, and toll of bell:
Yea, mock at even Loki's mischievous arts.

_____

* It was an old belief that dangerous arrows were shot down from the air
by elves.

Permission Theo. Stroefer, Nürnberg

MAX KLINGER

BEAR AND SPRITE

Make the most trifling gesture with thy hand,
These rocks shall turn to vaulted palace-halls,
Earth-men unnumbered shall buzz round, and
    stand
Ready to deck the floor, the walls, the board!
Yet — since by dark, fierce foes we are beset,
Wilt thou not flee into the earth with me?
There we need fear no icy giant's breath —
There the vast halls shall shine with dazzling
    light —

HEINRICH. Peace, child. No more. What were thy feast
    to me
So long as solemn, mute, and incomplete,
My work the hour awaits, wherein its voice
Shall loudly usher in the Feast of Feasts! . . .
I'll have one more good look at the great
    structure.
So shall new fetters bind me to it fast.
Take thou a torch, and light me on my way.
Haste! Haste! . . . Since now I feel my name-
    less foes
Busy at work to do me injury —
Since now the fabric's menaced at the base —
'Tis meet the Master, too, should toil — not
    revel!
For, should success his weary labor crown,
The secret wonder stand at last revealed,
In gems and gold expressed, and ivory,
Even to the faintest, feeblest, of its tones —
His work should live, triumphant, through the
    ages!
'Tis imperfection that draws down the curse,
Which, could we brave it here, we'd make a
    mock of.
Ay, we will make a mock of 't!
                [*He moves to the door and halts.*]
                          Well, child? . . .
Why dost thou linger! . . . Have I grieved thee?

RAUTEND.   No!
      No! No!

HEINRICH.   **What ails thee?**

RAUTEND.   **Nothing!**

HEINRICH.   Thou poor soul!
I know what grieves thee.— Children, such as
    thou,
Run lightly after the bright butterflies,
And often, laughing, kill what most they love.
But I am not a butterfly. I am more.

RAUTEND. And I? Am I a child? . . . No more than that?

HEINRICH. Ay, truly, thou art more! . . . That to forget
Were to forget the brightness of my life.
The dew that glistened in thy shining eyes
Filled me with pain. And then I pained thee, too.
Come! 'Twas my tongue, not I, that hurt thee so.
My heart of hearts knows naught, save only
    love,
Nay — do not weep so. See — now I am armed;
Thou hast equipped me for the game anew.
Lo, thou hast filled my empty hands with gold;
Given me courage for one more last throw!
Now I can play with Heaven! . . . Ah, and I feel
So blessed, so wrapped in thy strange love-
    liness —
Yet, when I, wond'ring, seek to grasp it all,
I am baffled. For thy charm's unsearchable.
And then I feel how near joy's kin to pain —
Lead on! And light my path!

W.-SPRITE (*without*).   Ho! Holdrio!
Up! Up! Bestir yourselves! Plague o' the
    dawdlers!
The heathen temple must be laid in ashes!
Haste, reverend sir! Haste, Master Barber,
    haste!
Here there is straw and pitch a-plenty. See!
The Master's cuddling his fair elfin bride —
And while he toys with her, naught else he heeds.

HEINRICH. The deadly nightshade must have made him
mad,
What art thou yelling in the night, thou rogue?
Beware!

W.-SPRITE (*defiantly*).   Of thee?

HEINRICH.   Ay, fool. Beware of me!
I know the way to manage such as thou,
I'll grab thee by thy beard, thou misshaped oaf;
Thou shalt be shorn and stripped, and when
thou'rt tamed,
When thou hast learned to know who's master
here,
I'll make thee work and slave for me — thou
goat-shank!
What? . . . Neighing, eh? . . . . Dost see this
anvil, beast?
And, here, this hammer?   It is hard enough
To beat thee to a jelly.

W.-SPRITE (*turning his back on* HEINRICH *insolently*).
Bah! Hammer away!
Many and many a zealot's flashing sword
Has tickled me, ere it was turned to splinters.
The iron on thy anvil's naught but clay,
And, like a cow's dung, at the touch it bursts.

HEINRICH. We'll see, thou windbag, thou hobgoblin
damned!
Wert thou as ancient as the Wester wood,
Or did thy power but match thy braggart
tongue —
I'll have thee chained, and make thee fetch and
carry,
Sweep, drudge, draw water, roll huge stones
and rocks,
And shouldst thou loiter, beast, I'll have thee
flayed!

RAUTEND. Heinrich! He warns thee!

W.-Sprite.   Ay! Go to! Go to!
          'Twill be a mad game when they drag thee hence
          And roast thee, like an ox! And I'll be by!
          But now to find the brimstone, oil, and pitch,
          Wherewith to make a bonfire that shall smoke
          Till daylight shall be blotted out in darkness.
              [*Exit.   Cries and murmurs of many voices
                    heard from below, without.*]
Rautend.   Dost thou not hear them, Heinrich?   Men are
              coming!
          Hark to their boding cries! . . . They are for
              thee!
              [*A stone flung from without strikes* Rauten-
                    delein.]
          Help, grandmother!
Heinrich.   So that is what was meant!
          I dreamed a pack of hounds did hunt me down.
          The hounds I hear.   The hunt has now begun!
          Their yelping, truly, could not come more pat.
          For, though an angel had hung down from
              Heaven,
          All lily-laden, and, with gentle sighs,
          Entreated me to tireless steadfastness,
          He had convinced me less than those fierce cries
          Of the great weight and purport of my mission.
          Come one, come all!   What's yours I guard for
              you!
          I'll shield you from yourselves! . . . Be that
              my watchword!   [*Exit with hammer.*]
Rautend. (*alone and in excitement*).
          Help, help, Bush-Grandmother! Help, Nickel-
              mann!
              [The Nickelmann *rises from the well.*]
          Ay, my dear Nickelmann, I beg of you —
          Bid water, quick, come streaming from all the
              rocks,
          Wave upon wave, and drive them all away!
          Do! Do!

NICKELM.   Brekekekex! What shall I do?

RAUTEND.   Let thy wild waters sweep them to the abyss!

NICKELM.   I cannot.

RAUTEND.   But thou canst, good Nickelmann!

NICKELM.   And if I should — what good were that to me?
I have no cause to wish well to the Master.
He'd love to lord it over God and men.
'Twould suit me if the fools should strike him
    down!

RAUTEND.   Oh, help him — help! Or it will be too late!

NICKELM.   What wilt thou give me, dear?

RAUTEND.   I give thee?

NICKELM.   Yes.

RAUTEND.   Ah, what thou wilt!

NICKELM.   Oho! Brekekekex!
Then strip thy pretty gown from thy brown
    limbs,
Take off thy crimson shoon, thy dainty cap.
Be what thou art! Come down into my well —
I'll spirit thee a thousand leagues away.

RAUTEND.   Forsooth! How artfully he'd made his plans!
But now I tell thee once, and once for all;
Thou'dst better clear thy pate of all thy schemes.
For, shouldst thou live to thrice thy hoary age —
Shouldst thou grow old as Granny — shouldst
    thou forever
Prison me close in thine own oyster shells,
I would not look at thee!

NICKELM.   Then . . . he must die.

RAUTEND.   Thou liest! . . . I'm sure of 't. Thou liest!
    Hark!
Ah, well thou knowest his clear-sounding voice!
Dost think I do not see thee shrink in fear?

[THE NICKELMANN *disappears in the well.*]

Enter HEINRICH *in triumph, and flushed with the excitement of the strife.*
    He laughs.

HEINRICH.   They came at me like hounds, and, even as
                    hounds,
            I drove them from me with the flaming brands!
            Great boulders then I rolled upon their heads:
            Some perished — others fled! Come — give me
                    drink!
            War cools the breast — 'tis steeled by victory.
            The warm blood rushes through my veins.
                    Once more
            My pulse throbs joyously. War does not tire.
            War gives a man the strength of twenty men,
            And hate and love makes new!

RAUTEND.   Here, Heinrich. Drink!

HEINRICH.   Yes, give it me, my child. I am athirst
            For wine, and light, and love, and joy, and thee!
                                        [*He drinks.*]
            I drink to thee, thou airy elfin sprite!
            And, with this drink, again I thee do wed.
            Without thee, my invention would be clogged,
            I were a prey to gloom — world-weariness.
            My child, I entreat thee, do not fail me now.
            Thou art the very pinion of my soul.
            Fail not my soul!

RAUTEND.   Ah, do not thou fail me!

HEINRICH.   That God forbid! . . . Ho! Music!

RAUTEND.   Hither! Hither!
            Come hither, little people! Elves and gnomes!
            Come! Help us to make merry! Leave your
                    homes!
            Tune all your tiny pipes, and harps, and flutes,
                                [*Faint elfin music heard without.*]
            And watch me dance responsive to your lutes!
            With glowworms, gleaming emerald, lo, I deck
            My waving tresses and my dainty neck.
            So jeweled, and adorned with fairy light,
            I'll make e'en Freya's necklace seem less bright!

HEINRICH (*interrupting*).

    Be still! . . . Methought . . .

RAUTEND.   What?

HEINRICH.   Didst not hear it then?

RAUTEND. Hear what?

HEINRICH.   Why — nothing.

RAUTEND.   Dearest, what is wrong?

HEINRICH. I know not . . . But, commingling with thy

    music . . .

    Methought I heard . . . a strain . . . a sound . . .

RAUTEND.   What sound?

HEINRICH. A plaint . . . a tone . . . a long, long, buried

    tone . . .

    No matter. It was nothing! Sit thou here!

    Give me thy rose-red lips. From this fair cup

    I'll drink forgetfulness!

      [*They kiss. Long and ecstatic pause. Then*
          HEINRICH *and* RAUTENDELEIN *move, locked*
          in each other's arms, through the door-
          way.]

    See! Deep and cool and monstrous yawns the

    gulf

    That parts us from the world where mortals

    dwell.

    I am a man. Canst understand me, child? . . .

    Yonder I am at home . . . and yet a stranger —

    Here I am strange . . . and yet I seem at home.

    Canst understand?

RAUTEND.   Yes!

HEINRICH.   Yet thou eyest me

    So wildly. Why?

RAUTEND.   I'm filled with dread — with horror!

HEINRICH. With dread? Of what?

RAUTEND.   Of what? I cannot tell.

HEINRICH. 'Tis nothing. Let us rest.

      [HEINRICH *leads* RAUTENDELEIN *toward the*
          doorway in the rocks, right. He stops sud-
          denly, and turns toward the open country.]

                                Yet may the moon,
That hangs so chalky-white in yonder heavens,
Not shed the still light of her staring eyes
On what's below . . . may she not flood with
    brightness
The valley whence I rose to these lone heights!
For what lies hid beneath that pall of gray
I dare not gaze on! . . . Hark! Child! Didst
    hear nothing?

RAUTEND. Nothing! And what thou saidst was dark to me!

HEINRICH. What! Dost thou still not hear 't?

RAUTEND.   What should I hear? —
The night wind playing on the heath, I hear —
I hear the cawing of the carrion-kite —
I hear thee, strangely uttering strange, wild
    words,
In tones that seem as though they were not thine!

HEINRICH. There! There! Below . . . where shines the
    wicked moon
Look! Yonder! — Where the light gleams on
    the waters!

RAUTEND. Nothing I see! Nothing!

HEINRICH.   With thy gerfalcon eyes
Thou seest naught? Art blind? What drags
    its way
Slowly and painfully along . . . There . . . See!

RAUTEND. Thy fancy cheats thee!

HEINRICH.   No! . . . It was no cheat,
As God shall pardon me! . . . Peace! Peace!
    I say!
Now it climbs over the great boulder, yonder —
Down by the footpath . . .

RAUTEND.   Heinrich! Do not look!
I'll close the doors and rescue thee by force!

HEINRICH. No! Let me be! . . . I must look down! I will!

RAUTEND. See — how the fleecy clouds whirl round and round,

As in a giant cauldron, 'mid the rocks!

Weak as thou art, beware! Go not too near!

HEINRICH. I am not weak! . . . 'Twas fancy. Now 'tis gone!

RAUTEND. That's well! Now be once more our Lord and Master!

Shall wretched visions so undo thy strength?

No! Take thy hammer! Swing it wide and high! . . .

HEINRICH. Dost thou not see them, where they climb and climb?

RAUTEND. Where?

HEINRICH.   There! . . . Now they have reached the rocky path . . .

Clad only in their little shifts they come!

RAUTEND. Who come?

HEINRICH.   Two little lads, with bare, white feet.

They hold an urn between them . . . 'Tis so heavy!

Now one, and now the other, bends his knee . . .

His little, baby knee, to raise it up . . .

RAUTEND. Oh, help him, mother — help him in his need!

HEINRICH. A halo shines about their tiny heads . . .

RAUTEND. Some will-o'-the-wisp!

HEINRICH.   No! . . . Kneel, and clasp thy hands!

Now . . . see . . . they are coming. Now . . . they are here!

[*He kneels, as the phantom forms of two* CHILDREN, *barefooted and clad only in their nightshifts, ascend from below and advance painfully toward him. Between them they carry a two-handled pitcher.*]

1ST CHILD (*faintly*).

Father!

HEINRICH.   My child!

1ST CHILD.   Our mother sends thee greeting.

HEINRICH. Thanks, thanks, my dear, dear lad!   All's well
          with her?

1ST CHILD (*slowly and sadly*).
          All's very well! . . .
          [*The first faint tones of the sunken bell are
          heard from the depths.*]

HEINRICH.   What have you brought with you?

2D CHILD. A pitcher.

HEINRICH.   Is 't for me?

2D CHILD.   Yes, father dear.

HEINRICH. What is there in the pitcher, my dear boy?

2D CHILD. 'Tis something salt! . . .

1ST CHILD   . . . And bitter!

2D CHILD.   Mother's tears!

HEINRICH. Merciful God!

RAUTEND.   What art thou staring at?

HEINRICH. At them . . . at them . . .

RAUTEND.   At whom?

HEINRICH.   Hast thou not eyes.
          At them!
                    (*To the* CHILDREN.)
          Where is your mother? Speak, oh, speak!

1ST CHILD. Our mother?

HEINRICH.   Yes! Where is she!

2D CHILD.   With . . . the . . . lilies . . .
          The water-lilies . . .   [*The bell tolls loudly.*]

HEINRICH.   Ah! The bell!

RAUTEND.   What bell?

HEINRICH. The old, old, buried bell! . . . It rings! It tolls!
          Who dealt this blow at me? . . . I will not
          listen!
          Help! Help me! . . . Help! . . .

RAUTEND.   Come to your senses, Heinrich!

HEINRICH.   It tolls! . . . God help me! . . . Who has dealt
                     this blow?
               Hark, how it peals!   Hark, how the buried tones
               Swell louder, louder, till they sound as thunder,
               Flooding the world! . . .
                          (*Turning to* RAUTENDELEIN.)
                                   I hate thee!   I abhor thee!
               Back!   Lest I strike thee!   Hence!   Thou witch!
               Thou trull:
               Accursèd spirit!   Cursed be thou and I!
               Cursed be my work! . . . And all! . . . Here!
               Here am I . . .
               I come! . . . I come! . . . Now may God pity
                     me! . . .
                  [*He makes an effort, rises, stumbles, rises
                  again, and tears himself away. The* CHIL-
                  DREN *have vanished.*]
RAUTEND.   Stay!   Heinrich!   Stay! . . . Woe's me!   Lost!
               . . . Lost for aye!

ACT V

The fir-clad glade seen in the first act. It is past midnight. Three ELVES
are resting near the well.

1ST ELF.   The flame glows bright!
2D ELF.   The wind of sacrifice —
               The red, red wind — blows in the vale!
3D ELF.   And lo,
               The dark smoke from the pine-clad peak
               streams down
               Into the gulf!
1ST ELF.   And, in the gulf, white clouds
               Lie thickly gathered!   From the misty sea
               The wond'ring herds lift up their drowsy heads,
               Lowing, impatient, for their sheltered stalls!

2D ELF.   A nightingale within the beechwood sang:
               It sang and sobbed into the waning night —
               Till, all a-quiver with responsive woe,
               I sank upon the dewy grass and wept.

3D ELF.   'Tis strange! I lay upon a spider's web.
               Between the blades of meadow-grass it hung,
               All woven out of marvelous purple threads,
               And softer than a royal shift it clung.
               I lay, and rested, while the glistening dew
               Flashed up at me from the green mead below:
               And so, my heavy lids did gently droop,
               Until at last I slept. When I awoke,
               The light had faded in the distant west:
               My bed had turned to gray. But, in the east,
               Thick clouds went up, and up, that hid the
                   moon,
               While all the rocky ridge was covered o'er
               With molten metal, glowing in the night.
               And, in the bloody glare that downward
                   streamed,
               Methought — 'twas strange — the fields did stir
                   with life,
               And whisp'rings, sighs, and voices low I heard
               That filled the very air with wretchedness.
               Ah, it was pitiful! . . . Then, quick, I hailed
               A fire-fly, who his soft, green lamp had trimmed.
               But on he flew. And so alone I lay,
               Trembling with fear, and lost in wonderment.
               Till, winged and gleaming as the dragon-fly,
               The dearest, loveliest, of all the elves,
               Who from afar his coming had proclaimed,
               Rustled and fell into my waiting arms.
               And, as we prattled in our cosy bed,
               Warm tears were mingled with our kisses
                   sweet,
               And then he sighed, and sobbed, and pressed me
                   tight,
               Mourning for Balder . . . Balder, who was dead!

1st ELF (*rising*).
>The flame glows bright!

2D ELF (*rising*). 'Tis Balder's funeral pyre!

3D ELF (*who meanwhile has moved slowly to the edge of the wood*).
>Balder is dead! . . . I'm chill!
>
>> [*She vanishes.*]

1st ELF. A curse doth fall
>Upon the land — as Balder's funeral pall!
>
>> [*Fog drifts across the glade. When it clears away the* ELVES *have vanished.*]

Enter RAUTENDELEIN, *slowly and wearily descending from the hillside. She drags herself toward the well, halting to rest, sitting and rising again with an effort, on her way. When she speaks, her voice is faint and strange.*

RAUTEND. Whither? . . . Ah, whither? . . . I sat till late,
>While the gnomes ran wild in my hall of state.
>They brought me a red, red cup to drain —
>And I drank it down, in pain.
>>For the wine I drank was blood!

> . . . .

>And, when I had drained the last red drop,
>My heart in my bosom seemed to stop:
>For a hand of iron had gripped the strings —
>And still with a burning pain it wrings
>>The heart that I long to cool!

> . . . .

>Then a crown on my wedding-board they laid —
>All of rose-red coral and silver made.
>As I set it upon my brow I sighed,
>Woe's me! Now the Water-man's won his
>>bride!
>>And I'll cool my burning heart!

> . . . .

>Three apples fell into my lap last night,
>Rose-red, and gold, and white —
>Wedding-gifts from my water-sprite.

I ate the white apple, and white I grew:
I ate the gold apple, and rich I grew —
And the red one last I ate!

. . . .

Pale, white, and rosy-red,
A maiden sat — and she was dead.
Now, Water-man, unbar thy gate —
I bring thee home thy dead, dead mate.
Deep down in the cold, damp darkness, see —
With the silver fishes I come to thee . . .
Ah, my poor, burnt, aching heart!
[*She descends slowly into the well.*]

THE WOOD-SPRITE *enters from the wood, crosses to the well, and calls down.*

W.-SPRITE. Hey! Holdrio! Old frog-king! Up with thee!
Hey! Holdrio! Thou web-foot wight bewitched!
Dost thou not hear me, monster? Art asleep?
I say, come up! — and though beside thee lay
Thy fairest water-maid, and plucked thy beard,
I'd still say, leave thy reedy bed and come!
Thou'lt not repent it: for, by cock and pie,
What I've to tell thee is worth many a night
Spent in the arms of thy most lovesick sprite.

NICKELM. (*from below*).
Brekekekex!

W.-SPRITE. Up! Leave thy weedy pool!

NICKELM. (*from below*).
I have no time. Begone, thou chattering fool!

W.-SPRITE. What? What? Thou toad-i'-the-hole, thou
hast no time
To spare from wallowing in thy mud and slime?
I say, I bring thee news. Didst thou not hear?
What I foretold's come true. I played the seer!
He's left her! . . . Now, an thou wilt but be
spry,
Thou'lt haply catch thy wondrous butterfly!

A trifle jaded — ay, and something worn:
But, Lord, what care the Nickelmann and Faun?
Rare sport thou'lt find her, comrade, even
    now —
Ay, more than thou hadst bargained for, I'll
    vow.

NICKELM. (*rising from the well and blinking slyly*).
Forsooth! . . . He's tired of her, the minx!
    And so
Thou'dst have me hang upon her skirts? . . .
    No, no!

W.-SPRITE. What? . . . Hast thou wearied of this beauty,
    too?
Why, then — I would her whereabouts I knew!

NICKELM. Go hunt for her!

W.-SPRITE.   I've sought her, like a dog:
Above — below, through mirk, and mist, and
    fog.
I've climbed where never mountain-goat had
    been,
And every marmot far and near I've seen.
Each falcon, glede, and finch, and rat, and
    snake,
I've asked for news. But none could answer
    make.
Woodmen I passed — around a fire they slept —
From them I stole a brand, and upward crept:
Till, grasping in my hand the burning wood,
At last before the lonely forge I stood.
And now the smoke of sacrifice ascends!
Loud roar the flames — each rafter cracks and
    bends!
The power the Master boasted once is fled:
For ever and for aye, 'tis past and dead!

NICKELM. I know. I know. Thy news is old and stale.
Hast thou disturbed me with this idle tale?

Much more I'd tell thee — ay, who tolled the
bell!
And how the clapper swung that rang the knell!
Hadst thou but seen, last night, as I did see,
What ne'er before had been, nor more shall be,
The hand of a dead woman, stark and cold,
Go groping for the bell that tossed and rolled.
And hadst thou heard the bell then make reply,
Peal upon peal send thundering to the sky —
Till, like the lioness that seeks her mate,
It thrilled the Master, even as the Voice of Fate!
I saw the woman — drowned. Her long, brown
hair
Floated about her face: 'twas wan with care.
And alway, when her hand the bell had found,
The awful knell did loud, and louder, sound!
I'm old, and used to many a gruesome sight:
Yet horror had seized me, and — I took to flight!
Hadst thou but seen, last night, what I have
seen,
Thou wouldst not fret about thine elfin quean.
So, let her flit at will, from flower to flower:
I care not, I! Her charm has lost its power.

W.-Sprite. 'Ods bodikins! I care, though, for the maid.
So — each to his own taste. I want the jade.
And once I hold her panting in these arms,
'Tis little I shall reck of dead alarms!

Nickelm. Quorax! Brekekekex! Oho, I see.
So that is still the flea that's biting thee?
Well — kill it, then. Go hunt her till thou'rt
spent.
Yet, though a-hunting twice ten years thou
went,
Thou shouldst not have her. 'Tis for me she
sighs!
She has no liking for thy goaty eyes.
A hen-pecked water-man, alack, I'm tied
By every whim and humor of my bride.

Now fare thee well. Thou 'rt free, to come, or
go:
But, as for me — 'tis time I went below!

[*He disappears in the well.*]

W.-SPRITE (*calling down the well*).
So sure as all the stars in heaven do shine —
So sure as these stout shanks and horns are
mine —
So sure as fishes swim and birds do fly —
A man-child in thy cradle soon shall lie!
Good-night. Sleep well! And now, be off to
bed!
On! On! Through brush and brier! . . . The
flea is dead!

[THE WOOD-SPRITE *skips off*. OLD WITTIKIN
*issues from the hut and takes down her
shutters.*]

WITTIKIN. 'Twas time I rose. I sniff the morning air.
A pretty hurly there has been to-night.

[*A cock crows.*]

Oho! I thought so. Kikereekikee!
No need to give thyself such pains for me —
Thou noisy rogue — as if we did not know
What 's coming, ere such cocks as thou did crow.
Thy hen another golden egg has laid?
And soon the sun shall warm the mirky glade?
Ay. Crow thy loudest, gossip! Sing and sing!
The dawn draws near. So strut thy fill and
sing.
Another day 's at hand. But — here 'tis dark . . .
Will no mad jack-o'-lantern give me a spark? . . .
I 'll need more light to do my work, I wis . . .
And, as I live, my carbuncle I miss.

[*She fumbles in her pocket and produces a
carbuncle.*]

Ah, here it is.

HEINRICH (*heard without*).

Rautendelein!

WITTIKIN.   Ay, call her!
        She'll answer thee, I wager, thou poor brawler!
HEINRICH (*without*).
        Rautendelein! I come. Dost thou not hear?
WITTIKIN.   Thou'lt need to call her louder, man, I fear.
        [HEINRICH, *worn and weary, appears on the*
            rocks above the hut. He is pale and in tat-
            ters. In his right hand he holds a heavy
            stone, ready to hurl it back into the depths.]
HEINRICH.   Come, if you dare! Be it priest, or be it barber,
        Sexton, or schoolmaster — I care not who!
        The first who dares another step to take,
        Shall fall and headlong plunge into the gulf!
        'Twas ye who drove my wife to death, not I!
        Vile rabble, witless wretches, beggars, rogues —
        Who weeks together mumble idle prayers
        For a lost penny! Yet, so base are ye,
        That, where ye can, God's everlasting love
        Ye cheat of ducats! . . . Liars! Hypocrites!
        Like rocks ye are heaped about your nether-
            land,
        Ringing it round, as with a dam of stone,
        Lest haply God's own waters, rushing in,
        Should flood your arid Hell with Paradise.
        When shall the great destroyer wreck your
            dam?
        I am not he . . . Alas! I am not the man.
        [*He drops the stone and begins to ascend.*]
WITTIKIN.   That way is barred. So halt! And climb no
            more.
HEINRICH.   Woman, what burns up yonder?
WITTIKIN.   Nay, I know not.
        Some man there was, I've heard, who built a
            thing,
        Half church, half royal castle. Now — he's
            gone!

And, since he's left it, up it goes in flame.

[HEINRICH *makes a feeble effort to press upward.*]

Did I not tell thee, man, the road was barred?
He who would pass that way had need o' wings.
And thy wings have been broken.

HEINRICH.   Ah, broken or no,
I tell thee, woman, I must reach the peak!
What flames up yonder is my work — all mine!
Dost understand me? . . . I am he who built it.
And all I was, and all I grew to be,
Was spent on it . . . I can . . . I can . . . no
    more!   [*Pause.*]

WITTIKIN. Halt here a while. The roads are still pitch-
    dark.
There is a bench. Sit down and rest.

HEINRICH.   I? . . . Rest? . . .
Though thou shouldst bid me sleep on silk and
    down,
That heap of ruins still would draw me on.
The kiss my mother — long she's joined the
    dust —
Did press years since upon my fevered brow,
Would bring no blessing to me now, no peace:
'Twould sting me like a wasp.

WITTIKIN.   Ay, so it would!
Wait here a bit, man. I will bring thee wine.
I've still a sup or two.

HEINRICH.   I must not wait.
Water! I thirst! I thirst!

WITTIKIN.   Go, draw, and drink!

[HEINRICH *moves to the well, draws, sits on the edge of the well, and drinks. A faint, sweet voice is heard from below, singing mournfully.*]

THE VOICE (*from below*).

> Heinrich, my sweetheart, I loved thee true.
> Now thou art come to my well to woo.
> Wilt thou not go?
> Love is all woe —
> Adieu! Adieu!

HEINRICH. Woman, what voice was that? Speak—
answer me!

> What called and sang to me in such sad tones?
> It murmured, "Heinrich!" . . . from the
> depths it came . . .
> And then it softly sighed, "Adieu! Adieu!"
> Who art thou, woman? And what place is this?
> Am I awaking from some dream? . . . These
> rocks,
> Thy hut, thyself, I seem to know ye all!
> Yet all are strange. Can that which me befell
> Have no more substance than a peal that sounds,
> And, having sounded, dies away in silence?
> Woman, who art thou?

WITTIKIN.　　　　　　　　I? . . . And who art thou?

HEINRICH. Dost ask me that? . . . Yes! Who am I? God
wot!

> How often have I prayed to Heaven to tell
> me! . . .
> Who am I, God! . . . But Heaven itself is mute.
> Yet this I do know: that, whatsoe'er I be,
> Hero or weakling, demi-god or beast —
> I am the outcast child of the bright Sun —
> That longs for home: all helpless now, and
> maimed,
> A bundle of sorrow, weeping for the Light
> That stretches out its radiant arms in vain,
> And yearns for me! . . . What dost thou there?

WITTIKIN. Thou'lt learn that soon enough.

HEINRICH (*rising*).　　　　　　Nay, I'll begone!

> Now, with thy bloody lamplight, show me a way
> Will lead me onward, upward, to the heights!

Once I am there, where erst I Master stood,
Lonely I'll live — thenceforth a hermit be —
Who neither rules, nor serves.

WITTIKIN.   I doubt it much!
What thou would'st seek up yonder is not that.

HEINRICH. How canst thou know?

WITTIKIN.   We know what we do know.
They'd almost run thee down, my friend? . . .
    Ay, ay!
When life shines bright, like wolves ye men do
    act,
Rend it and torture it. But, when death comes,
No bolder are ye than a flock of sheep,
That tremble at the wolf. Ay, ay, 'tis true!
The herds that lead ye are but sorry carles
Who with the hounds do hunt and loudly yelp:
They do not set their hounds to hunt the wolf:
Nay, nay: their sheep they drive into its
    jaws! . . .
Thou'rt not much better than the other herds.
Thy bright life thou hast torn and spurned
    away.
And when death fronted thee, thou wast not
    bold.

HEINRICH. Ah, woman, list! . . . I know not how it came
That I did spurn and kill my clear bright life:
And, being a Master, did my task forsake,
Like a mere 'prentice, quaking at the sound
Of my own handiwork, the bell which I
Had blessed with speech. And yet 'tis true!
    Its voice
Rang out so loud from its great iron throat,
Waking the echoes of the topmast peaks,
That, as the threatening peal did rise and swell,
It shook my soul! . . . Yet I was still the
    Master!

Ere it had shattered me who molded it,
With this same hand, that gave it form and life,
I should have crushed and ground it into atoms.

WITTIKIN.   What's past, is past: what's done, is done, for
aye.
Thou'lt never win up to thy heights, I trow.
This much I'll grant: thou wast a sturdy shoot,
And mighty — yet too weak. Though thou wast
called,
Thou'st not been chosen! . . . Come. Sit down
beside me.

HEINRICH.   Woman! Farewell!

WITTIKIN.   Come here, and sit thee down.
Strong — yet not strong enow!
Who lives, shall life pursue. But be thou sure,
Up yonder thou shalt find it nevermore.

HEINRICH.   Then let me perish here, where now I stand!

WITTIKIN.   Ay, so thou shalt. He who has flown so high,
Into the very Light, as thou hast flown,
Must perish, if he once fall back to Earth!

HEINRICH.   I know it. I have reached my journey's end.
So be it.

WITTIKIN.   Yes! Thou hast reached the end!

HEINRICH.   Then tell me —
Thou who dost seem to me so strangely wise —
Am I to die and never more set eyes
On what, with bleeding feet, I still must seek?
Thou dost not answer me? . . . Must I go
hence —
Leave my deep night, and pass to deepest dark-
ness —
Missing the afterglow of that lost light?
Shall I not see her once . . . ?

WITTIKIN.   Whom wouldst thou see?

HEINRICH.   I would see her. Whom else? . . . Dost not
know that?

WITTIKIN.   Thou hast one wish! . . . It is thy last! . . .
So — wish.

HEINRICH (*quickly*).
    I have wished!
WITTIKIN.   Then thou shalt see her once again.
HEINRICH (*rising and ecstatically*).
    Ah, mother! . . . Why I name thee thus, I know
       not . . .
    Art thou so mighty? . . . Canst thou do so
       much? . . .
    Once I was ready for the end, as now:
    Half hoping, as each feeble breath I drew,
    That it might be the last. But then she came —
    And healing, like the breeze in early Spring,
    Rushed through my sickly frame: and I grew
       well . . .
    All of a sudden, now I feel so light,
    That I could soar up to the heights again.
WITTIKIN.   Too late!   [HEINRICH *recoils in terror*.]
                Thy heavy burdens weigh thee down:
    Thy dead ones are too mighty for thee. See!
    I place three goblets on the table. So.
    The first I fill with white wine. In the next,
    Red wine I pour: the last I fill with yellow.
    Now, shouldst thou drain the first, thy vanished
       power
    Shall be restored to thee. Shouldst drink the
       second,
    Once more thou shalt behold the spirit bright
    Whom thou hast lost. But an thou dost drink
       both,
    Thou must drain down the last.
       [*She turns to enter the hut. On the threshold*
       she halts and utters the next words with
       solemn emphasis.]
                  I say thou must!
       [*She goes into the hut.* HEINRICH *has listened*
       to the preceding speech like a man dazed.
       As OLD WITTIKIN *leaves him, he rouses*
       himself and sinks on a bench.]

HEINRICH.   Too late! . . . She said, "Too late!" . . . Now
all is done!
O heart, that knowest all, as ne'er before:
Why dost thou question? . . . Messenger of
Fate!
Thy fiat, as the ax, doth sharply fall,
Cutting the strand of life! . . . It is the end!
What's left is respite! . . . But I'll profit by 't.
Chill blows the wind from the abyss.   The day
That yonder gleam so faintly doth forerun,
Piercing the sullen clouds with pale white shafts,
I shall not see.   So many days I have lived:
Yet this one day I shall not live to see!
                    [He raises the first goblet.]
Come then, thou goblet, ere the horror come!
A dark drop glistens at the bottom.   One!
A last one . . . Why, thou crone, hadst thou no
more?
So be it! *[He drinks.]* And now to thee, thou
second cup!   *[He raises the second goblet.]*
It was for thee that I did drain the first.
And, wert thou missing, thou delicious draught,
Whose fragrance tempts to madness, the carouse
Whereunto God has bid us in this world
Were all too poor, meseems — unworthy quite,
Of thee, who dost the festal board so honor.
Now I do thank thee — thus!   *[He drinks.]*
                    The drink is good.
    *[A murmur as of æolian harps floats on the
    air while he drinks. RAUTENDELEIN rises
    slowly from the well. She looks weary and
    sad. She sits on the edge of the well, comb-
    ing her long flowing locks. Moonlight.
    RAUTENDELEIN is pale. She sings into
    vacancy. Her voice is faint.]*

RAUTEND.   All, all alone, in the pale moon-shine,
             I comb my golden hair,
                 Fair, fairest Rautendelein!
             The mists are rising, the birds take flight,
             The fires burn low in the weary night . . .
NICKELM. (*from below*).
                 Rautendelein!
RAUTEND.   I'm coming!
NICKELM. (*from below*).   Come at once!
RAUTEND.   Woe, woe is me!
             So tight I am clad,
             A maid o' the well, bewitched and so sad!
NICKELM. (*from below*).
                 Rautendelein!
RAUTEND.   I'm coming!
NICKELM. (*from below*).   Come thou now!
RAUTEND.   I comb my hair in the moonlight clear,
             And think of the sweetheart who loved me
                 dear.
             The blue-bells all are ringing.
             Ring they of joy? Ring they of pain?
             Blessing and bane —
             Answers the song they are singing!
             Now down I go, to my weedy well —
             No more I may wait:
             I must join my mate —
             Farewell! Farewell!
                         [*She prepares to descend.*]
             Who calls so softly?
HEINRICH.   I.
RAUTEND.   Who'rt thou?
HEINRICH.   Why — I.
             Do but come nearer — ah, why wouldst thou fly?
RAUTEND.   I dare not come! . . . I know thee not. Away!
             For him who speaks to me, I am doomed to slay.

HEINRICH.   Why torture me?   Come.   Lay thy hand in mine,
And thou shalt know me.

RAUTEND.   I have never known thee.

HEINRICH.   Thou know'st me not?

RAUTEND.   No!

HEINRICH.   Thou hast never seen me?

RAUTEND.   I cannot tell.

HEINRICH.   Then may God cast me off!
I never kissed thee till thy lips complained?

RAUTEND.   Never.

HEINRICH.   Thou'st never pressed thy lips to mine?

NICKELM. (*from below*).
              Rautendelein!

RAUTEND.   I'm coming!

NICKELM.   Come.   I wait.

HEINRICH.   Who called to thee?

RAUTEND.   'Twas the Water-man — my mate!

HEINRICH.   Thou seest my agony — the pain and strife
That rend my soul, and eat away my life!
Ah, torture me no longer.   Set me free!

RAUTEND.   Then, as thou wilt.   But how?

HEINRICH.   Come close to me!

RAUTEND.   I cannot come.

HEINRICH.   Thou canst not?

RAUTEND.   No.   I am bound.

HEINRICH.   By what?

RAUTEND. (*retreating*).
              I must begone to join the round,
A merry dance — and though my foot be sore,
Soon, as I dancing go, it burns no more.
Farewell!   Farewell!

HEINRICH.   Where art thou?   Stay, ah stay!

RAUTEND. (*disappearing behind the well*).
              Lost, lost, forever!

PERMISSION E.A. SEEMANN, LEIPZIG

HEINRICH.   The goblet — quick, I say!
  There . . . there . . . the goblet! . . . Magda?
  Thou? . . . So pale!
  Give me the cup. Who brings it, I will hail
  My truest friend.
RAUTEND. (*reappearing*).   I bring it.
HEINRICH.   Be thou blessed.
RAUTEND.   Yes. I will do it. Leave the dead to rest!
                    [*She gives* HEINRICH *the goblet.*]
HEINRICH.   I feel thee near me, thou dear heart of mine!
RAUTEND. (*retreating*).
  Farewell! Farewell! I never can be thine!
  Once I was thy true love — in May, in May —
  Now all is past, for aye! . . .
HEINRICH.   For aye!
RAUTEND.   For aye!
  Who sang thee soft to sleep with lullabies?
  Who woke thee with enchanting melodies?
HEINRICH.   Who, who — but thou?
RAUTEND.   Who am I?
HEINRICH.   Rautendelein!
RAUTEND.   Who poured herself into thy veins, as wine?
  Whom didst thou drive into the well to pine?
HEINRICH.   Thee, surely thee!
RAUTEND.   Who am I?
HEINRICH.   Rautendelein!
RAUTEND.   Farewell! Farewell!   [*He drinks.*]
HEINRICH.   Nay: lead me gently down.
  Now comes the night — the night that all would
      flee.
        [RAUTENDELEIN *hastens to him, and clasps
        him about the knees.*]
RAUTEND. (*exultingly*).
  The Sun is coming!
HEINRICH.   The Sun!

RAUTEND. (*half sobbing, half rejoicing*).   Ah, Heinrich!

HEINRICH.   Thanks!

RAUTEND. (*embracing* HEINRICH, *she presses her lips to his, and then gently lays him down as he dies*).

    Heinrich!

HEINRICH (*ecstatically*).

        I hear them!   'Tis the Sun-bells' song!
      The Sun . . . the Sun . . . draws near! . . .
      The Night is . . . long!

                          [*Dawn breaks.   He dies.*]

MICHAEL KRAMER*

DRAMATIS PERSONÆ

MICHAEL KRAMER, *teacher at the Royal College of Art, painter*
MRS. KRAMER, *his wife*
MICHALINE KRAMER, *his daughter, painter*
ARNOLD KRAMER, *his son, painter*
LACHMANN, *painter*
ALWINE LACHMANN, *his wife*
LIESE BANSCH, *daughter of the restaurant keeper* BANSCH
ASSISTANT JUDGE SCHNABEL, ⎫
ARCHITECT ZIEHN,   ⎪
VON KRAUTHEIM,   ⎬ *Frequenters of* BANSCH'S *restaurant*
QUANTMEYER,   ⎭
KRAUSE, *chief janitor in the College of Art*
BERTHA, *maid at the Kramers'*
FRITZ, *waiter in* BANSCH'S *restaurant*
    The events of this drama take place in a provincial capital

TO

THE MEMORY OF MY DEAR FRIEND

HUGO ERNST SCHMIDT

* Permission B. W. Huebsch, New York.

[211]

MICHAEL KRAMER (1900)

By Gerhardt Hauptmann

TRANSLATED BY LUDWIG LEWISOHN, A.M.
Assistant Professor of the German Language and Literature, Ohio State University

ACT I

A large room, having a single window in one corner, in Kramer's *apartment. Time: A winter morning toward nine o'clock. On a table beside the window that looks out on the court a burning lamp and the breakfast dishes are still standing. The furnishings of the room are quite ordinary.* Michaline, *a dark girl with an interesting face, having pushed her chair slightly away from the table, is smoking a cigarette and holding a book in her lap.* Mrs. Kramer *enters by the door in the rear on some household errand. She is a white-haired woman about fifty-six years old. Her demeanor is restless and anxious.*

Mrs. Kramer. Are you still there, Michaline? Isn't it time for you to go?

Michaline (*pausing before she answers*). No, mother, not yet.—Anyhow, it's quite dark outside yet.

Mrs. Kramer. Be careful that you don't neglect anything, Michaline; that's all.

Michaline. There's no danger, mother.

Mrs. Kramer. Because really . . . you shouldn't miss any opportunity; there's worry enough left anyhow.

Michaline. Yes, mother, surely! [*She smokes and looks into her book.*]

Mrs. Kramer. What are you reading there? You always have your nose in a book!

Michaline. Am I not to read?

Mrs. Kramer. You may read for all I care!—I'm only surprised that you have the peace of mind to do it.

Michaline. Dear me, if one were to wait for that! Would one ever get to do anything?

[212]

MRS. KRAMER. Didn't papa say anything at all when he went?

MICHALINE. No.

MRS. KRAMER. That's always the worst sign when he doesn't say anything.

MICHALINE. Oh yes, he did though. I almost forgot. Arnold is to come to him at the studio at eleven o'clock sharp.

MRS. KRAMER (*opens the door of the stove and fastens it again. As she draws herself up, she sighs*). Ah, yes, yes! Oh, dear, dear, dear!

MICHALINE. Do as I do, mother. Divert your mind!— There's nothing new! it's the same old story. Arnold's not going to change in that respect either.

MRS. KRAMER (*sits down at the table, supports her head with her hand and sighs*). Oh, you don't understand the boy—none of you! You don't understand him! And as for father—he'll be the ruin of him.

MICHALINE. Oh, I don't think it right for you to make such an assertion. You're bitterly unjust. Papa does his very best by Arnold. He's tried every way. If you and Arnold fail to recognize that, mother—why, so much the worse.

MRS. KRAMER. You're your father's daughter; I know that very well.

MICHALINE. Yes, I'm your daughter and father's.

MRS. KRAMER. No, you're father's daughter much more than mine. Because if you were more my daughter you wouldn't always be taking sides with father.

MICHALINE. Mother, we'd better not excite ourselves by such talk.—One tries merely to exercise simple justice and at once one is told: You take sides with so and so or so and so.—You make life pretty difficult, you can believe me.

MRS. KRAMER. I side with my boy and there's an end to it! You can all of you do what you please.

MICHALINE. I don't see how one can bear to say a thing like that.

Mrs. Kramer. Michaline, you're not a woman at all; that's it! You're not like a woman! You talk like a man! You think like a man! What comfort can a woman get of such a daughter?

Michaline (*shrugging her shoulders*). Well, mother, if that's really true . . .! I don't suppose I'll be able to alter that either.

Mrs. Kramer. You can alter it, only you don't want to!

Michaline. Mama . . . I'm afraid it's time for me to go. And do, mother, be sensible and don't excite yourself. You don't really mean what you've just been saying.

Mrs. Kramer. As truly as that I'm standing here — every syllable!

Michaline. Then I'm very sorry for us all, mother.

Mrs. Kramer. The truth is we all suffer under papa.

Michaline. Do me a favor, mother, once and for all: I have never suffered under papa and I do not suffer under him now. I honor father as you very well know! And it would be the damndest lie . . . .

Mrs. Kramee. I'm ashamed of the way you swear, Michaline.

Michaline. . . . if I were to say that I am suffering under him. There isn't any human being in the world to whom I am so boundlessly grateful.

Mrs. Kramer. Not to me either?

Michaline. No. I'm sorry. What father really is and what he is to me seems clearer to strangers than to you — I mean you and Arnold, mother. That's just the fatality of it. Those who ought to be closest to papa are most alien to him. He'd be lost among you alone.

Mrs. Kramer. As if I didn't remember how often you cried when father . . .

Michaline. That's true. I cried often. He did hurt me at times. But I always had to admit to myself finally that, though he hurt me, he was never unjust, and that I always learned something in the process.

MRS. KRAMER. Whether you learned anything or not, father has never helped you to be happy. If you had a comfortable home of your own, a husband and children . . . and all that . . .

MICHALINE. Father didn't rob me of that!

MRS. KRAMER. And now you work yourself sick just as papa does and nothing comes of it except discontent and worry.

MICHALINE. Oh, mother, when I hear such talk I always feel so shut in! So caged and throttled and depressed, you would scarcely believe it! (*With bitter sadness.*) If Arnold weren't just — Arnold, how grateful would he be to father!

MRS. KRAMER. Why, he whipped the boy when he was fifteen!

MICHALINE. I don't doubt that father can be hard, and that he lost control of himself at times. I neither palliate nor excuse. But I ask you, mother, whether on that occasion Arnold hadn't provoked father's anger! He forged his signature that time!

MRS. KRAMER. In the terror of his soul! Because he was so frightened of papa!

MICHALINE. No, mother, that doesn't quite explain it all.

MRS. KRAMER. The boy is wretched; he isn't well; he's been sickly from the beginning.

MICHALINE. That may be true. He must resign himself and settle that with his own soul. That's the fate of all men, mother. To keep a grip on oneself and fight one's way through to something higher — that's what everybody has had to do. He has the best example of that in father.— By the way, mother, here are twenty marks; I can't spare more this month. I've had to pay the bill for paint; that alone mounted up to twenty-three marks. I must have a winter hat, too. I've had to trust two pupils for their tuition.

MRS. KRAMER. That's it. You work yourself to death for those women and then they cheat you of your little earnings.

MICHALINE. No, mother, there's no question of cheating at all. One is a poor, hunch-backed girl without means, and Miss Schäffer saves the fees from her food. [*The outer door-bell rings.*] The bell just rang; who could it be?

MRS. KRAMER. I don't know. I'll just blow out the lamp. — wish I were lying in my grave.

[BERTHA *goes through the room.*]

MICHALINE. Ask what name first, Bertha.

MRS. KRAMER. Is Mr. Arnold still asleep?

BERTHA. He didn't stop to lie down at all.

[BERTHA *exit.*]

MICHALINE. But who do you think it can be, mama?

[BERTHA *returns.*]

BERTHA. A painter named Lachmann and his wife. He used to study with the professor.

MICHALINE. Papa is not a professor. You know that he wants to be called simply Mr. Kramer.

[MICHALINE *goes out into the hall.*]

MRS. KRAMER. Just wait a bit! I just want to straighten up here a little. Hurry, Bertha! Then I'll look in later.

[*She and* BERTHA *leave the room, carrying dishes with them.*]

The sounds of greeting are heard from the outer hall. Thereupon appear the painter ERNEST LACHMANN, *his wife* ALWINE, *and finally* MICHALINE. LACHMANN *wears a top-hat and overcoat and carries a stick;* MRS. LACHMANN *wears a dark, small hat with feathers, a feather boa, etc. The clothes of both show signs of wear.*

MICHALINE. Where do you come from, and what are you doing here?

LACHMANN (*introducing the two women*). Alwine: Michaline Kramer.

MRS. LACHMANN (*thoroughly surprised*). Well! Is it possible? So that's you!

MICHALINE. Does that surprise you so greatly?

MRS. LACHMANN. Yes! If I'm to be honest. A little bit, anyhow. I had such a different idea of you.

MICHALINE. Did you think I was even older and more wrinkled than I really am?

MRS. LACHMANN (*immediately*). No, quite the contrary, to tell you the truth.

[MICHALINE *and* LACHMANN *laugh with amusement.*]

LACHMANN. I foresee great things. You're making a fine start.

MRS. LACHMANN. Why? What did I do again?

LACHMANN. How is your father, Michaline?

MICHALINE. Well. He is about as usual. I doubt whether you'll find him at all changed.— But please, sit down! Won't you, please, Mrs. Lachmann? And you will pardon us, won't you? Everything is still a bit upset here. [*They all sit down at the table.*] Do you smoke? [*She offers* LACHMANN *cigarettes.*] Or did you drop the habit? Do forgive me; I've been puffing away! I know it isn't womanly, but the realization came to me too late. I dare say you don't smoke? No? And doesn't it annoy you, either?

MRS. LACHMANN (*shakes her head*). Ernest sucks away at something all day at home.

LACHMANN (*taking a cigarette from* MICHALINE'S *case*). Thank you.— You don't understand that.

MRS. LACHMANN. What is there about it to understand?

LACHMANN. A great deal, dear Alwine.

MRS. LACHMANN. How's that? I don't see.

MICHALINE. It's much easier to talk freely if one smokes.

MRS. LACHMANN. Then it's a mighty good thing I don't smoke. According to my husband I chatter too much as it is.

LACHMANN. It all depends on *what* one says.

MRS. LACHMANN. Well, you talk nonsense yourself sometimes, dear Ernest.

LACHMANN (*changing the subject violently*). Yes . . .
what is it I wanted to say! . . . Oh, yes: So your
father is well; I'm glad of that.

MICHALINE. Yes; as I said before: He is as usual. By
and large, anyhow. I suppose you've come here to see
your mother?

MRS. LACHMANN (*talkatively*). What he wanted to do was
to look around here a bit — if there wasn't something
or other to be done here. There's absolutely no chance
in Berlin any longer. Are things just as dull here, do
you think?

MICHALINE. In what respect? I don't know. . . . Just
what do you mean?

MRS. LACHMANN. Well, I thought you'd established a
school. Doesn't that pay you pretty well?

LACHMANN. Look here! Tell me when you're through!
Will you?

MICHALINE. My school? I earn something. Oh, yes. Not
much. But something, no doubt; I get along. (*To*
LACHMANN.) Do you intend to offer me competition?

MRS. LACHMANN. Why, of course not! Gracious! What
do you think? My husband's crazy about you, I can
tell you. My husband would never do that. But a
man's got to do something, you know. People have to
eat and drink, don't they? My husband . . .

LACHMANN. *My* husband; I am not *your* husband. That
expression always makes me nervous.

MRS. LACHMANN. Did you ever hear the like of that?

LACHMANN. Ernest is my name, Alwine. Try to remember that. You may say my coal shovel or my coffee
strainer or my false hair. But slavery is abolished.

MRS. LACHMANN. But hubby . . .

LACHMANN. That sounds like a dog's name.

MRS. LACHMANN. Now you see how it is. That's the
kind of husband a woman has. Do me one favor —
don't marry at any price! Old maids are a sight
better off.   [MICHALINE *laughs heartily.*]

LACHMANN. Alwine, that ends it! You'll kindly take your boa and wait somewhere else for me. Do you understand? For otherwise my coming here will be quite futile! Just take your boa, that most tasteful favorite adornment of yours. Then have the kindness either to ride out to mother's or wait in the restaurant across the way. I'll even come for you.

MRS. LACHMANN. Did you ever? That's the way a wife's treated, you see. I don't hardly say a word, but what —Lord, Lord!

LACHMANN. It isn't necessary for you to say anything. There's nothing but folly at the bottom of it, anyhow.

MRS. LACHMANN. I'm not as clever as you, to be sure.

LACHMANN. Agreed! I agree with everything you're about to say.

MICHALINE. But please, Mrs. Lachmann, won't you stay?

MRS. LACHMANN. For heaven's sake! What are you thinking of! But you needn't feel a bit sorry for me. He'll come running after me again. Good-by.— There's a pastry-cook at the corner across the street. You understand, hubby? That's where you report.

[*Exit, accompanied by* MICHALINE.]

LACHMANN. But don't eat thirteen pieces of pastry again.

[MICHALINE *returns.*]

MICHALINE. Old maids are a sight better off! She really is a little direct.

LACHMANN. She babbles like a brook.

MICHALINE (*sitting down again*). You do make short work with her, though. Not every woman would endure that, Lachmann.

LACHMANN. Michaline, she presses me hard. I have no choice.— She wanted to make your acquaintance; otherwise I wouldn't have brought her with me.— How are you, anyhow?

MICHALINE. Well, thank you. And you?

LACHMANN. Oh, so, so. Not brilliant.

MICHALINE.   I feel the same way.— You're getting gray about the temples, too.

LACHMANN.   The donkey reveals itself more and more.

[*Both laugh.*]

MICHALINE.   And so you think of settling down here?

LACHMANN.   I never dreamed of such a thing. She fancies all kinds of things, bubbles over with them, and then asserts roundly that I had expressed myself to the same purpose. [*Pause.*]   How's your brother?

MICHALINE.   Well, thank you.

LACHMANN.   Does he work steadily at his painting?

MICHALINE.   On the contrary.

LACHMANN.   What else does he do?

MICHALINE.   He dawdles about, of course. He wastes his time.   What else do you think?

LACHMANN.   Why didn't he stay in Munich? He succeeded in doing something there now and then.

MICHALINE.   Do you still expect anything of Arnold?

LACHMANN.   Why do you ask? I don't quite understand. I thought that was pretty well settled.

MICHALINE.   Well, if he has talent . . . then he isn't worthy of it.— By the way, to change the subject: Father has asked after you repeatedly. He will be glad to see you again. And leaving myself quite out of the question, of course, I'm very glad, for father's sake, that you came over again. He is really in need of some intellectual refreshment.

LACHMANN.   And so am I. Probably more than he is. And — leaving you out of the question once more — what exclusively drew me here — everything else could well have waited — was the wish to be with your father once again. To be sure I'd like to have a look at his picture too.

MICHALINE.   Who told you anything about the picture?

LACHMANN.   There's a report that the public gallery has bought it.

MICHALINE. The director of the gallery was here, but I don't know whether he bought it. Father is excessively reticent and conscientious. I hardly think so. I think he'll want to finish it entirely first.

LACHMANN. You know the picture? Of course you do.

MICHALINE. It's two years ago that I saw it. I can't quite judge it any longer. Papa has been at work on it a very long time.   [*Pause.*]

LACHMANN. Do you think he will show it to me? I don't know why, but I have a presentiment that it is something extraordinary. I can't help it: I have great faith in it. I have known many men, but no other of whose inner life one has so deep a wish to see a bit. And anyhow — if I haven't quite gone under artistically — and really, I still have some grip on myself — I owe it primarily to your father alone. The things he said to a fellow, and the way he said them — no one can forget. There isn't another teacher like him. I always say that any one whom your father has once influenced can never become quite shallow again.

MICHALINE. That's what I always think, Lachmann; just that.

LACHMANN. He stirs one up to the very depths. One learns a good many things from different men; I've known some excellent ones. But your father always seemed to loom up behind them and then not one could hold his own any longer. He ploughed up the very souls of us, his pupils, he turned us inside out, made us over again — thoroughly. He knocked all the wretched philistinism out of one. A man can feed on his teaching for a lifetime. For instance, to any one who has known his unflaggingly loyal seriousness in the service of art, the outside world seems at first entirely frivolous . . .

MICHALINE. Well, and you see, father's deep seriousness . . . you say yourself that you feel it in your very blood; it's become my best possession: his seriousness has made an impression on the shallowest donkeys, but not on Arnold. He doesn't profit by it. [*She has arisen during her last words.*] I must correct my pupils' work now, Lachmann. You're laughing because you think my own ability is pretty small.

LACHMANN. You're your father's daughter, after all. But it's something I was always shy of. I imagine it must be terribly bleak to bother oneself with women who want to paint.

MICHALINE. Oh, there's something to be accomplished. They make the most honest efforts. That in itself is a reconciling element. What more do you want? Whether in the end they really achieve something — ? The striving in itself is an achievement. And, beyond that, I feel the way father does — it amuses me to influence people. Then, too, one grows young again in one's pupils. And, as time goes on, that's rather necessary. [*She opens the door and calls out into the rear of the apartment.*] Good-by, mama, we're going now.

ARNOLD (*outside in a mocking voice*). Good-by, mama, we're going now.

LACHMANN. Why, who was that?

MICHALINE. Arnold. He won't stop that kind of thing. There's no good dwelling on it. Come on!

[LACHMANN *and* MICHALINE *leave.*]

ARNOLD *enters. He is a homely fellow with black, fiery eyes behind spectacles, dark hair and indications of a beard. His figure is slightly bowed and slightly deformed. The color of his face is a dirty pale. He is dressed only in coat, trousers and bedroom slippers. He shuffles up to the mirror, takes off his spectacles and regards the impurities in his skin, making faces the while. His whole appearance is slovenly.* MICHALINE *returns.*

MICHALINE (*taken by surprise*). Why, Arnold! — I forgot my umbrella. — By the way, do you know that Lachmann is here?

ARNOLD (*with gestures warding off her interference and demanding silence*). That worthy is in the highest degree indifferent to me.

MICHALINE. Will you kindly tell me what Lachmann has done to you?

[ARNOLD *does not answer.*]

MICHALINE (*shrugging her shoulders, but calmly*). Don't forget to meet father at eleven.

[ARNOLD *puts his fingers into both ears.*]

MICHALINE. Look here, Arnold, do you think that decent?

ARNOLD. Yes.— You'd better lend me a mark.

MICHALINE. Surely I can lend it to you. Why not? Only in the end I have to reproach myself that I . . .

ARNOLD. Run along! Take to your heels, Michaline! I know your miserliness.

[MICHALINE *is about to answer, shrugs her shoulders instead and leaves the room.* ARNOLD *shuffles up to the breakfast table, nibbles a bit of sugar and glances carelessly at his mother who has just entered. Thereupon he returns to the mirror.*]

MRS. KRAMER (*dries her hands on her apron and sits down on a chair, sighing heavily and anxiously*). Oh, dearie me! Yes, yes.

ARNOLD (*turns around, pushes his spectacles forward on his nose, draws up his shoulders, and assumes a comical attitude in keeping with his remarks*). Mother, don't I look like a marabout?

MRS. KRAMER. Oh, Arnold, I don't feel a bit like fooling. I can't laugh at your nonsense.— Who unlocked the door for you last night?

ARNOLD (*approaching her and still keeping the mock-gravity of the animal he is imitating*). Father.

MRS. KRAMER. He went down all the three flights of stairs?

ARNOLD (*still staring comically through his spectacles*). Yes.

Mrs. Kramer. No, really, Arnold, the way you act is repulsive! Do please stop your nonsense. Can't you be serious for once? Be sensible! Tell me what papa said.

Arnold. Everything's repulsive to you people. Well, you're all of you pretty repulsive to me now and then.

Mrs. Kramer. Was father very angry when he opened the door for you?

[Arnold, *absent-minded, does not answer.*]

Mrs. Kramer. What did he say to you?

Arnold. Nothing.

Mrs. Kramer (*approaching him with tenderness*). Arnold, try to do better. Try for the love of me. Lead a different kind of life!

Arnold. How do I live?

Mrs. Kramer. Dissolutely! Idly! Whole nights long you're out of the house! You gad about . . . O Lordy, Lord. You're leading a horrible life, Arnold!

Arnold. Don't take on so frightfully, mother. I'd like to know where you get your information.

Mrs. Kramer. It's very nice, I must say, the way you treat your mother.

Arnold. Then have the kindness to leave me in peace! The whole crowd of you is always yelping at me! It's enough, actually, to drive any one crazy.

Mrs. Kramer. You call it yelping at you, Arnold, when we come to you for your own sake? Isn't your own mother to plead with you? Arnold, Arnold, you're sinning and blaspheming!

Arnold. Mother, all that doesn't do me any good! The eternal whining can't help me. And, anyhow, I have a horrible headache! Let me have a bit of money of my own and I'll manage to get along without you . . .

Mrs. Kramer. Is that so? You want a chance to go to the dogs entirely? [*Pause.*]

Arnold (*at the table, picks up a roll*). Supposed to be a roll? The thing's hard as a rock!

MRS. KRAMER. Get up earlier and you'll find them fresher.

ARNOLD (*yawning*). The day's disgustingly long and empty enough as it is.

MRS. KRAMER. With your carrying on it's no wonder you feel that way. Take a decent night's rest and you'll be refreshed through the day.— Arnold, I won't let you go this way today! Oh, yes, you can fly up at me if you want to, I know that! But I can't bear to see things going on this way any longer. [ARNOLD *has sat down by the table and she pours him a cupful of coffee.*] You can make faces all you want to; I'm up to your tricks. There's something wrong with you. I ought to know you. There's something that weighs on you and worries you. D'you think I haven't heard you sigh! You do nothing but sigh all the time. You don't seem to realize it yourself any longer!

ARNOLD. Good Lord, this eternal spying! The devil, I say! The number of times a fellow sneezes and things like that; the number of times a fellow spits and sighs and so forth! It's enough to make one want to jump out of the window!

MRS. KRAMER. You can say what you please. I care little about that. I know what I know and that's all about it. Something or other, Arnold, is weighing you down. I know that from your very restlessness. Of course, you always were a little restless, but not the way you are now. I know that!

ARNOLD (*beats his fist on the table*). Mother, leave me in peace, d'you understand?— Otherwise you'll drive me out into the street entirely — What business is it of yours *how* I carry on, mother? I'm not a child any longer and what I don't want to tell, I won't. I'm sick of your nagging! I've been pestered by you all long enough. Your help I don't want either. You can't help me, I tell you. The most you can do is to cry: Help! Murder!

Mrs. Kramer (*dissolved in tears*). Arnold, did you do
something awful? Merciful God! Arnold, for God's
sake, what have you done?

Arnold. Murdered an old Jew, mama.

Mrs. Kramer. Don't jeer, Arnold. Don't mock me! Tell
me, if you've done something. I know very well that
you're not really bad, but sometimes you're so full of
hate and so rash. And when you act in rage and
rashness . . . who knows what misfortunes you'll be
guilty of yet.

Arnold. Mama, mama! Calm yourself! I haven't murdered an old Jew. I haven't even sold a forged pawn-
ticket, although I needed a bit of money pretty badly.

Mrs. Kramer. I stick to my point: You're keeping something from us! Why, you can't look into any one's
eyes! You always did have something shrinking and
secretive about you, but now, Arnold — you don't notice
it yourself, of course — now you act as if you were
branded. You're drinking. You couldn't bear the
sight of beer formerly. Now you drink to deaden your
soul, Arnold!

Arnold (*has been standing at the window and drumming
on the panes*). Branded! Branded! And what else,
I'd like to know? — Say what you please, for all I
care. — I'm branded, you're quite right there. But in
that respect, at least, it seems to me that I'm not to
blame.

Mrs. Kramer. You always thrust about you and hit out
at us and try to stab, and sometimes you stab deep —
to our very hearts. Surely, we've done our best by
you. That you grew up to be what you are now . . .
One has to bear that, as God wills it.

Arnold. Very well! Then kindly go ahead and bear it!
[*Pause.*]

Mrs. Kramer. Arnold, listen to me! Don't harden yourself! Do tell me what the trouble is. We live in fear
and trembling day and night. You don't know how

papa tosses about at night. And I haven't slept either
these many days. Take this burden from us that drags
us down, my boy. Maybe you can do it by one frank
word. You're frail, I know that well . . .

ARNOLD. Oh, mother, let the whole business be. Otherwise I'll sleep in my studio after this — in my hayloft,
I should have said. I'd rather freeze stiff. There *is*
something! Very well. I don't deny that at all. But
do you want me to raise a row on that account? That
would only make the whole business still worse.

MRS. KRAMER. Arnold, you are . . . Is it still the same
thing? Weeks ago you betrayed yourself once! Then
you tried to hush it all up.— Is it still the affair with
that girl, Arnold?

ARNOLD. Mother, are you quite crazy?

MRS. KRAMER. My boy, don't inflict that misery on us!
Don't entangle yourself in love affairs. If you fasten
your heart to a creature like that, you'll be dragged
through all the slime on earth. I know how great the
temptation is here. You find these pitfalls here wherever you set your foot. You hear that wild rabble
when you pass. And the police tolerate all that!—
And if you don't listen to your mother's warning,
you'll come to harm some day. There are crimes committed daily in those places.

ARNOLD. Just let any one try to touch me, mother, that's
all. [*With a gesture toward his back pocket.*] I've
provided myself against that contingency.

MRS. KRAMER. What do you mean by that?

ARNOLD. I mean that I'm prepared for anything. There
are ways and means to be had nowadays, thank heaven.

MRS. KRAMER. Doesn't the very sight and sound of it all
disgust you — the strumming on the piano, the red
lanterns, the whole vile, repulsive atmosphere! Arnold,
if I had to believe that you pass your nights there
. . . in such holes, I mean . . . in such vile resorts
. . . then I'd rather die and be out of it.

ARNOLD. Oh, mother, I wish the day were over. You make me feel confused; my ears just buzz. I've got to keep a firm hold on myself not to fly up the chimney. I'll buy a knapsack and drag you all around with me.

MRS. KRAMER. Very well. But I tell you this one thing. You won't leave this house tonight.

ARNOLD. No? Then I'll leave it this minute.

MRS. KRAMER. You go to meet papa at eleven and then come back here.

ARNOLD. I wouldn't dream of doing such a thing! Good heavens!

MRS. KRAMER. Where do you intend to go then?

ARNOLD. I don't know yet.

MRS. KRAMER. So you don't want to come home to dinner?

ARNOLD. With your faces around the table? No. And anyhow I don't eat anything.

MRS. KRAMER. And tonight you mean to stay out again?

ARNOLD. I'll come and go exactly as I please.

MRS. KRAMER. Very well, my son. In that case it's all over between us. And, besides, I'll track you down! I won't rest before I do; depend upon it! And if I find out that it's a wench like that, I swear to you and God is my witness — I'll turn her over to the police.

ARNOLD. Well, mother, you'd better not do that.

MRS. KRAMER. On the contrary, I'll tell father. And father, he'll know how to bring you to reason. You just let him find this out: he'll be beside himself.

ARNOLD. All I have to say is: You'd better not. When father thunders out his moral preachments all I do, as you know, is to put my fingers in my ears. It doesn't affect me in the slightest. Good Lord! Anyhow, you've all grown to be so strange to me . . . How did I get here — tell me that!

MRS. KRAMER. Is that . . . . ?

ARNOLD. How? How? Where am I when I'm here, mother? Michaline, father, you — what do you want of me? What have you to do with me? How, when all's said and done, do you concern me?

MRS. KRAMER. How? What?

ARNOLD. Yes, what is it? What do you want of me?

MRS. KRAMER. What shocking talk that is.

ARNOLD. Oh, yes, shocking; I'll admit that. But true, mother, true! No lying about that. You can't help me, I tell you. And if, some day, you cut up too rough for me, then, maybe, something will happen, mama . . . something, some day, that'll leave you all with foolish faces!—That'll put an end to all this trouble.

ACT II

The studio of MICHAEL KRAMER in the College of Art. The studio proper is shut off from the room visible to the spectator by drawn hangings of gray. To the right of the hangings a door which is led up to by several steps. Also to the right but farther forward an old leather sofa with a covered table before it. To the left one-half of a great studio window, of which the other half is hidden by the hangings. Beneath this window a small table on which are lying etching tools and an unfinished plate. On the table in front of the sofa writing utensils, paper, an old candle-stick with candle, etc. On the wall are hanging plaster casts: An arm, a foot, a female bust, as well as the death mask of Beethoven. All these casts have a bluish-gray hue. Emerging from behind the hangings which reach to only about two-thirds the height of the room, the top of a great easel is visible.—Above the table by the sofa a gas-pipe.— Two simple cane chairs complete the furnishings of the room. Cleanliness and the nicest order predominate. MICHAEL KRAMER is sitting on the sofa and, heavily groaning, is signing a number of documents for which KRAUSE, the head janitor, is waiting, cap in hand. KRAUSE is broad and com-fortably stout. KRAMER is a bearded man over fifty, with many white splotches in his black beard and hair. His shoulders are high, his neck is bent forward as if under a yoke. His eyes lie deep in their sockets; they are dark, glowing and at the same time restless. He has long arms and legs; his gait is ungraceful, with long steps. His face is pale and thought-worn. He has a habit of groaning. In his speech there is an unconscious fierceness. He keeps the points of his ugly, highly polished shoes far outward. His garb consists of a long black coat, black waist-coat, black trousers, old-fashioned turn-down collar, topshirt and small, black string-tie, all scrupulously laundered and kept. He has taken off his cuffs and placed them on the window-sill. All in all, his appearance is odd, distinguished, and at first glance repellent rather than attractive. LACHMANN is standing by the window at the left, his back turned to the room. He is waiting and looking out.

KRAMER (*to* LACHMANN). You see, we worry along just as
we used to. (*To* KRAUSE.) So. Give my best regards
to the director. [*He rises, puts the documents together
and hands them to* KRAUSE. *Then he sets about restoring the disturbed order of his little table.*] You're
looking at my poplars, eh?

LACHMANN (*who has been looking at the copper-plate, is
slightly startled and draws himself up*). I beg your
pardon.

KRAUSE. Good-mornin', Mr. Kramer. Good-mornin', Mr.
Lachmann.

LACHMANN. Good-morning, Mr. Krause.

KRAMER. Good-by.   [KRAUSE *exit.*]

KRAMER. Five years ago Böcklin visited me. He stood
by that very window, I tell you . . . and he couldn't
look enough.

LACHMANN. The poplars are really remarkably beautiful.
Years ago, when I first came here, they used to impress
me greatly. The rows stand there with so much dignity, that the grove has almost something of a temple
about it.

KRAMER. That's deceptive, I tell you.

LACHMANN. Oh, but only partly so.— I didn't know, though,
that Böcklin was ever here.

KRAMER. At that time they had the notion that he was to
provide the grand entrance over there, in the Museum
of the province, with mural paintings. In the end one
of their professors did it. Ah, I tell you, there's a
great deal of sinning done about such things.

LACHMANN. Oh, it's boundless!

KRAMER. But let me tell you this: It was always so. Only
one feels especially sorry nowadays. What treasures
the present could lay up for the future with the huge
expenditure and display that are going on in the country today. As it is, the best men must stand aside.
[LACHMANN *has picked up the proof of an etching and*
KRAMER *continues to speak, referring to it.*] That's a

MOONLIGHT NIGHT

From an Etching by Max Klinger

COPYRIGHT THEO STROEFER NÜRNBERG

page for my decorative work. But the plate wasn't properly prepared. The whole thing doesn't suit me yet. I must get a better insight first.

LACHMANN. I tried my hand at etching too, once, but I soon gave it up.

KRAMER. What have you been working at, Lachmann?

LACHMANN. Portraits and landscapes, one thing and another. Not much has come of it, God help me!

KRAMER. Always work, work, work, Lachmann. I tell you, we must work, Lachmann. Or the dry rot'll eat into our living bodies. Look at a life like Böcklin's. The work that man does. But something's accomplished in such a life. Not only what he paints; the whole man! I tell you — work is life, Lachmann.

LACHMANN. I'm thoroughly conscious of that, too.

KRAMER. I'm a wretched creature without my work. In my work I become something.

LACHMANN. With me, unfortunately, the time slips by and I can't get down to any real work.

KRAMER. Why so? Tell me that!

LACHMANN. Because I have other things to do — work which is no work at all.

KRAMER. How am I to understand that, eh?

LACHMANN. I used to be a painter and nothing else. Nowadays I'm forced to sling copy.

KRAMER. What does that mean?

LACHMANN. I write for the papers.

KRAMER. Is that so?

LACHMANN. In other words, Mr. Kramer, I use most of my precious time to earn a little dry bread by writing. There isn't enough to be made for butter too. When a man has a wife and child . . .

KRAMER. A man ought to have a family, Lachmann. That's quite right and quite befitting. And as for your scribbling: Write from your conscience! You have a sense for the genuine in art. You can advance the cause not a little.

LACHMANN. But it's only a kind of Sisyphus labor. No change takes place in the public taste. There you drag up your stone daily . . .

KRAMER. Tell me, what would we be without that?

LACHMANN. And after all, it's a sacrifice of one's very self. Then, too, if one fails to make an impression by one's real work, this . . .

KRAMER. I tell you, it doesn't matter a jot. If my son had become a cobbler and did his duty in that station, I'd honor him, I tell you, just as much. Have you any children?

LACHMANN. One. A son.

KRAMER. Then you've accomplished something, I tell you. What better thing can a man do? Your articles must almost write themselves, eh?

LACHMANN. I can hardly say that, Mr. Kramer.

KRAMER. Duties, duties — they're the main thing. That's what makes a man into a man, I tell you. To realize the nature of life in all its seriousness — that's it. When you've done that, you can rise above it.

LACHMANN. Often enough that's not easy, though.

KRAMER. That ought to be hard, I tell you. It's meant to bring out the manhood in us. A fellow can show, in that struggle, what he's made of. These vagabonds of today think the whole world is a whore's bed! A man must recognize duties, I tell you.

LACHMANN. But surely the duties he owes himself, too.

KRAMER. You're right. Yes, there's no doubt. And a man who recognizes the duties he owes himself, will not fail to recognize those he owes to others. How old is your son?

LACHMANN. Three years old, Mr. Kramer.

KRAMER. I tell you, that time when my boy was born . . . I'd set my heart on a son . . . and I waited fourteen long years till my wife gave birth to one. I tell you, I trembled on that day. And I wrapped up the man-child, I tell you, and I took him into my chamber and

locked the door, and it was like a temple, Lachmann.
I placed him there before God. You fellows don't
know what it is to have a son. I knew it, by the
Eternal! And I thought to myself: Not I, but you!
Not I, I thought to myself, you — perhaps! — (*Bitterly.*)
My son is a good-for-nothing, Lachmann! But I tell
you I would do the same thing over again.

LACHMANN. Surely, Mr. Kramer, he isn't that.

KRAMER (*vehemently and grimly*). I tell you: Let that
be! He's a vagabond and nothing else. But let's not
talk about it any more.— And I'll tell you something,
Lachmann: That's the worm that eats into my life,
gnaws at my marrow! But let's say no more.

LACHMANN. Surely all that will change.

KRAMER (*vehemently, bitterly and fiercely*). It will not
change! It will not change! There's not a sound
fibre in his being! The boy's nature is poisoned at
the root. A bad fellow he is; a vulgar soul. That
can't change; that doesn't change. I tell you, I can
forgive anything, but I can't forgive the fundamentally
ignoble. A vulgar soul revolts me, and that's what
he has, I tell you, a vulgar soul — cowardly and low.
It revolts me. [*He goes to a simple, gray wall closet.*]
And, oh, I tell you, the scamp has gifts. It's enough
to make one want to tear one's hair out! Where we
have to toil and torment ourselves days and nights —
the finished product seems to fall down to him from
heaven. Look here! See his sketches and studies!
Isn't it tragic? He has but to sit down to accomplish
something. Whatever he does has quality and solidity.
Look at the firmness, the perfection of it! One could
shed bitter tears. [*He strides up and down in the foreground repeatedly while* LACHMANN *looks through the
sketches and studies. A knocking at the door is heard.*]
Come in!   [MICHALINE *enters in street costume.*]

MICHALINE. Father, I've come for Lachmann.

KRAMER (*looking over his spectacles*). Eh? And you leave your school in the lurch?

MICHALINE. I've just been correcting.— Lachmann, I've just met your wife. She said she didn't want to grow fast to the restaurant, so she went out to your mother.

KRAMER. Why didn't you bring her with you?

LACHMANN. Her social presentableness isn't exactly of the . . .

KRAMER. Nonsense! What's that mean? Don't understand that.

MICHALINE (*has stepped up behind* LACHMANN *and looks at the study which he is just scrutinizing*). I painted that mill, too, once.

KRAMER. Hm. But differently.

MICHALINE. It was a different view of it.

KRAMER. Yes, yes, I am of the same view.

[LACHMANN *laughs.*]

MICHALINE. Father, that doesn't hit me in the least. If one does the very best that is in one — more than that can't be required.

KRAMER. Girl, you know how things are.

MICHALINE. To be sure, I know. I know very well indeed. Your opinion of me is of the smallest.

KRAMER. Listen, how do you infer that? If Arnold were half as industrious as you are and half as well provided in the matter of brains — the boy would be all of a man. In those respects he simply can't be compared with you. But beyond that — the spark — you haven't it. Every human being should be quite clear about himself. You are that and that is your advantage. For that reason one can speak seriously with you. You've made the best of yourself that can be made by industry and tenacity of purpose and character, and with that you may be satisfied. [*He consults his watch.*] Ten o'clock.— Lachmann, there's no more chance for work this morning. I'm glad that you've come. I'll be glad to go with you later; we could even go and drink a glass of beer somewhere. I must first look in at my class once more and at eleven I have an appointment with my son.

MICHALINE (*earnestly*). Father, aren't you going to show your picture to Lachmann?

KRAMER (*turning swiftly*). No, Michaline! What made you think of it?

MICHALINE. It's quite simple. He heard of it and told me he would like to see it.

KRAMER. Don't bother me with such things. There they all come and want to see my picture. Paint your own pictures, as many as you please! I can't show it to you, Lachmann.

LACHMANN. Mr. Kramer, I didn't mean to be insistent . . .

KRAMER. This is getting too much for me, too much! I've been living with this picture for seven years. Michaline has seen it just once — the boy never asked after it — now Director Müring comes along! No, it's getting too much for me. That won't do, I tell you; that can't be done. Suppose you have a mistress, and everybody wants to get into bed with her . . . a sty is the result, no more, no less. What ardor will you have left? — Lachmann, it isn't possible! I don't like it.

MICHALINE. I don't understand how your illustration applies. That kind of reticence strikes me as weakness.

KRAMER. Think of it as you please! On the other hand, mark well what I say: The original, the genuine, the deep and strong in art grows only in a hermitage — is born only in utter solitude. The artist is always the true hermit. So! And now go and bother me no more.

MICHALINE. It's a pity, father. I'm very sorry. If you barricade yourself in that way, even keep Lachmann out . . . I'm surprised. You deny yourself any possible stimulus. And in addition, if you were to be quite frank you would admit that Director Müring's visit the other day did really refresh you. You were quite jolly afterward.

KRAMER. There's nothing to it. It isn't anything yet. I tell you, don't make me unhappy. You must have something to show before you show it. Do you think it's a jest? I tell you, if a man has the impudence to want to paint that Man with the Crown of Thorns — he needs a lifetime to do it, I tell you. And not a life, I tell you, of revelry or noise, but lonely hours, lonely days, lonely years, I tell you. The artist must be alone with his sorrow and with his God. He must sanctify himself daily, I tell you! Nothing low or mean must be about him or within him! Then, I tell you, the Holy Ghost may come — when a man digs and strives in his solitude. Something may come to him then; the work begins to take shape, I tell you, and one feels it. You rest in the Eternal, I tell you, and it lies before you in quietness and beauty. It comes to you without your knowing. You see the Saviour then and you feel him. But when once the doors begin to slam, Lachmann, then you see him no longer, you feel him no longer. He is gone, I tell you, gone far away.

LACHMANN. I assure you, Mr. Kramer, I'm truly sorry I ever . . .

KRAMER. There's nothing to feel sorry about, I tell you. In that respect each man must go his own way. The place on which you stand is holy ground — that's what you must say to yourself at your work. You others: Out with you! Away with you! There is space enough in the world for your vanity fair. Art is religion. If thou prayest, go into thy secret chamber. Money-changers and chafferers — out from the temple!

[*He turns the key in the entrance door.*]

MICHALINE. We are hardly moneychangers and chafferers.

KRAMER. You are not. God forbid. But for all that and all that! It's getting too much for me. I understand it very well in Lachmann. He wants to see what's behind it all. He's had to swallow big words all this time; he wants to see something tangible at last. There's nothing behind all the talk, I tell you. There's nothing in the old fellow. Sometimes he gets a glimpse, a hint — then he takes a scalpel and scratches it all off again. [*A knocking is heard.*] Some one is knocking. Perhaps later, another time, Lachmann! Come in! — Nothing more to be done this morning, anyhow.— D'you hear? Some one has knocked — Come in!

MICHALINE. But you locked the door, father.

KRAMER. I? When?

MICHALINE. Just now; this moment. Just as you were walking through the room.

KRAMER. Open the door and look.

MICHALINE (*opens the door slightly*). A lady, papa.

KRAMER. A model, probably. I need none.

LIESE BÄNSCH (*still without*). Might I speak to the professor?

MICHALINE. Would you mind telling me your errand?

LIESE BÄNSCH. I'd like to speak to the professor himself.

MICHALINE. What professor do you mean?

KRAMER. Tell her that no professor lives here.

LIESE BÄNSCH. Doesn't Professor Kramer live here?

KRAMER. My name is Kramer. Please come in.

LIESE BANSCH *enters, a slender, good-looking young woman, tricked out in the finery of the half-world.*

LIESE BÄNSCH. If you'll permit me, I'll take the liberty.

KRAMER. Go over into the museum, children. That's where you intended to go. I'll expect you at twelve o'clock, Lachmann. [*He accompanies* LACHMANN *and* MICHALINE *to the door. They leave.*] With whom have I the honor? I'm at your service.

LIESE BÄNSCH (*not without embarrassment, but with a good deal of affectation*). Professor, I'm Liese Bänsch. I've come to you about a delicate matter.

KRAMER. Please sit down. You are a model?

LIESE BÄNSCH. Oh, no, professor; you're mistaken there. I don't have to do things like that, thank heaven. No, I'm not a model, professor.

KRAMER. And I, thank heaven, am no professor. Well then, to what am I to attribute the honor of your visit?

LIESE BÄNSCH. You want to know that, right straight off? You don't mind my getting my breath a bit? I just wore myself out, that's a fact. First I really wanted to turn back at the door downstairs, but then I got up my courage.

KRAMER. As you please. Whenever you're ready.

LIESE BÄNSCH (*has taken a seat, coughs, and taps her rouged face under her veil carefully with her handkerchief*). No, to think that you'd imagine such things of me! It's a good thing that George didn't hear that! My intended, you know, he's in the legal profession, he gets awful angry at the least thing. Do I really look like a model?

KRAMER (*drawing a window-shade*). That depends entirely on who wants to paint you. In certain circumstances any one may be a model. If you imagine, however, that being a model involves a slur, you are guilty of a mistake.

LIESE BÄNSCH. No, you know, I'm really scared. Don't be offended, Mr. Kramer, but I was that frightened of you!

KRAMER. Let's come to the point, however. What brings you here?

LIESE BÄNSCH. I made inquiries about you and they all acted as if you were, well, I don't know what . . . a kind of old Nick or something.

KRAMER. Sincerely obliged. What do you wish? I can give you the assurance that not a hair of your head will be harmed.

LIESE BÄNSCH. And Arnold is so frightened of you, too.

KRAMER (*stunned and confused*). Arnold? What's the meaning of that? What's the fellow's name?

LIESE BÄNSCH (*rises fearfully*). Oh, but what eyes you're making, Mr. Kramer! I'd much rather get out of this. Arnold has just that expression in his eyes . . .

KRAMER. Arnold? I don't know the fellow.

LIESE BÄNSCH (*frightened and soothingly*). Please, Mr. Kramer, I'm not doing anything special. I'd rather let it all go. I've come here without telling my parents . . . it is, as I said, a delicate matter. But I'd rather not speak of it at all.

KRAMER (*mastering himself*). I see you for the first time today. You must be so kind as to pardon me therefore. I have a son who is named Arnold. And if you speak of Arnold Kramer . . .

LIESE BÄNSCH. I'm talking about Arnold Kramer, of course!

KRAMER. Very well, then. That doesn't . . . after all . . . surprise me.—And what have you to tell me about him?

LIESE BÄNSCH. Oh, he's so silly and so crazy and he just won't leave me alone.

KRAMER. H-m. Is that so? In what respect? How do you mean?

LIESE BÄNSCH. Why, he makes me a regular laughing-stock. I can't make him behave sensible any way I try.

KRAMER. Is that so? Yes, that is difficult. I can believe that.

LIESE BÄNSCH. I've said to him: Go home, Arnold! Not he! There he squats all night long.

KRAMER. So he was with you last night?

LIESE BÄNSCH. Why, nobody can get him to move an inch. Papa's tried it, mama's tried it, the gentlemen who are our regular guests have tried it, and I've tried it — but it's no use. There he sits and glowers just the way you do and he won't move or budge till the last guest is gone.

KRAMER. Your father is an innkeeper?

LIESE BÄNSCH. Proprietor of a restaurant.

KRAMER. And who are these gentlemen who are your regular guests?

LIESE BÄNSCH. Assistant Judge Schnabel, architect Ziehn, my intended and several other gentlemen.

KRAMER. And these gentlemen have taken all possible pains, so to speak, to assist him out?

LIESE BÄNSCH. They always call him the marabout. (*Laughing.*) That's a kind of a bird, you know. They think he looks exactly like one. I suppose that's because he's a little deformed . . .

KRAMER. Ah, yes, quite true!—And these gentlemen, I take it, are very jolly?

LIESE BÄNSCH. Awfully! Fit to kill! I should say so! Sometimes it's such a joke—you can hardly imagine it. Enough to make you split your sides, I tell you. You know Arnold always eats an awful lot of the bread that stands around free in little baskets on the tables. So the other day they took the basket and hung it up from the ceiling right over the place where he always sits. You see? But high enough up so he couldn't reach it from where he was. Everybody in the place just fairly roared.

KRAMER. And so my son sits at the same table with these gentlemen?

LIESE BÄNSCH. Oh, no. My intended wouldn't stand that. He just crouches alone in a corner. But sometimes he takes out a leaf of paper and looks over at the gentlemen so spiteful! And they don't like it, of course. Once one of them got up and went over to him and called him to account.

KRAMER. The gentlemen are of the opinion that he ought not to draw?

LIESE BÄNSCH. Yes, because they're such horrid pictures. People can't allow such things, Mr. Kramer. Why, he once showed me a drawing—a little dog, you know, and a lot of big ones after it. It was so vulgar . . . horrible.

KRAMER. Does Arnold pay for what he eats and drinks?

LIESE BÄNSCH. Oh, yes. I didn't come on that account. He drinks a couple of glasses of beer, three at most — and if there wasn't nothing more, Mr. Kramer . . .

KRAMER. But you're a sensitive soul, as it were.— If I understand you correctly, then, my son is a kind of — what shall I call it — a kind of butt in your house, but one that one would rather, after all, be rid of. Furthermore, I may probably assume that neither the gentlemen who are your regular guests — most estimable gentlemen, doubtless — nor yet the beer or the bread of your excellent father form the attraction that draws Arnold to you —?

LIESE BÄNSCH (*coquettishly*). But it really isn't my fault.

KRAMER. No, no, assuredly not. Why should it be? — But what am I to do in the matter?

LIESE BÄNSCH. Mr. Kramer, I'm that scared of him! He lies in wait for me at all corners and then I can't get rid of him for hours and I just feel sometimes, I do declare, as if he might do me some harm.

KRAMER. H-m. Has he ever uttered a definite threat?

LIESE BÄNSCH. No, not exactly. I can't say that. But anyhow, it's in the way he acts. Sometimes I just get frightened all over when I look at him. When he sits that way, too, just brooding, . . . for hours and don't say a word, half the night through, just as if he didn't have good sense! And then, too, when he tells his stories. He tells such awful lies! . . . Ugh! And then, you know, he looks at me so . . .

KRAMER. And you're not drawn to him either, eh?

[*A bell rings.*]

LIESE BÄNSCH. . . . Oh, heavens alive! Surely not!

KRAMER. Very well. Do you wish to meet Arnold here?

LIESE BÄNSCH. For heaven's sake! On no account!

KRAMER. It is exactly eleven o'clock and the bell has rung. Arnold has been ordered to come here at eleven. [*Opening the door of a small side room and ushering* LIESE BÄNSCH *into it.*] Step in here, please. I can assure you that everything in my power will be done. [LIESE BÄNSCH *disappears.* KRAMER *opens the main door and admits* ARNOLD *in whose feeble countenance defiance, repugnance and fear are struggling.*] Wait in the rear; I'll come to you in a moment. [KRAMER *leads* ARNOLD *behind the hangings, closes them and opens the door of the side room.* LIESE *appears. He lays his finger on his lips and points to the hangings.* LIESE *imitates the gesture. He leads her to the main door through which she slips out.* KRAMER *remains standing, groans heavily, grasps his forehead and then begins to walk up and down in the foreground. It is evident that it takes all his will power to become master of his profound emotion and to suppress a moan of spiritual pain. After several struggles he controls himself. He opens the hangings and speaks through them.*] Arnold, I simply wanted to talk to you. [ARNOLD *comes slowly forward. He has a gay colored tie on and betrays other attempts at foppishness.*] Why are you so tricked out?

ARNOLD. How?

KRAMER. I mean your red tie, for instance.

ARNOLD. Why?

KRAMER. I'm not used to seeing such things on you. You had better let them be, Arnold.— Have you made your designs?

ARNOLD. What designs, father? I don't know of any.

KRAMER. H-m. To be capable of forgetting such things! You have forgotten. Well, if it's not too much trouble, perhaps you wouldn't mind trying to think a little.

ARNOLD. Oh, yes; you mean those for the cabinet maker?

KRAMER. Yes, those for the cabinet maker, for all I care. It's not to the purpose what they were for. So I suppose you haven't made much progress with them? Say: No, quite simply, please. Don't think of excuses. But how do you pass your time?

ARNOLD (*feigning astonishment*). I work, father.

KRAMER. What do you work at?

ARNOLD. I draw, I paint—the usual thing.

KRAMER. I thought you were wasting your days. I am glad to know that I've been deceived. Furthermore, I won't keep watch on you any longer. I'm not your gaoler.—And I want to take the opportunity of telling you that, if you have anything on your heart, I am, after all—if you don't mind my saying it—your father. Do you understand? Remember that, please.

ARNOLD. But I haven't anything on my heart, father.

KRAMER. I didn't say you had. I made no such assertion. I said: *If* you have! In that case I might be of some little help to you. I know the world somewhat more thoroughly than you do. I was trying to take a precaution; do you understand?—You were away from home again last night. You are ruining yourself. You are making yourself ill. Take care of your health. A sound body means a sound spirit; a sound life means sound art. Where were you so long yesterday? Never mind; it doesn't concern me after all. I don't want to know what you don't care to tell me. Tell me voluntarily or be silent.

ARNOLD. I was out of town with Alfred Fränkel.

KRAMER. Is that so? Where? In Pirscham, or where?

ARNOLD. No; over by Scheitnig and thereabouts.

KRAMER. And you were both there all night?

ARNOLD. No, later we were at Fränkel's house.

KRAMER. Until four o'clock in the morning.

ARNOLD. Yes, almost until four. Then we took a stroll through the streets.

KRAMER. You and Fränkel? You two alone? Then you're very great friends indeed. And what do you do together when you sit there while other people are in their beds?

ARNOLD. We smoke and talk about art.

KRAMER. Is that so?—Arnold, you're a lost soul!

ARNOLD. Why?

KRAMER. You're a lost soul! You're depraved to the very core.

ARNOLD. You've said that more than once.

KRAMER. Yes, yes; I have been forced to say it to you. I have been forced to say it a hundred times and, what is worse, I have felt it. Arnold, prove to me that I am lying; prove to me that I am doing you wrong! I'll kiss your feet in gratitude!

ARNOLD. It doesn't much matter what I say, I believe . . .

KRAMER. What? That you *are* rotten?

[ARNOLD, *very pale, shrugs his shoulders.*]

KRAMER. And what's to be the end of it all, if that's true?

ARNOLD (*in a cold and hostile voice*). I don't know that myself, father.

KRAMER. But I know! You're going straight to your ruin!

[*He walks about violently, stops at the window, holding his hands behind him and tapping his foot nervously on the floor.* ARNOLD, *his face ashy pale and distorted, grasps his hat and moves toward the door. As he presses the knob of the door,* KRAMER *turns around.*]

KRAMER. Have you nothing else to say to me?

[ARNOLD *releases the knob. He has hardened himself and peers watchfully at his father.*]

KRAMER. Arnold, does nothing stir in you at all this? Do you not feel how we are all in torment for your sake? Say something! Defend yourself! Speak to me as man to man! Or as friend to friend! I am willing! Do I wrong you? Teach me to deal more justly, then; but speak! You can speak out like the rest of us.

Why do you always slink away from me? You know how I despise cowardice! Say: My father is a tyrant. My father torments me and worries me; my father is at me like a fiend! Say that, but say it out openly. Tell me how I can do better by you! I will try to improve, I give you my word of honor. Or do you think that I am in the right in all I say?

ARNOLD (*strangely unmoved and indifferent*). Maybe it's true that you're right.

KRAMER. Very well, if that is your opinion. Won't you, then, try to do better? Arnold, here I give you my hand. There; take it; I want to help you. Let me be your comrade; let me be your friend at the eleventh hour. But don't deceive yourself! The eleventh hour has come; it has come now! Pull yourself together; rise above yourself! You need only to will it and it can be done. Take the first step toward good; the second and third will cost no effort. Will you? Won't you try to be better, Arnold?

ARNOLD (*with feigned surprise*). Yes, but how? In what respect?

KRAMER. In all respects . . .

ARNOLD (*bitterly and significantly*). I don't object. Why should I? I'm not very comfortable in my own skin.

KRAMER. I gladly believe that you're not comfortable. You haven't the blessing of labor. It is that blessing, Arnold, that you must strive for. You have alluded to your person! [*He takes down the death mask of Beethoven.*] Look, look at this mask! Child of God, dig for the treasures of your soul! Do you believe *he* was handsome? Is it your ambition to be a fop? Or do you believe that God withdraws himself from you because you are near-sighted and not straight? You can have so much beauty within you that the fops round about you must seem beggars in comparison.— Arnold, here is my hand. Do you hear? Confide in me this one time. Don't hide yourself from me; be open with me — for your own sake, Arnold! What do I care, after all, where you were last night? But tell me, do you hear, tell me for your sake! Perhaps you will learn to see me as I truly am. Well, then: Where were you last night?

ARNOLD (*after a pause, deathly pale, with visible struggles*). Why . . . I've told you already, father.

KRAMER. I have forgotten what you said. So: Where were you? I don't ask you in order to punish you. I ask you for the sake of truth itself! Prove yourself truthful! That is all!

ARNOLD (*with bold front, defiantly*). Why, I was with Alfred Fränkel.

KRAMER. Is that so?

ARNOLD (*wavering again*). Why, where should I have been?

KRAMER. You are not my son! You can't be my son! Go! Go! My gorge rises at you! My gorge . . .!

[ARNOLD *slinks out at once.*]

ACT III

The restaurant of BANSCH. *A moderately sized tap-room with old German decorations. Wainscoting. Tables and chairs of stained wood. To the left a neat bar with a marble top and highly polished faucets. Behind the bar a stand for cordial bottles, glasses, etc. Within this stand a small square window to the kitchen. To the left, behind the bar, a door that leads to the inner rooms. A large show window with neat hangings; next to it a glass door opening on the street. To the right a door to the adjoining room. Twilight.*

LIESE BANSCH, *neatly and tastefully dressed, with long white apron, comes slowly through the low door behind the bar. She looks up carelessly from her crocheting work and perceives* ARNOLD *who is sitting over his glass of beer at a table in the foreground to the right. Shaking her head she continues to crochet.*

ARNOLD (*very pale, tapping gently and nervously with his foot, stares over at her as if in ambush and says*): Good evening.

[LIESE BÄNSCH *sighs ostentatiously and turns away.*]

ARNOLD (*with emphasis*). Good evening. [LIESE *does not reply.*] Well, if you don't want to answer, you needn't. I'm not exactly crazy about it. [*Continues to regard her with feverish excitement.*] But why do you open a hole like this if you're going to be rude to your customers?

LIESE BÄNSCH. I'm not rude. Leave me alone.

ARNOLD. I said good evening to you.

LIESE BÄNSCH. And I answered you.

ARNOLD. That isn't true.

LIESE BÄNSCH. Is that so? Very well, then! Your opinion don't bother me.

[*Pause.*]

[ARNOLD *shoots a paper arrow at* LIESE *from a rubber sling.* LIESE BÄNSCH *shrugs her shoulders arrogantly and contemptuously.*]

ARNOLD. D'you think that kind of thing impresses me?

LIESE BÄNSCH. I suppose I'll think what I please.

ARNOLD. I pay for my beer as well as anybody else. D'you understand me? I want you to remember that!—Does one have to wear a monocle here?—I'd like to know who frequents this grand place of yours, after all? D'you think I'm going to be driven out? By those Philistines? Not at all!

LIESE BÄNSCH (*threatening*). Well, you better not carry on too much!

ARNOLD. Aha! I'd like to see one of them do anything about me. He'd be surprised, I give you my word. Provided he had time left to be surprised.

[LIESE BÄNSCH *laughs.*]

ARNOLD. If any one touches me—d'you understand—there'll be a bang!

LIESE BÄNSCH. Arnold, some fine day soon I'll give notice to the police, if you go on making such threats.

ARNOLD. What about?—If some one touches me, I say!—And if I box their ears that'll bang too.

LIESE BÄNSCH. Don't insult our guests.

ARNOLD (*laughs maliciously to himself, sips his beer and says:*) Bah! How do these nonentities concern me!

LIESE BÄNSCH. Why, what are you, that you act so high and mighty? What have you accomplished, tell me that!

ARNOLD. Unfortunately you don't understand that.

LIESE BÄNSCH. Oh, yes, anybody could say that. Go ahead first and do something! And when you've shown what you can do, then you can abuse the others.

[*Pause.*]

ARNOLD. Liese, listen to me. I'll explain all that to you.

LIESE BÄNSCH. Oh, pshaw! You criticize everybody! According to you Mr. Quantmeyer isn't the right kind of lawyer, and Mr. Ziehn is no architect! Why that's pure rot!

ARNOLD. On the contrary, it's the solemn truth. In this place, of course, a plaster slinger like that can put on airs even if he hasn't a notion of what art is. If he goes among artists he doesn't count for more than a cobbler.

LIESE BÄNSCH. But you're an artist, I suppose? (*Pityingly.*) Lord, Lord!

ARNOLD. Surely I am an artist; that's just what I am! All you have to do is to come to my studio . . .

LIESE BÄNSCH. I'll take good care not to do that . . .

ARNOLD. You just go to Munich and ask the professors there about me. They're people of international fame! And they have a most thorough respect for me.

LIESE BÄNSCH. Well, it's you who do the boasting, not Mr. Ziehn . . .

ARNOLD. They respect me and they know why. I can do more than all these fellows together . . . with one hand. Ten thousand times more than they — including my own father.

LIESE BÄNSCH. Anyhow, it's you who boast and not Mr. Ziehn. If you were really such a very big man you'd look a bit different, I think.

ARNOLD. How?

LIESE BÄNSCH. How? Well, that's simple enough: famous painters make a great deal of money.

ARNOLD (*vehemently*). Money? And do you suppose I haven't made money? Money like dirt. Just ask! All you need do is to ask my father! Go and ask him; I give you my word.

LIESE BÄNSCH. Well, what do you do with all that money?

ARNOLD. I? Just wait till I'm of age. If a fellow has a miserly father—? Liese, do be a bit decent.

LIESE BÄNSCH. Fritz!

FRITZ (*starts up from his sleep*). Yes!

LIESE BÄNSCH. Fritz! Go into the kitchen, will you? New champagne glasses have come, and I believe the gentlemen are going to drink champagne today.

FRITZ. Certainly! With pleasure, Miss Bänsch.

[*Exit.*]

[LIESE BÄNSCH *stands by the bar, her back turned to* ARNOLD, *takes several hairpins from her hair and arranges it anew.*]

ARNOLD. You do that in a dashing way!

LIESE BÄNSCH. You can be as vain as you please. [*Suddenly she turns around and observes* ARNOLD *glaring at her from over his glasses.*] Dear Lord, there he glares again!

ARNOLD. Liese!

LIESE BÄNSCH. I'm not " Liese " to you!

ARNOLD. Oh, you little Liese, if you'd only be a bit sensible. You good for nothing little bar maid! I feel so awful horrible.

[LIESE BÄNSCH *laughs, half amused, half jeering.*]

ARNOLD (*more passionately*). Laugh, laugh if you can! Laugh! Go on laughing! Maybe I am really ridiculous. On the outside, I mean; not within. If you could look within me you'd see that I could scorch all those fellows off the earth.

LIESE BÄNSCH. Arnold, don't excite yourself. I believe
you; I'm willing to believe you. But in the first place
you're far too young, and in the second, third, fourth,
fifth place . . . why, it's just madness, child! Now
listen and be sensible, won't you? I do feel sorry for
you. But what can I do?

ARNOLD (*moaning heavily*). It's like a pestilence in my
blood. . . .

LIESE BÄNSCH. Nonsense!— Get up on that bench and hand
me down the pail. [ARNOLD *does it groaning.*] I'm
just a girl like many others. There! Come on! [*She
has stretched out her hand to him; he grasps it and
jumps down. He holds her hand and as he bends down
to kiss it,* LIESE *withdraws it.*] Can't be done, little
boy! That's it! You can get ten others instead of me,
my dear.

ARNOLD. Liese, what do you want me to do for you —
plunder, rob on the highway, steal? What? What?

LIESE BÄNSCH. You are kindly to leave me alone.

[*The door is heard opening in the next room.*]

LIESE BÄNSCH (*listens. With suddenly changed demeanor
she withdraws behind the bar and calls into the
kitchen:*) Fritz! Customers! Quick, hurry up!

[*The door resounds again and a noisy company is
heard to enter the adjoining room.*]

ARNOLD. Please: I would like another glass of beer. But
I'm going into the other room.

LIESE BÄNSCH (*adopting a formal tone*). But you're very
comfortable here, Mr. Kramer.

ARNOLD. Yes, but I can draw much better inside.

LIESE BÄNSCH. Arnold, you know there'll only be trouble
again. Do be sensible and stay here.

ARNOLD. For nothing in the world, Miss Bänsch.

ARCHITECT ZIEHN *enters in a very jolly mood.*

ZIEHN. Hurrah, Miss Lizzie, the crowd is here, the whole
moist and merry brotherhood. What are you doing?

How are you? Your intended is already languishing after you! [*He observes* ARNOLD.] Well, well, the deuce! I beg your pardon!

LIESE BÄNSCH. Fritz! Fritz! Our gentlemen are here!

ZIEHN (*cuts the end of his cigar on the cigar-cutter*). Fritz! Beer! Beer's what's wanted, in the devil's name!—How's your papa?

LIESE BÄNSCH. Oh, not at all well. We've had to call in the doctor twice today.

ASSISTANT JUDGE SCHNABEL *enters.*

SCHNABEL. Well, sir, are we going to have a game of skat tonight?

ZIEHN. I thought we were going to throw dice today and drink a bottle of champagne.

SCHNABEL (*raises his arms, sings and prances*).

"Lizzie had a little birdie,
And a cage to keep it in."

Don't let your friend in there perish with longing.

ZIEHN (*softly, with a side glance at* ARNOLD). He'll get his share.

SCHNABEL (*noticing* ARNOLD, *also furtively*). Ah, yes! There is our stony guest—our pocket edition of Raphael.—Please let me have a great deal of bread, Miss Lizzie! With my order I want a great deal of bread.

[FRITZ *has entered and busies himself behind the bar.*]

LIESE BÄNSCH. What was your order?

SCHNABEL. Oh, yes. A veal chop with paprika and bread. A tremendous lot of bread, dear Lizzie. You know what huge quantities of bread I eat.

ZIEHN. They should hang the bread-basket out of your reach, then.

VON KRAUTHEIM *enters; he is a law-student of long standing.*

VON KRAUTHEIM. For heaven's sake, where's the stuff, Fritz?

FRITZ. Gentlemen, we've just broached a new keg.

SCHNABEL (*peers at the beer faucet through his monocle*). Nothing for the present but air, air, air! Nothing but air!

[ARNOLD *takes his hat, rises, and goes into the adjoining room.*]

VON KRAUTHEIM. Now the air is not contaminated, at least. It's air still, but pure air.

SCHNABEL (*sings*).

"You're a crazy kid
    Berlin is your home."

Thank heaven, he fleeth, he departeth from hence!

FRITZ. Don't you believe that. He just goes in there to be sitting where you gentlemen sit.

LIESE BÄNSCH (*affectedly*). I think that's really ridiculous.

ZIEHN. Let's take up our rest in this room.

VON KRAUTHEIM. Well now, look here, I beg of you, that would be the last straw for us to run away from any monkey that happens to turn up.

QUANTMEYER *enters. Dashing exterior. Monocle.*

QUANTMEYER. Good evening. How are you, my dear? [*He takes hold of* LIESE's *hands; she turns her head aside.*] That wretched fellow Kramer is here again too . . .

SCHNABEL. And I would like to have you see where that fine fellow passes his time! Early yesterday morning I saw him — a sight for gods and men, I assure you — 'way out, in the vilest kind of a hole, in an incredible condition. When he leaves here, he just begins.

QUANTMEYER. Are you angry at me, sweetheart, tell me!

LIESE BÄNSCH (*frees herself from him, laughs, and calls out through the window into the kitchen*). Veal chop with paprika for Mr. Schnabel.

SCHNABEL. But bread, too — a lot of bread. Don't forget that. A tremendous lot of bread — a gigantic lot!

[*General laughter.*]

FRITZ (*enters, carrying four full beer glasses*). Here is the beer, gentlemen!

[*He goes into the adjoining room.* ZIEHN, SCHNABEL, *and* VON KRAUTHEIM *follow the waiter.*]

[*Pause.*]

QUANTMEYER. Look here, you kitten, why are you so spiteful today?

LIESE BÄNSCH. Me? Spiteful? Do I act spiteful? You don't say so?

QUANTMEYER. Come, you little devil, don't pout. Come, be sensible and hold up your little snout quickly. And day after tomorrow you can come to see me again. Day after tomorrow is Sunday, as you know. My landlady and her husband'll both be out. Not a mouse at home, I give you my word.

LIESE BÄNSCH (*still resisting a little*). Are we engaged to be married or not?

QUANTMEYER. To be sure we are! Why shouldn't we be, I'd like to know? I'm independent; I can marry whom I please.

LIESE BÄNSCH (*permits herself to be kissed, taps him lightly on the cheek, and then escapes from his arms*). Oh, go on! I don't believe a word you say any more.

QUANTMEYER (*about to follow her*). Kiddie, what makes you so pert today?

The street door opens and MICHALINE *enters.*

LIESE BÄNSCH. Sh!

QUANTMEYER (*with feigned innocence, cutting the end of his cigar*). You just wait, Lizzie; I'll have my revenge.

[*Exit into the other room.* MICHALINE *comes farther forward into the tap-room.* LIESE BÄNSCH *has taken up her position behind the bar and observes.*]

LIESE BÄNSCH (*after a brief pause*). Are you looking for any one, Miss?

MICHALINE. Is this the restaurant of Bänsch?

LIESE BÄNSCH. Certainly.

MICHALINE. Thank you. In that case it's all right. The friends whom I'm expecting will be here.

[*She is about to go into the adjoining room.*]

LIESE BÄNSCH. Only the gentlemen who come every night are in there.

MICHALINE. Ah? I'm expecting a young couple. So I'll sit down somewhere here.

LIESE BÄNSCH. Here, please? Or here? Or, maybe, over there?

MICHALINE (*sitting down on a bench that runs along the wall*). Thank you, I'll sit down here.—A small glass of beer.

LIESE BÄNSCH (*to* FRITZ, *who is just returning*). Fritz, a small glass of beer. [*She leans back, assumes a very decent and dignified air, adjusts details of her toilet, observes* MICHALINE *with great interest, and then says:*] The weather is very bad out, isn't it?

MICHALINE (*taking off first her overshoes, then her coat and finally her hat*). Yes, I'm grateful that I put on my galoshes. It looks very bad in the streets.

[*She sits down, straightens her hair and dries her face.*]

LIESE BÄNSCH. May I offer you a comb? I'd be pleased to fetch you one.

[*She approaches and hands her comb to* MICHALINE.]

MICHALINE. You are very good. Thank you.

[*She takes the comb and busies herself rearranging her hair.*]

LIESE BÄNSCH (*gathering some strands of* MICHALINE'S *hair*). Let me help you, won't you?

MICHALINE. Thank you. I'll be able to adjust it now.

[LIESE BÄNSCH *returns to the bar and continues to observe* MICHALINE *with interest.* FRITZ *brings the beer and places it in front of* MICHALINE. *Then he takes up a box of cigars and carries it into the next room. Loud laughter is heard from within.*]

LIESE BÄNSCH (*shrugs her shoulders and speaks not without affectation*). Oh, yes; there's nothing to be done about that. The gentlemen can't get on any other way. [*She comes forward a little again.*] You see, I don't like all this: the noise and the roughness and all that. But you see, my father was taken sick; my mother can't stand the smoke and, of course, she nurses papa. So what is there left to do? I had to come in and help out.

MICHALINE. Surely; that was your duty in the circumstances.

LIESE BÄNSCH. And, anyhow, I'm young, don't you see? And there are some very nice gentlemen among them, really well-educated, nice gentlemen. And you do learn a great deal from people.

MICHALINE. Surely. Of course you do.

LIESE BÄNSCH. But do you know what is horrid? (*Suddenly confidential.*) They can't get along without quarreling. First they drink and then they quarrel. Heavens, I have to be careful then! Sometimes I'm supposed to be too pleasant to one of them, or not to give my hand to another, or not touch a third with my arm. Half the time I don't know that I've done all that. And another one I'm not to look at, and another I'm to get out of the place. And you can't please every one, can you? But oh, in just a minute, they'll all be fighting.

VOICES (*from the adjoining room*). Liese! Liese! Where are you keeping yourself?

LIESE BÄNSCH (*to* MICHALINE). I'll stay with you; I won't go in. I'm never comfortable any more with them. One of the gentlemen is my intended. Now, I leave it to you: that isn't very nice, is it? Of course, he wants to take liberties with me. Now I ask any one . . . that isn't possible?

MICHALINE. Surely he can't demand such things of you, your intended.

LIESE BÄNSCH. No, no, and of course he doesn't demand it, but even so . . . [*She looks up again as* FRITZ *returns with the empty beer glasses.*] Do take my advice and don't get mixed up with men admirers.

[LACHMANN *enters from the street, observes* MICHALINE *at once and holds out his hand to her.*]

LACHMANN (*hanging up his overcoat and hat*). Michaline, we've grown real old.

MICHALINE (*amused*). Heavens, how suddenly you come out with that!

LACHMANN. I have, at least; I. Not you, but I. Surely so if I compare myself with your father.

[*He sits down.*]

MICHALINE. Just why?

LACHMANN. There are reasons and reasons.— D'you remember when I entered the school of art here . . . by heaven! . . . And look at me today. I've advanced backward a bit!

MICHALINE. But why? That's the question after all: Why?

LACHMANN. Well, in those days . . . what didn't a fellow want to do? Reconcile God and the devil! What didn't we feel equal to doing? What a noble and exalted idea of ourselves didn't we have? And now? Today we're pretty well bankrupt.

MICHALINE. Why bankrupt? In respect of what?

LACHMANN. In respect of a good many things and a few more. Our illusions, for instance.

MICHALINE. H-m. I'm under the impression we get along very fairly without them! Do you still lay so much weight on that?

LACHMANN. Yes. Everything else is doubtful. The power to nurse illusions, Michaline — that is the best possession in the world. If you think it over, you'll agree with me.

MICHALINE. What you really mean is imagination. Without that, of course, no artist can exist.

LACHMANN. Yes. Imagination and faith in its workings. —A pint of red wine please, the same as yesterday.

LIESE BÄNSCH (*who has the wine in readiness and has opened the bottle*). I recognized you again right away. [*She places the bottle and glass in front of* LACHMANN.]

LACHMANN. Is that so? Very happy, I'm sure. If I had the necessary wherewithal we'd be drinking champagne today.

[*Pause.*]

MICHALINE. You go from one extreme to another, Lachmann. What connection is there between these things?

LACHMANN. There isn't any. That's the joke of the whole business.—It's all over with me, that's all. There you are! All that's left is to have a jolly time. [*Laughter and noise resound again from the adjoining room.* LIESE BÄNSCH *shakes her head disapprovingly and goes in.*]

MICHALINE. You're strangely excited.

LACHMANN. Do you think so? Really? Well, usually my soul's asleep. I thank God that I'm a bit wrought up. Unfortunately, it won't last very long.—"Age with his stealing steps!" We're dying slowly.

MICHALINE. You don't impress me as being so old, Lachmann.

LACHMANN. Very well, Michaline. Then marry me!

MICHALINE (*surprised and amused*). Well, hardly that! I wouldn't go that far. We're both really too old for such things.—But it seems to me that so long as you keep your good humor, as you seem to do, you can't be so badly off.

LACHMANN. Oh, yes, I am, though; I am! I am! But the less said about that the better.

MICHALINE. Tell me: What has depressed you so?

LACHMANN. Nothing. Because I'm not really depressed. Only I've looked back over the past today and I've seen that we're really no longer among the living.

MICHALINE. But why? I must ask you again.

LACHMANN. Fishes are adapted to a life in water. Every living thing needs its proper atmosphere. It's just the same in the life of the spirit. And I've been thrust into the wrong atmosphere. When that happens, whether you want to or not, you must breathe it in. And then your real self is suffocated. You cease to have the sensation of your own individuality; you're no longer acquainted with yourself; you know nothing about yourself any longer.

MICHALINE. In that case I seem to be better off in my voluntary loneliness.

LACHMANN. You're better off here for other reasons — all of you. You see nothing and you hear nothing of the great philistine orgy of the metropolis. When once you've sunk into that, it whirls you hither and thither through — everything!—When one is young, one wants to go out into the wide world. I wish I had stayed at home.— The world is not wide, at all, Michaline! It is no wider anywhere than here! Nor is it smaller here than elsewhere. He for whom it is too small, must make it wider for himself. That's what your father has done here, Michaline.—As I was saying, when I entered the art school here, long ago, in spring . . .

MICHALINE. It was in autumn.

LACHMANN. Nothing but spring remains in my memory. Ah, weren't we liberated from the philistine yoke. And it really seemed in those days . . . we could truly say . . . the world opened itself to us, great and wide. Today one is back again in it all—buried in domesticity and marriage.

MICHALINE. I seem still to see you standing there, Lachmann, with your fair, silken hair—there, in the passage, do you remember, at father's door? Father's studio was still upstairs in those days; not in the small wing by itself. Do you remember that or have you forgotten?

LACHMANN. Forgotten? I? One doesn't forget such things. I've forgotten nothing that happened then. The least little detail still clings to my memory. But those were our great days.— It isn't possible to express — to come near to expressing — the mysterious change that came over us then. A fellow had been a flogged urchin: suddenly he became a knight of the spirit.

MICHALINE. Not every one felt that as you did, dear Lachmann. Many felt oppressed by father's personality.

LACHMANN. Yes. But what kind were they! There wasn't one who had a grain of promise, but he ennobled him at one stroke. For he opened the world of heroes to us. That was enough. He deemed us worthy of striving to emulate their work. He made us feel toward the lords of the realm of art, that we and they were of one blood. And so a divine pride came upon us, Michaline!— Ah, well.— I drink to you! How do the fairy tales say: It *was* — once upon a time! [*He observes that* MICHALINE *has no glass and turns to* FRITZ *who is about to carry champagne into the other room.*] Let us have another glass, please.

[FRITZ *brings it at once and then hurries off with the champagne.*]

MICHALINE. Something very special must have happened to you, Lachmann.

LACHMANN (*filling her glass*). I have seen your father's picture.

MICHALINE. Is that so? You have been with him?

LACHMANN. Yes. Just now. I came straight here.

MICHALINE. Well, and did the picture impress you so deeply?

LACHMANN. As deeply as possible. Yes.

MICHALINE. Quite honestly?

LACHMANN. Honestly. Honestly. Without doubt.

MICHALINE. And you are not at all disappointed?

LACHMANN. No. No. By no means.—I know what you mean and why you ask. But all art is fragmentary. What there is, is beautiful; beautiful and deeply moving. And all that is yet unattained but felt, Michaline, is equally so. The final expression in which all is to culminate—therein one recognizes most fully what your father is.—The great failure can be more meaningful—we see it in the noblest works—can move us more deeply, can lead us to loftier heights—deeper into immensity—than the clearest success.

MICHALINE. And what was father's state of mind about other things?

LACHMANN. He dragged me over the coals thoroughly; a futile process, unfortunately. But do you know, if a fellow were to close his eyes and let those great reprimands and encouragements pour down upon him he might imagine, if he cared to, that it is still the first storm of his spiritual spring and that he might still grow to touch the stars.

ZIEHN and SCHNABEL *enter. They are both tipsy, speak loudly and freely and then again whisper suddenly as if communicating secrets, yet distinctly enough for all to hear. Laughter in the next room.*

ZIEHN. Fritz, hurry! Another bottle of that extra dry! Eight marks per bottle—small matter! This thing is beginning to amuse me.

SCHNABEL. A deuce of a fellow, this Quantmeyer, eh? He's got notions like I don't know what!

ZIEHN (*laughing*). I thought I'd roll under the table!

SCHNABEL (*looking at* MICHALINE). Fritz, is the circus in town again?

FRITZ (*busy with the champagne bottle*). Why, your honor? I didn't hear nothing.

SCHNABEL. Why? Why? Why, you can almost smell it! Don't you scent the stables?

ZIEHN. To the noble art of bareback riding! May it flourish!

Von Krautheim (*enters on his way to the bar. In passing he says to* Ziehn *and* Schnabel). Man and woman created he them. Which is that?

Ziehn. Better go and investigate. (*Whispering to* Schnabel.) Tell me, how is that about Quantmeyer? Is that fellow really a lawyer? I can't make head or tail of it all. What's he live on?

Schnabel (*shrugging his shoulders*). Money, I suppose.

Ziehn. Yes, but who gives it to him?

Schnabel. He's got plenty of it, anyhow, and that's the main thing.

Ziehn. And this talk about an engagement, d'you believe in that?

Schnabel. Ziehn! You must be pretty far gone!

Ziehn. Well, in that case the girl is damned stupid. A girl may be a bit of a fool — all right! But, look here, to throw herself away . . . well! [*He whispers something into* Schnabel's *ear upon which both break out into ribald laughter and blow great clouds of smoke. Then* Ziehn *continues.*] I want you to look around here. [*He draws his arm through* Schnabel's *and leads him, regardless of* Lachmann *and* Michaline, *close up to their table. Without asking pardon, he presses close up to them and points with outstretched arm and loud and boastful speech to the details of the room.*] This whole business here — I designed it all. Made it all myself: wainscoting, ceiling, bar, whole thing! Designed it all myself; all my work. That's the reason I like to come here. We've got some taste, eh? Don't you think so? Damned tasteful tap-room, this! [*He releases* Schnabel *and lights a cigar with a match which he strikes with rude circumstantiality against the table at which* Lachmann *and* Michaline *are sitting. Again the sound of laughter is heard from the other room.* Fritz *carries in the champagne.* Ziehn *turns around and says:*] He'll end by driving that young man quite crazy.

[Schnabel *shrugs his shoulders.*]

ZIEHN. Come on in. It's starting again.

[*Both go into the adjoining room.* MICHALINE *and* LACHMANN *look at each other significantly. Pause.*]

LACHMANN (*taking his cigar-case from his pocket. Drily*). These types are rather deficient in interest. . . . Do you mind if I smoke a little?

MICHALINE (*somewhat disquieted*). Not at all.

LACHMANN. Will you smoke too?

MICHALINE. No, thank you, not here.

LACHMANN. Yes, there's no doubt, we've made admirable progress—we wonderful fellows of this generation! Or, tell me, do you doubt it?

MICHALINE. I don't think it's very comfortable here.

LACHMANN (*smoking*). And if you were to take the wings of the morning, you would not escape these or their kind.—Heavens, how we started out in life! And to-day we chop fodder for a society of this kind. There's not a point concerning which one thinks as they do. They stamp into the mud all that is pure and bare. The meanest rag, the most loathsome covering, the most wretched tatter is pronounced sacred. And we must hold our tongues and work ourselves weary for this crowd.—Michaline, I drink to your father! And to art that illuminates the world.—In spite of everything and everything!—[*They clink their glasses.*]— Ah, if I were five years younger than I am today. . . . I would have secured one thing which is now lost to me, alas, and then much would look brighter now.

MICHALINE. Do you know what is sometimes hardest to bear?

LACHMANN. What?

MICHALINE. Among friends?

LACHMANN. Well, what?

MICHALINE. The command not to divert each other from their erring ways! Well, then, again: Once upon a time . . . !

[*She touches her glass significantly to his.*]

LACHMANN. Surely. Surely. I deserve your reproach. That time is irrevocably past. Once upon a time we were so near it . . . Oh, you may shake your head today. I need but have beckoned to you then.

[*Hallooing and laughter in the next room.*]

MICHALINE (*grows pale and starts up*). Lachmann, listen! Did you hear that?

LACHMANN. Yes; does that really excite you, Michaline?

MICHALINE. I really don't know myself why it should. I suppose it's connected with the fact that the relations between father and Arnold are very much strained just now and that I have been worrying over it.

LACHMANN. Yes, yes. But just how, just why does that occur to you here?

MICHALINE. I don't know. Wouldn't it be better for us to go? Oh, yes, your wife! Oh, yes, we will wait, of course. But really, I have an uncanny feeling here.

LACHMANN. Don't pay any attention to that vulgar crowd.

[LIESE BÄNSCH *comes from the next room.*]

LIESE BÄNSCH. O dear Lord! No, no, such things! Those gentlemen drink so much champagne that they don't know what they're doing any longer. I tell you, it's a miserable business.

[*Unembarrassed, she sits down at* LACHMANN'S *and* MICHALINE'S *table. Her great excitement makes it clear that some incident has taken place which really annoys her.*]

LACHMANN. I dare say the gentlemen are not very tactful in their behavior.

LIESE BÄNSCH. Oh, they're not so bad as far as that goes. They're decent enough. But you see, there's a young fellow, they just make him . . . [*Imitating what she is trying to describe she lets her head hang back, shakes it in a kind of unconsciousness and makes wild gestures with her hands.*] . . . They make him . . . oh, I don't know what!

LACHMANN. I suppose that is your betrothed?

LIESE BÄNSCH (*acts as though shaken with cold, looks down upon her bosom and pulls the laces straight*). Oh, no, he's just a foolish fellow that's taken all kinds of silly things into his head. The young fool is no concern of mine, is he? I wish he'd go where he belongs! [*To* MICHALINE.] Or would you stand it if some one always sat there like a marabout? I can do what I please, can't I? What do I care for a spy like that! [*She looks up in her excitement.*] And, more'n that, my intended is drunk; and if he wants to get drunk I'd thank him to do it elsewhere and not here.

[*She crouches in a corner behind the bar.*]

LACHMANN. You may imagine how the contrast impresses me: your father in his studio and here this — let us say, this noble company.— And if you imagine his picture, in addition, the solemn, restful picture of the Christ, and imagine it in this atmosphere in all its sublime quietude and purity — it gives you a strange feeling . . . most strange.— I'm glad my other half isn't here. I was actually afraid of that.

MICHALINE. If we only knew whether she is coming. Otherwise I'd propose . . . Do you feel at ease here?

LACHMANN (*replacing his cigar-case in his overcoat pocket*). Oh, yes. Since we clinked our glasses awhile ago, I do. In spite of everything and everything. For if two people can say, as we have said: *Once* upon a time! . . . something of that old time is not quite dead, and to that remnant we must drink again.

After a last outburst of laughter, there takes place in the adjoining room, with growing boisterousness, the following colloquy:

QUANTMEYER. What's your name? What are you? What? Why d'you always sit here and glare at us? Eh? And stare at us? Why? What? It annoys you, eh, if I kiss my intended? Is that it? Well, d'you think I'm going to ask you for permission? Why, you're, you're crazy! Crazy! That's what you are!

VOICES (*of the others amid confused laughter*). Give him a cold douche! A cold douche! That's what he needs!

QUANTMEYER. Can't I show my own garter here? Do you think that I may not? [*Laughter.*]

LACHMANN. That seems to be a nice crowd, I must say.

QUANTMEYER. So you think I oughtn't to, eh? Well, I wear lady's garters. That's all. And if it isn't mine, then it isn't. Maybe it's even Lizzie's, come to think of it! [*Laughter.*]

LIESE BÄNSCH (*to* MICHALINE *and* LACHMANN). He lies. Oh, what meanness to lie so. And that fellow pretends to be my intended!

QUANTMEYER. What's that? What? All right! Come on! Come ahead! I don't care if you look like a chalk wall, my boy, that's not going to upset me a little bit! A dauber like that! A sign painter! Just say one more word and out you fly! You can all depend on it!

LIESE BÄNSCH (*hastily and confused in her overeagerness*). It all came about this way, you know . . . You mustn't think that I'm to blame for all this scandalous business. But it happened this way. Just as I'm going to tell you. My intended, you know, he's just a bit tipsy and so he kept pinching my arm because they'd all made up their minds that they'd make him jealous . . .

LACHMANN. Whom did they want to make jealous?

LIESE BÄNSCH. The young fellow that I was talking about. I've been to see his father about him. What haven't I tried to do? But nothing does any good! He comes here and sits in a corner and carries on till things happen this way.

LACHMANN. What exactly does he do?

LIESE BÄNSCH. Why, nothing, really. He just sits there and watches all the time. But that isn't very nice, is it? He needn't be surprised if they try to scare and worry him out in the end. [QUANTMEYER *is heard speaking again.*] There you are. It's starting up again. I'm really going up to father. I don't know what to do no more.

QUANTMEYER. D'you hear what I said to you just now? You didn't? You forgot it, eh? Well, I'll say it again, word for word: I can kiss my intended how I want to — where I want to — when I want to! I'd like to see the devil himself come and prevent me. There! Now you just say one more word, and when you've said it you'll be flying out at the end of my boot!

LIESE BÄNSCH. Oh, goodness me! And that fellow pretends to be my intended! And then he goes and tells such lies and behaves that way!

[*From a sudden violent outcry of the voices in the next room the following words are distinguishable:*]

ZIEHN. Hold on, my good fellow, that's not the way we do business!

SCHNABEL. What's that? What? Call the police! Put that scamp in jail!

VON KRAUTHEIM. Take it away, Quantmeyer. No use fooling!

QUANTMEYER. Try it! Just try! I advise you!

ZIEHN. Take it away from him!

SCHNABEL. Grab it! One, two, three.

QUANTMEYER. Put it down! Do you hear? Put it down, I tell you!

ZIEHN. Are you going to put that thing down or not?

SCHNABEL. You see that fellow, just simply an anarchist.

[*A brief, silent struggle begins in the next room.*]

MICHALINE (*has suddenly jumped up in inexplicable dread and grasps her garments*). Lachmann, I beg of you. Come, come away from here.

ZIEHN. There, fellows, I've got it! Now we've got you.

SCHNABEL. Hold him! Hold the scoundrel!

[ARNOLD, *deathly pale, rushes madly in and out at the street door.* ZIEHN, SCHNABEL *and* VON KRAUTHEIM *pursue him with the cry:* Hold him! Stop him! Get hold of him! *They run out into the street after him and disappear. Their cries and the cries of several passersby are still heard for some moments. Then, growing fainter and fainter, the sounds die away.*]

MICHALINE (*as if stunned*). Arnold! Wasn't that Arnold?

LACHMANN. Don't speak.

QUANTMEYER *and* THE WAITER *enter.*

QUANTMEYER (*exhibiting a small revolver*). You see, Lizzie, that's the kind of a scoundrel he is. I wish you'd come and look at this thing. Dirt cheap article no doubt, but it could have done harm enough.

LIESE BÄNSCH. I wish you'd leave me alone.

FRITZ. Beggin' your pardon, if you please. But I don't hold with servin' customers who pull out revolvers and put them down next to their glasses.

LIESE BÄNSCH. If you don't want to, you don't have to — that's all.

LACHMANN (*to* FRITZ). Did the gentleman threaten you?

QUANTMEYER (*regards* LACHMANN *with a look of official suspicion*). Oho! *Did* he? The *gentleman!* Maybe you doubt it! By God, that's a fine state of affairs! Maybe it's we who'll have to give an account of ourselves!

LACHMANN. I merely ventured to address a question to the waiter — not to you.

QUANTMEYER. You ventured, did you? Who are you, anyhow? Have you any reason to interfere? Maybe you're related to that fine little product, eh? Then we could make a clean sweep of the crowd, so to speak.— The gentleman! [*Laughing derisively.*] I think he has enough for today, the gentleman! I think that lesson'll stick in his mind. But do you imagine the coward defended himself . . .

MICHALINE (*awakening from her stunned condition arises and, as if beside herself, walks up to* QUANTMEYER). Arnold!! Wasn't that Arnold!!

LIESE BÄNSCH (*suspecting the connection, steps with lightning like rapidity between* QUANTMEYER *and* MICHALINE. *To* QUANTMEYER). Go on! Don't interfere with our guests or I'll call papa this minute!

MICHALINE (*approaches the door in intense dread with a cry of pain and despair*). Arnold!! Wasn't that Arnold?

LACHMANN (*following her and holding her*). No! No, no, Michaline! Control yourself!

ACT IV

The studio of MICHAEL KRAMER *as in the second act. It is afternoon, toward five o'clock. The hangings which conceal the studio proper are drawn, as always.* KRAMER *is working at his etching. He is dressed as in the second act.* KRAUSE *is taking blue packages of stearin candles from a basket which he has brought with him.*

KRAMER (*without looking up from his work*). Just put down the packages, back there, by the candlesticks.

KRAUSE (*has placed the packages on the table upon which stand several branched candlesticks of silver. He now produces a letter and holds it in his hands*). I suppose there's nothing else, professor?

KRAMER. Professor? What does that mean?

KRAUSE. Well, I suppose it's that. Because this here letter 's from the ministry.

[*He places the letter in front of* KRAMER *on the little table.*]

KRAMER. H-m. Eh? Addressed to me? [*He sighs deeply.*] All due respect.

[*He lets the letter lie unopened and continues to work.*]

KRAUSE (*picking up his basket and about to go*). Don't you want me to watch tonight, professor? You ought to take a bit o' rest, really.

KRAMER. We'll let things be as they have been, Krause. In regard to the watching too, I tell you. And, anyhow, it's provided for. I've made an agreement with Lachmann. You recall him, don't you?

KRAUSE (*takes up his cap and sighs*). Merciful Father in Heaven! Dear! Dear! So there's nothing else just now, I suppose?

KRAMER. Is the director in his office?

KRAUSE. Yes, sir, he's there.

KRAMER. Thank you; that's all.— Hold on. Just wait a moment. On Monday evening . . . where was that? Where did your wife meet Arnold?

KRAUSE. Why, it was down by the river, where the boats are lying . . . right under the brick bastion. Where they rent boats by the hour.

KRAMER. On the little path that leads around down there? Close by the Oder?

KRAUSE. Yes; that's where it was.

KRAMER. Did she address him or he her?

KRAUSE. No, sir. He was sittin', you see, on the parapet or on the wall, you might say, where people sometimes stand an' look down to watch the Polacks cooking potatoes on their rafts. An' he seemed so queer to my wife an' so she just said good-ev'nin' to him.

KRAMER. And did she say anything else to him?

KRAUSE. She just said as how he'd catch a cold.

KRAMER. H-m. And what did he answer?

KRAUSE. Why, the way she says, he just laughed. But he laughed in a kind o' way, she was thinkin', that was terrible. Kind o' contemptuous. That's all I know.

KRAMER. He who desires to scorn all things, I tell you, will find good reasons for his scorn.— I wish you had come to me.— But I believe it was too late even then.

KRAUSE. If only a body had known. But how is you to know? Who'd be thinkin' of a thing like that straight off? When Michaline came to me — she came to me, you know, with Mr. Lachmann — then the fright got hold o' me. But by that time it was half-past twelve at night.

KRAMER. I tell you, I will remember that night. When my daughter wakened me, it was one o'clock.—And when, at last, we found the poor boy, the cathedral clock was striking nine.

[KRAUSE *sighs, shakes his head, opens the door in order to go and, at the same time, admits* MICHALINE *and* LACHMANN *who enter.* KRAUSE *exit.* MICHALINE *is dressed in a dark gown; she is deeply serious and shows signs of weariness and of tears.*]

KRAMER (*calls out to them*). There you are, children. Well, come in. So you are going to watch with me tonight, Lachmann. You were his friend too, in a way, at least. I am glad that you are willing to watch. A stranger, I tell you, I could not bear.— [*He walks up and down, stands still, reflects and says:*] I will leave you alone for five minutes now and go over to see the director. To tell him the little that is to be told. You won't go in the meantime, I dare say.

MICHALINE. No, father. Lachmann, at all events, will stay here. As for me, I have to go on some errands.

KRAMER. I'm very glad that you'll stay, Lachmann. I won't take long; I'll be back presently.

[*He puts on a muffler, nods to both and leaves.* MICHALINE *sits down, draws up her veil and wipes her eyes with her handkerchief.* LACHMANN *puts aside his hat, stick and overcoat.*]

MICHALINE. Does father seem changed to you?

LACHMANN. Changed? No.

MICHALINE. Dear me, there's something that I forgot again! I didn't send an announcement to the Härtels. One loses the little memory that's still left.—There's another wreath.— [*She gets up and examines a rather large laurel wreath with riband that is lying on the sofa. She takes up a card that was fastened to the wreath and continues with an expression of surprise.*] Why, it's from Miss Schäffer.—There's another soul left solitary now. She had but one thought—Arnold. And Arnold didn't even know of it.

LACHMANN. Is she that slightly deformed person whom I saw in your studio?

MICHALINE. Yes. She painted simply because Arnold did. She saw in me just — Arnold's sister. That's the way life is — she'll pay for this wreath by living for weeks on tea and bread.

LACHMANN. And probably be very happy doing it, in addition.— Do you know whom else I met? And who is going to send a wreath too?

MICHALINE. Who?

LACHMANN. Liese Bänsch.

MICHALINE. She . . . needn't have done that.

[*Pause.*]

LACHMANN. If only I had been able to talk to Arnold. About Liese Bänsch too! Perhaps it would have done some good!

MICHALINE. No, Lachmann, you're mistaken. I don't believe it.

LACHMANN. Who knows? But what could I do? He avoided me! I could have made several things clear to him . . . never mind what, now! And from my very own experience. Sometimes our most ardent desires are denied us. Because, Michaline, were they granted us . . .! A wish like that was granted me once and I—I needn't conceal it from you—I am much worse off than I was before.

MICHALINE. Experience is not communicable, at least not in the deeper sense.

LACHMANN. It may be so, and yet . . . I've had my lesson. [*Pause.*]

MICHALINE. Yes, yes, that's the way it goes. That's the way of the world. The girl was playing with fire, too, I dare say. And of course it never occurred to her, naturally, that the end might be this! [*At her father's small table.*] Look what father has been etching here.

LACHMANN. A dead knight in armor.

MICHALINE. Mh-m.

LACHMANN (*reads:*)
> "With armor am I fortified
> Death bears my shield for me."

MICHALINE (*with breaking voice, then with tears*). I have never seen father weep, and look—he wept over this.

LACHMANN (*involuntarily taking her hand*). Michaline, let us try to be strong; shall we?

MICHALINE. The paper is quite wet! Oh, my God. [*She masters her emotion, walks a few paces and then continues in a higher strain:*] He controls himself, Lachmann, assuredly. But how does it look in his soul? He has aged by ten years.

LACHMANN. I have buried my father and my brother, too. But when life discloses itself to us in its deepest seriousness—in fateful moments in the course of time—when we survive what is hardest—surely our ships sail more calmly and firmly—with our beloved dead—through the depths of space.

MICHALINE. But to survive at all! That, surely, is hardest.

LACHMANN. I never felt it to be so.

MICHALINE. Oh, yes. It was like lightning! Like a stroke from heaven! I felt at once: If we find him—well! If we don't find him, it's over. I knew Arnold and I felt that. So many things had heaped themselves up in him and when this affair grew clear to me, I knew that he was in danger.

LACHMANN. Yet we followed him almost immediately.

MICHALINE. Too late. We didn't go till I had pulled myself together. Just one word, one little word! If we could have said one word to him, it would probably have changed everything. Perhaps if they had caught him, those people, when they chased after him, I mean—if they had brought him back! I wanted to cry out: Arnold, come!   [*Her emotion overpowers her.*]

LACHMANN. Things wouldn't have turned out so badly then. There was nothing against him except the childish fooling with the revolver . . .

MICHALINE. Oh, but there was the girl, and the shame of it all, and father and mother! He fled from his own terror. He acted as though he were as old and sophisticated as possible. And yet he was, to any one who knew him as I did, quite inexperienced and childish. I knew that he was carrying the weapon.

LACHMANN. Why, he showed it to me in Munich, long ago.

MICHALINE. Yes, he thought himself pursued everywhere. He saw nothing but enemies all around him. And he wouldn't be persuaded out of that opinion. It's nothing but veneer, he always said. They only hide their claws and fangs and if you don't look out, you're done for.

LACHMANN. It wasn't so foolish. There's something to it. There are moments when one feels just so. And he probably suffered a great deal from coarseness of all kinds. If one tries to realize his situation: he probably wasn't so far wrong as far as he was concerned.

MICHALINE. We should have given more time and care to him. But Arnold was always so gruff. However kindly one's intention was, however good one's will, he repelled any advances.

LACHMANN. What did he write to your father?

MICHALINE. Papa hasn't shown the letter to any one yet.

LACHMANN. He intimated something to me. A mere intimation — nothing more. He spoke of it quite without bitterness, by the way. I believe there was something like this in the letter, that he couldn't endure life, that he felt himself quite simply unequal to it.

MICHALINE. Why didn't he lean on father! Of course he is hard. But there's something defective in any one who can't get beyond the exterior, and doesn't feel father's humanity and goodness. I was able to do it, and I am a woman. It was so much harder for me than for Arnold. Father strove to get Arnold's confidence; I had to fight for father's. Father is tre-

mendously veracious, but that's all. In that respect
he hit me harder than Arnold. Arnold was a man.
Yet I stood the test.

LACHMANN. Your father could be my confessor —

MICHALINE. He fought his way through a similar experience.

LACHMANN. One feels that.

MICHALINE. Yes. I know it for a certainty. And he would
have understood Arnold without a doubt.

LACHMANN. Ah, but who knows the word that will save?

MICHALINE. Well, you see, Lachmann, this is the way
things go: Our mother is a stranger to father's inmost
self. But if ever she had a quarrel with Arnold, she
threatened him at once with father. In this way —
what has she brought about? Or, at least, has helped
to bring about?

[KRAMER *returns*.]

KRAMER (*takes off his muffler*). Here I am again. How is
mama?

MICHALINE. She doesn't want you to wear yourself quite
out. Are you going to sleep at home tonight or not?

KRAMER (*gathering cards of condolence from the table*).
No, Michaline. But when you go home, take these
cards to mama. [*To* LACHMANN.] See, he had his
friends, too, only we didn't know of it.

MICHALINE. There were many callers at home today, too.

KRAMER. I wish people would refrain from that. But if
they think they are doing good, it is not for us to
restrain them, to be sure.— You are going again?

MICHALINE. I must. Oh, these wretched annoyances and
details!

KRAMER. We mustn't by any means let that vex us. The
hour demands our last strength.

MICHALINE. Good-by, papa.

KRAMER (*holding her back gently*). Good-by, my dear child.
I know you don't let it vex you. You are probably
the most reasonable of us all. No, no, Michaline, I

don't mean it in that way. But you have a sane, temperate mind. And her heart, Lachmann, is as warm as any. [MICHALINE *weeps more intensely.*] But listen: Approve yourself now too, my child. We must show now how we can stand the test.

[MICHALINE *calms herself resolutely, presses her father's hand, then* LACHMANN'S *and goes.*]

KRAMER. Lachmann, let us light the candles. Open these packages for me. [*Going to work himself.*] Sorrow, sorrow, sorrow! Do you taste the full savor of that word? I tell you, that is the way it is with words: They become alive only at times. In the daily grind of life they are dead. [*He hands a candlestick, into which he has placed a candle, to* LACHMANN.] So. Carry this in to my boy.

[LACHMANN *carries the candlestick behind the hangings and leaves* KRAMER *alone in the outer room.*]

KRAMER. When the great things enter into our lives, I tell you, the trivial things are suddenly swept away. The trivial separates, I tell you, but greatness unites us. That is, if one is made that way. And death, I tell you, always belongs to the great things — death and love. [LACHMANN *returns from behind the hangings.*] I have been downstairs to see the director and I have told him the truth, and why should I lie? I am surely in no mood for it. What is the world to me, I should like to know? The director took it quite sensibly too.— But, you see, the women want concealment. Otherwise the parson won't go to the grave and then the matter is irregular. I tell you, all that is of secondary importance to me. God is everything to me. The parson is nothing.— Do you know what I have been doing this morning? Burying my heart's deepest wishes. Quietly, quietly, I've done it, all by myself, I tell you. And there was a long train of them — little ones and big ones, thin ones and stout ones. There they lie, Lachmann, like wheat behind the scythe.

LACHMANN. I have lost a friend before. I mean by a
voluntary death.

KRAMER. Voluntary, you say? Who knows how true that
is?—Look at the sketches yonder. [*He fumbles in
his coat and draws from his breast-pocket a sketch-
book. He leads* LACHMANN *to the window where one
can barely see by the dim light of evening, and opens
the book.*] There he assembled his tormentors. There
they are, look you, as he saw them. And I tell you, he
had eyes to see. It is almost the evil eye. But vision
he had, surely, surely.—I am perhaps not so shattered
as you think nor so disconsolate as many imagine.
For death, I tell you, leads us into the divine. Something comes upon us and bows us down. But that
which descends to us is sublime and overwhelming at
once. And then we feel it, we see it almost, and we
emerge from our sorrows greater than we were.—How
many a one has died to me in the course of my life!
Many a one, Lachmann, who is still alive today. Why
do our hearts bleed and beat at once? Because they
must love, Lachmann: that is the reason. Man and
nature yearn toward oneness, but upon us is the curse
of division. We would hold fast to all things, yet all
things glide from our grasp even as they have come.

LACHMANN. I have felt that too, in my own life.

KRAMER. When Michaline awakened me on that night, I
must have cut a pitiable figure. I tell you, I knew it all
at once.—But the bitterest hours came when we had
to leave him, to let him lie there—alone. That hour!
Great God, Lachmann, was that hour sent to purify
me as by fire or not? I scarcely knew myself. I tell
you, I would never have believed it of myself! I rebelled so bitterly; I jeered and I raged at my God. I
tell you, we don't know what we are capable of! I
laughed like a fetishist and called my fetish to account!
The whole thing seemed to me a devilish bad joke on
the part of the powers that be, a wretched, futile kind

of trick, Lachmann, damnably cheap and savorless and poor.— Look you, that's the way I felt; that's the way I rebelled. Then, later, when I had him here near me, I came to my senses.— A thing like this — we can't grasp it at first. Now it's entered the mind. Now it's become part of life. It's almost two days ago now. I was the shell; there lies the kernel. If only the shell had been taken!

[MICHALINE *enters softly without knocking.*]

MICHALINE. Papa, Liese Bänsch is downstairs at the janitor's. She's bringing a wreath.

KRAMER. Who?

MICHALINE. Liese Bänsch. She'd like to speak to you. Shall she come in?

KRAMER. I do not blame her and I do not forbid her. I know nothing of hatred; I know nothing of revenge. All that seems to me small and mean. [MICHALINE *exit.*] Look you, it has struck me down! And it's no wonder, I tell you. We live alone, take our accustomed ways for granted, worry over small affairs, think ourselves and our little annoyances mightily important, groan and complain . . . And then, suddenly, a thing of this kind comes down upon us as an eagle swoops down among sparrows! Then, I tell you, it is hard to stand one's ground. But I have my release from life now. Whatever lies before me in the future, it cannot give me joy, it cannot cause me dread; the world holds no threat for me any more!

LACHMANN. Shall I light the gas?

KRAMER (*pulls the hangings apart. In the background of the large, almost dark studio, the dead man, swathed in linen, lies upon a bier*). Behold, there lies a mother's son! Are not men ravening beasts? [*A faint afterglow comes through the tall windows at the left. A branched candlestick with burning candles stands at the head of the bier.* KRAMER *comes forward again and pours wine into glasses.*] Come, Lachmann, refresh yourself. There is some wine here; we need to be strengthened. Let us drink, Lachmann, let us pour a libation; let us calmly touch our glasses to each other! He who lies there is I—is you—is the majestic symbol of us and our fate. What can a parson add to its meaning? [*They drink. Pause.*]

LACHMANN. I told you about a friend of mine a while ago. His mother was a clergyman's daughter. And she took it deeply to heart that no priest went to her son's grave. But when they were lowering the coffin, the spirit, so to speak, came upon her and it seemed as if God himself were speaking through her praying lips . . . I had never heard any one pray like that.

[MICHALINE *leads* LIESE BÄNSCH *in. The latter is dressed in a simple, dark dress. Both of the women remain standing near the door.* LIESE *holds her handkerchief to her mouth.*]

KRAMER (*apparently without noticing* LIESE, *strikes a match and lights more candles.* LACHMANN *does the same until two branched candlesticks and about six separate candles are burning*). What did those coxcombs know of him: these stocks and stones in the form of men? Of him and of me and of our sorrows? They baited him to his death! They struck him down, Lachmann, like a dog.—And yet, what could they do to him; what? Come hither, gentlemen, come hither! Look at him now and insult him! Step up to him now and see whether you can! I tell you, Lachmann, that is over now! [*He draws a silken kerchief from the face of the dead.*] It is well to have him lie there as he does; it is well; it is well! [*In the glimmer of the candles an easel is seen to have been placed near the bier.* KRAMER, *who has been painting at it, sits down before it again, and continues, calmly, as though no one were present but he and* LACHMANN.] I have sat here all day. I have drawn him; I have painted him; I have modeled a death mask of him . . . It's lying yonder, in that silken cloth. Now he is equal to the greatest of us all. [*He points to the mask of Beethoven.*] And yet to try to hold that fast which now lies upon his face, Lachmann, is but a fool's effort. Yet all that . . . all that was in him. I felt it, I knew it, I recognized it in him; and yet I could not bring that treasure to light. Now death has brought it to light instead. All is clarity about him now; his countenance is radiant with that heavenly light about which I flutter like a black, light-drunken butterfly. I tell you, we grow small in the presence of death. All his life long I was his schoolmaster. I had to maltreat him and now he has risen into the divine.— Perhaps I smothered this plant. Perhaps I shut out his sun and he perished in my shadow. But, look you, Lachmann, he would not let me be his friend. He needed a friend and it was not granted me to be that one.— That day when the girl came to me, I tried my best, my very best. But the evil in him had power over him that day, and when that happened it did him good to wound me. Remorse? I do not know what that is. But I have shriveled into nothingness. I have become a wretched creature beside him. I look up to that boy now as though he were my farthest ancestor.

> [MICHALINE *leads* LIESE BÄNSCH *toward the background.* LIESE *lays down her wreath at the feet of the dead.* KRAMER *looks up and meets her glance.*]

LIESE BÄNSCH. Mr. Kramer, I, I, I . . . I'm so unhappy, so . . . People point at me on the street!

> [*Pause.*]

KRAMER (*half to himself*). Wherein does the lure lie that is so deadly? And yet, any one who has experienced it and still lives, lives with the thorn of it in his palm, and whatever he touches, the thorn pricks him.— But you may go home in quiet. Between him and us all is peace! [*Pause.*]

> [MICHALINE *and* LIESE BÄNSCH *leave the studio.*]

KRAMER (*absorbed in the contemplation of his dead son and of the lights*). These lights! These lights! How strange they are! I have burned many a light, Lachmann; I have seen the flame of many a light. But I tell you: This light is different.—Do I frighten you at all, Lachmann?

LACHMANN. No. What should I be frightened of?

KRAMER (*rising*). There are people who take fright. But I am of the opinion, Lachmann, that one should know no fear in this world . . . Love, it is said, is strong as death. But you may confidently reverse the saying: Death is as gentle as love, Lachmann. I tell you that death has been maligned. That is the worst imposture in the world. Death is the mildest form of life: the masterpiece of the Eternal Love. [*He opens the great window. The chimes of evenfall are ringing softly. He is shaken as by frost.*] All this life is a fever — now hot, now cold.—Ye did the same to the Son of God! Ye do it to him today even as then! Today, even as then, he will not die! . . . The chimes are speaking, do you not hear them? They are telling a story to the folk on the streets—the story of me and of my son. They are saying that neither of us is a lost soul! You can hear their speech clearly, word for word. Today it has come to pass; this day is the day. — The chime is more than the church, Lachmann, the call to the table more than the bread.—[*His eye falls upon the death-mask of Beethoven. He takes it down and, contemplating it, continues:*] Where shall we land? Whither are we driven? Why do we cry our cries of joy into the immense incertitude — we mites abandoned in the infinite? As though we knew whither we are tending! Thus you cried too! And did you know — even you? There is nothing in it of mortal feasts! Nor is it the heaven of the parsons! It is not this and it is not that. What . . . (*he stretches out his hands to heaven*) . . . what will it be in the end?

PEACE IN THE METROPOLIS

From the Painting by Fritz Kalimoyzen

PEACE IN THE METROPOLIS

From the Painting by Fritz Kallmorgen

PERMISSION BERLIN PHOTO. CO. "NEW YORK

COPYRIGHT PHOTOGRAPHISCHE GESELLSCHAFT

THE CONTEMPORARY GERMAN LYRIC

By Paul H. Grummann, A.M.

Professor of Modern German Literature, University of Nebraska

SINCE the days of Schiller and Goethe Germany has been conscious of a cultural unity. The whole course of her history during the nineteenth century is marked by attempts to assert this unity through political devices varying from a federation of states to a German republic. Political unification was finally accomplished at the hands of Bismarck by means of the wars of 1864, 1866, and 1870. The exultation arising from three successful wars and the fulfilment of the national yearning of a century would have been sufficient causes for an era of quickened literary activity.

But Germany was destined to have more than a literature of national rejuvenation, for this rejuvenation came at a time when the most remarkable social, economic, and ethical transformations were at hand and, in consequence, Germany has produced a literature which will stand out as epochmaking in the modern world. The reasons for this exceptional literary activity are not quite so accidental as might appear at first sight. For a century Germany had occupied the front rank in scientific research. After the successful wars, it grew in financial resources and became intoxicated with the spirit of initiative. In a very short time agrarian Germany became an industrial Germany. This change involved a reconstruction of its economic and social life unparalleled in its history. The appearance of a new money aristocracy and a new caste of industrial wage-earners raised a large number of vital problems.

Spiritually, an equally portentous revolution was preparing. Metaphysics had run its course from Kant through Fichte, Schelling, and Hegel to Schopenhauer. Not without a certain influence from Germany's unsuccessful experiments at political regeneration, this movement had ended in complete pessimism. This pessimism found its most complete expression in the neo-romantic literature with its devotion to the doctrine of art for art's sake. Sometimes this pessimism was open and avowed, as in Hamerling, and again it was more veiled, more subconscious, as in Wagner.

But a new German *Weltanschauung* was developing in an entirely new field. The evolutionary theory of Darwin found enthusiastic advocates in Germany. Ernst Haeckel not only accepted it, but did much to fortify it scientifically. What is most important, he pointed out the possibilities of the evolutionary theory in new fields of thought and made it possible for Wundt to do his important work in evolutionary psychology. The direct result was that science was transferred from a metaphysical to a psychological basis and religion itself now came to be viewed from this angle.

It was greatly to be feared that under such circumstances the prevailing philosophy might become deterministic. If man was to be viewed as the result of an evolutionary process modified by his environment, his own initiative might readily seem a negligible quantity. Such a deterministic attitude was clearly the result of evolutionary ethics in England, where the doctrine of the survival of the fittest was interpreted as applicable to man in a special sense only. Evolution did not become a spur to activity, but was accepted as an assurance that " somehow good must be the final goal of ill."

Fortunately for Germany, a thinker appeared who read the lessons of evolution in a more positive manner. Whatever we may think of some of the details of Nietzsche's philosophy, it does remain true that he had the power of transforming the thought of a whole generation.

Instead of passively complying with the laws of evolution, Nietzsche insisted that we take an active part in them. Instead of looking backward, he enjoined us to look forward. Instead of accepting static laws, he taught us to apply the law of growth. Instead of accepting man in his present state, he preached the development of the over-man — a stronger, better disciplined, more effective man than the man of today. In the general shipwreck of moral criteria, Nietzsche pointed the way to a more substantial and robuster morality.

It is true that a considerable number of weaklings seized the fringes of Nietzsche's philosophy and made it a passport for libertinism. They liked the external aspects of his blond beasts, and emulated them without heeding the gospel of the superman. Deplorable as this by-product of the movement may be, it should not blind us to the fact that Nietzsche's influence is present in a positive form in most of the remarkable poetry which has been produced in this generation.

The tremendous influence of Nietzsche at once becomes apparent when we compare the contemporary literature of Germany with the foreign literature which preceded it. It differs from the naturalism of Zola, it differs from the individualistic, critical analysis of Ibsen, it is completely at odds with Tolstoy and it has even grown away from the psychology of Dostoyevski.

The influence which it exerted was not always felt directly. At first sight Detlev von Liliencron might be regarded as the very counterpart of Nietzsche. But in another sense he is a partial fulfilment of Nietzsche's prophecy. He is militant, optimistic, self-assertive and robust. Far from being a casual singer of battle songs, he has a singularly quick eye for modern life in all of its aspects. What he sees he casts into poems of charming simplicity and plastic reality. In the matter of diction he has been a source of strength to his generation. This becomes apparent at once when we compare his sturdy sentences with the German of Wagner. In the case of Wagner we have an attempt to create a pure German shorn of foreign elements, but no one but half mythical stage characters would ever think of using it. In the case of Liliencron we have a language which, with all of its simplicity, is instinct with life — a language which people and poets alike are glad to imitate.

But Liliencron may justly be regarded a transition type. The new movement more consciously asserted itself in the works of Heinrich and Julius Hart, Michael Georg Conrad and Hermann Conradi. But in all of these writers there was more promise than accomplishment. Arno Holz may be regarded the first important figure of contemporary German literature, and since he proclaimed himself the apostle of the new movement he affords a convenient point of departure.

With the self-assurance and dash of Heine, Holz published a series of lyrics that arrested the attention of the thoughtful. He broke completely with the neo-romantic pessimists and glorified the now and here. Instead of looking for poetical material in the old pastoral fields, he made the modern city the background of his songs. Technically he also broke with the past by demanding new poetic forms. In this connection two writers clearly influenced Holz and a number of his followers. The irregular metres of Whitman, so instinct with life and energy, appealed to the young writers, and Ibsen's complete rupture with metrical form also played its part. The most important innovation of Holz, however, remains his utilization of psychology. This is clearer in his *Papa Hamlet* and *Familie Selicke* than in his lyrics. Since the two former works had been written in conjunction with Johnannes Schlaf, much of the credit for this achievement may be due to him.

Holz did not confine himself to the writing of lyrics and dramas, but also ventured forth upon the field of esthetics. In a rather brief essay, *Art, its Essence and Laws* (1890), he attempted to define the nature of art. Railing at the voluminous writings of the philosophers, he attempted to go directly to the core of the whole matter by asserting that art is nature — *the means of reproducing nature*. Under the second term of his equation he included the personality of the artist and the means of representation, or the artis-

tic medium employed. As a corollary he stated that art is
never identical with nature, that it has the tendency to re-
approach nature, that it cannot equal nature, but can only
approximate it. After the publication of this essay crit-
icisms appeared from many sources; these in turn evoked
a reply on the part of Holz which was thoroughly characteristic of the man. He wrote himself down as a brilliant but narrow iconoclast. He delivered the evidence upon
which he can conveniently be judged, for the deficiencies of
his esthetic essay have turned out to be his deficiencies as
a poet.

The deficiencies become at once apparent when one com-
pares his essay with the works of Volkelt, Elster, and
Lange. These writers study art in its relation to life, and
do not manipulate it to suit a mathematical formula. They
approach the question in a large, comprehensive manner
and are able to correlate poetic activity with other artistic
and rational activities, thus restoring it to a commanding
position in life. By ignoring the narrow polemic side they
are able to do really constructive work. Thus Elster has
given us a psychological basis for the study of literature,
and Lange has taught us the value of the artistic illusion.
Elster has promoted criticism; Lange has given a stimulus
to artistic activity which even the most critical artist can
accept with gratitude. Holz failed because he confined himself in polemic limitations from the outset.

A man so constituted may give evidence of a noisy ado-
lescence, but he is not likely to achieve a fertile maturity.
Holz may have prepared the way, but other writers who had
a larger view of life have completely eclipsed him. This is
conspicuously true of the drama, in which Hauptmann,
Schnitzler, Halbe, and Ernt Rosmer (Else Bernstein)
showed possibilities of growth unknown to him. It is
equally true of the lyric, where Hauptmann, Dehmel, Hesse,
Rilke and Isolde Kurz have overshadowed him.

We are so accustomed to view Hauptmann merely as a
dramatist that we forget his solid accomplishments in the

lyric. It will be remembered that he cast his first works in verse. In *Hannele* the lyric impulse again asserts itself, and in *The Sunken Bell* it breaks forth with elemental force. The lyrical portions of *The Sunken Bell* enable us to account for Hauptmann's success in comparison with Holz's failure. Here the lyric is an outgrowth of the popular consciousness, not a thing artificially constituted. It involves Schiller's distinction between " the *Naïve and the Sentimental.*" It is the difference between Heine and Goethe. But Hauptmann's lyrical development does not stop with *The Sunken Bell.* It deepens and broadens in the later dramas. *Henry von Aue, Pippa dances* and *Griselda* give evidence of continued growth in this direction.

But the greatest lyrical genius of the period, and one of the greatest since Goethe, is Richard Dehmel. His first poems, like those of Holz, were strongly reminiscent of Heine. They showed the same spirit of rebellion—they were not free from a certain iconoclasm. Moreover, they cut a great breach into our conventions and reasserted the right of the individual to happiness. But it soon became apparent that the deeper lessons of Nietzsche and other intellectual leaders of modern Germany had been acquired by him. He no longer espoused the bibulous, complacent joyousness of Bodenstedt and Scheffel, but a joy that springs from the rational mastering of the environment. Self-culture is almost a dominant note in his poetry. In his erotic poems, which occupy a surprisingly large share of his pages, there is also a new note. We might almost say that the poet has consistently applied Nietzsche's philosophy to the problem of sex—a thing that Nietzsche himself failed signally to do when he failed to include the superwoman in his program. According to Dehmel woman has the same innate rights to happiness and self-direction as man. Not every woman is by nature divine, but, just as in the case of man, she shows transitions from the lowest to the highest, culminating in modern times in a type including both Venus and the Madonna. The realism of Dehmel is at times shocking, but it is exhibited over so wide a range that its effect is distinctly wholesome. This is particularly true in an age when man is alternately proclaimed by social theorists a paragon and a beast. Dehmel clearly points out that he is an eternally varying combination of the two.

Germans have frequently been in danger of lapsing into mawkish sentimentalism — *Gefühlsduselei.* This tendency was most pronounced during the Storm and Stress, the Romantic and the Neo-romantic movements. The reactions to these movements have generally been marked by a shallow, sterile rationalism. Such a period seemed to be foreshadowed in the writings of David Friedrich Strauss, and it is one of Nietzsche's greatest services to German Literature that he pointed out the viciousness of Strauss's influence. Nietzsche insisted that Strauss robbed the universe of its tantalizing mystery and suggestiveness, and therefore caused individual effort to stagnate. Man's duty is to continue to work at the riddles and to find ever new ones to take the place of those already solved. Here again Dehmel is the fulfilment of Nietzsche. He shows us a world full of mysteries, and exhorts us to fathom them to the best of our ability. Instead of discrediting the feelings, as did Strauss, he stresses their importance; instead of divorcing them from our rational activity, he never tires of linking our intelligence with our feelings, making this union the basis of a really robust initiative.

Independent in the use of metrical schemes, Dehmel nevertheless gives the impression of classical finish. This is due to the fact that he is a master in finding the proper form for the thought which he wishes to convey. In diction he is simple and clear. Many of his poems do require repeated reading in order to be understood, but the depth of the conception and not the obscurity of the statement engages the activity of the reader. It is too early to venture upon a final statement of Dehmel's work. Goethe has remained Germany's supreme lyricist because he continued to broaden and deepen up to his death. One at times doubts

Dehmel's ability to live up to this promise, but there is clearly no one on the horizon today who threatens to eclipse him.

Of the many poets who resemble Dehmel in a general way, two deserve special attention. Although Carl Busse lacks the virility and versatility of Dehmel, a perusal of his works will lead to the conclusion that many of his superb mood-pictures will find a permanent place in the national lyric. Less turbulent than Dehmel, but endowed with the same instinct for fathoming feelings and defining moods, is Hermann Hesse. His poems are of rare beauty, and all of them show a mastery of inner and outer form. He has impressed his individuality upon each one of his works without obtruding it upon them. It is too early to say what may be expected of him; as yet his interests and his outlook are confined, but the quality of work which he has produced up to the present warrants the hope that he may become one of the most interesting poets of the period.

Although Gustav Falke has been accorded recognition in this group of poets, it is doubtful whether he will maintain his present ratings. His poetry shows many characteristics of modernism. The themes are striking and vital, the language is terse, vigorous and direct, but the metrical resources of the poet are limited. This is particularly surprising because Falke is primarily a musician. For a similar reason Otto Julius Bierbaum will probably fail to make a lasting impression as a lyricist. Unlike Falke, Bierbaum has attempted many metrical forms, but his poems give the impression of experiments in a new field.

Heralded by a small group as a deliverer from naturalism, Stefan George has not been without influence. George's poetry represents a conscious return to mysticism. He puts his mystic thought into a mystic garb, and his publishers have further mystified the products of his muse by printing them in type that obtrudes itself between the poem and the mind of the reader in a tantalizing manner. There is more obscurity than in Browning. It is difficult to state whether he himself had any rational conception of what he wished to convey. To be sure, Professor Kummer has found his poems reminiscent of Goethe's *Divan* and *The Hymns to Night* by Novalis. The language is so individualistic that a special code of syntactical rules is necessary to fathom it. Since the value of the subject matter remains in doubt, it is a question whether it is really worth while to acquire the new code in order to get to the core of the matter.

Somewhat in harmony with the mystical tendency of George, Rainer Maria Rilke avoids the pose of that writer. Retiring and sensitive, he developed along the lines lying far away from the main current of thought in the period. After he had turned in despair from the universities he came into contact with a number of artists in Germany and Italy. Later he entered into very close friendship with Rodin, whose impress is to be found in his later poetry. His poetry betrays a craving for a new spirituality. It is singularly delicate and chaste, but lacks virility.

Although he was hailed as a leading spirit by some discriminating critics, Alfred Mombert has failed to make a strong impression upon his times. He is quite as individualistic as Nietzsche, but his metaphysical bent has rendered him comparatively ineffective as a poet. His fondness for abstraction and his imagery are reminiscent of Shelley, whose strong popular sympathies he does not, however, share.

A group of young writers in Vienna broke with naturalism; they lacked the ability, however, to launch a really vigorous movement. Their poetry does not carry that conviction which grows out of actual experience and individual effort. Hugo von Hofmannsthal is the most brilliant exponent of this group. He has devoted himself especially to the drama, and has produced work which gives evidence of astounding ability. His dramas have a marked lyrical note, but upon further analysis it becomes evident that this lyrical element lacks genuine feeling. It is pervaded by an artistic atmosphere acquired by idling in art museums rather than in immediate contact with life.

Singularly out of tune with the prevailing spirit of progress is the note struck by Freiherr Börries von Münchhausen. His lapse to traditionalism is almost complete. A descendant of the old nobility, he glorifies the old landed aristocracy with its vices as well as its virtues. He loves war —looks upon it as the regenerative force of the nation. He recasts much heroic ballad material without giving it a really new significance. His lyrics, however, are charged with genuine emotion. He has shown such a marvelous development in simplicity and directness of appeal that he must be considered one of the most promising poets of the day.

The literary activity of women has been quite remarkable in the present generation. Especially in the early years it had many of the ear-marks of newly acquired liberties. It sometimes reeked with excesses which, with all of our modernism, shocks us particularly when it comes from the pen of a woman. But the work of the most significant poetesses shows a growth in naturalness, a diminution of fitful hyperbole — in a word a greater sanity, greater self-control.

The most conspicuous figure among the women of the period is Ricarda Huch. Her fame properly rests upon her novels rather than her poems. Strong as a pioneer in the new fields of thought, Alberta von Puttkammer and Marie Janitschek deserve a large share of recognition. The vigorous, sane, and clearly conceived poetry of Anna Ritter gives evidence of the new spirit present in literary women. In Isolde Kurz, however, we have the best representative of the woman lyricist. Without violating the best traditions of her sex she is able to grapple with the deepest problems in a most interesting way; without the slightest sentimentalism she is able to portray those feminine sides of life which women can more clearly reveal than men.

Johanna Ambrosius (Voigt), an obscure peasant woman whose poetry was brought into vogue some years ago, has lost the halo which, for a time, surrounded her. Although the exaggerated praise which was temporarily bestowed upon her must be tempered, her poetry does give evidence of the rich inner life of the humble classes of German society.

The German lyric in America has had a development quite distinct from the currents in Germany. The civil war enlisted the Germans in the anti-slavery cause. After that issue had been settled a certain lethargy characterized German literary efforts. Young Germans in America were laying the foundations of material welfare, and the intellectual and literary activity confined itself largely to attacks upon American jingoism and to a propaganda for liberal religious views. The attacks upon American jingoism, well founded as they frequently were, had more than a touch of jingoism about them, and the liberal religious activity was narrow because it lost touch with the deeper German and English thought. Worst of all, the writers suffered the penalty of exiles. Uprooted from one civilization, they did not gain a firm footing in the new world. They found no distinct German consciousness to which they could appeal. The Germans in America have been even more particularistic than their fathers in Germany before 1870. They have been isolated by their American environment and have not come under the inspiration of the new Empire. Whether the conscious efforts to organize the German-Americans will lead to a solidarity that may culminate in a German-American culture with a German-American literature is a question which the future must decide.

Fortunately, what happened in America did not happen in Germany. Literary activity did not become confined in narrow currents from which it could not rescue itself. There was too much intellectual activity to make it possible to foist programs upon it — socialistic, anarchistic, naturalistic, or what not. Many forms of propaganda have helped to enrich it; but the writers who have clung to a propaganda have been supplanted by men of wider fields and a deeper furrow.

FERDINAND VON SAAR (1833–1906)

GIRLS SINGING*

PRING-TIME: in the evening shade
I was strolling through the vale —
All at once before me strayed
Gentle sounds across the dale.

I drew nearer; all serene
Two were sitting hand in hand —
Maidens as by day are seen
Working in the furrowed land.

And their faces both were brown
From the kissing sunbeams' glow;
Underneath each ragged gown
Bare a sun-burnt foot would show.

But they sang, their heads held high,
Songs that from their bosoms sprang
To the stars that lit the sky,
Sang, and knew not how they sang.

Thus they sang the old, old lays
All of love, its joy and pain,
Heedless, seeking no one's praise, —
Through the wide and lonely plain.

* Translator: Margarete Münsterberg.

FERDINAND VON SAAR

DETLEV VON LILIENCRON (1844–1909)

WAR AND PEACE*

ID flower-beds I chanced to stand,
And gazed upon a gorgeous land
That blooming wide before me lay
Beneath the harvest sun's hot ray.
And in the apple-tree's fair shade
My host and I together stayed
And listened to a nightingale,
And peace was over hill and dale.
There whizzed, the distant rails along,
A train that brought a happy throng.
What magic! And besides it bore
Of blessed goods a heavy store.
But once I saw the iron track
Destroyed and torn for miles. Alack—
And here where flowers now abound
Was then a wild and stirred-up ground.

A summer morn was glowing bright,
Like this one; down from every height,
" With pack and knapsack all day long "
From ambuscades there poured a throng
Prepared to storm, a dazzling sea,
The army of the enemy.
I stood as though of iron cast,
Upon my sabre leaning, fast.
With lips apart and open-eyed
Into the mouth of hell I spied.
" Quick fire! " " Stand still! " Now they are
    there!
High waves the flag through smoky air!
And up and down men rush in rows,
And many sink in deadly throes.

* Translator: Margarete Münsterberg.

Now some one stabs me as I fall,
Stabs hard — I have no strength at all;
Before, beneath me, round about,
A frightful struggle, rage and rout.
And o'er this tangle wild, in fear
I see a shying war-horse rear.
The hoof I see like lightning whir,
The clotted scar from pricking spur,
The girth, the spattered mud, the red
Of nostrils swelling wide with dread.
Between us now with clanging sound
The bomb-shell bursts its iron bound;
A dragon rears, the earth is rent,
Down falls the whole wide firmament.
They wail and moan, and dust is spread
Upon the laurels and the dead.

'Mid flower-beds I chanced to stand
And gazed upon a gorgeous land
That far and wide before me lay
Beneath the peace-fan's lulling sway.
And in the apple-tree's fair shade
My host and I together stayed
And harkened to the nightingale,
And roses bloomed on hill and dale.

PARTING AND RETURN *

I

ALL over, over — and my eyes
Afar are straying in despair.
All over — but the sea-gull flies,
My plaintive escort, through the air.

* Translator: Margarete Münsterberg.

DETLEV VON LILIENCRON

The gull returns: far, far away
I leave my fatherland behind,
An outcast from my home I stray
Where I my grave had hoped to find.

When yesterday, in parting pain,
Enraged the linden bough I shook,
And heard the partridge in the grain,
A fever-spell my limbs o'ertook.

My ship is pitching, tossed by waves,
The mates are singing while they sail;
My heart is tossed, it storms and raves,
And homeless, I must feel the gale.

II

'Mid waves there gleams the pallid strand,
Afar through blurring tears is seen
The sea-coast of my fatherland;
Exhausted, by the mast I lean.

The lilacs bloom, the swallows stray,
The starlings' chatter fills the air,
The organ-grinder grinds his lay,
The wind's light kiss is on my hair.

Before the guard-house soldiers stand,
And arm in arm laugh damsels young,
While from the school there pours a band
That frolic in my native tongue.

My heart cries out in rapture wild,
Rejoicing my old home to greet,
And all I lived with as a child
Like echoes on my ways I meet.

FLOWRETS*

LITTLE blossoms, unpretentious flowrets,
From the forest border or the meadow,
Red and white and blue and yellow flowrets
Did I gather as I wandered homeward.
Happy memories of youth came back then;
In the fields the grass was softly waving,
From an alder bush the goldfinch warbled,—
What a world of innocence he sang there
For us two!

Many years now have your hands been weaving
Strings of pearls and roses in your tresses.
Sweetlier though the little flowers adorned you,
Dearest wife, which once we used to gather,—
I and you!

THE NEW RAILROAD*

THE skull cries out: "I'm an ambassador,
I am a baron, and 'twas I that made
The treaty between Germany and Holland.
Who's this that shakes my marble casket so?
Who breaks the lid? Is't Resurrection Day?
The commonest clodhoppers, a pack of slaves
Have torn away the ribbon from my breast,
The brave blue Order of the Elephant.
Besides, the picture of my gracious master,
Of Frederick the Fifth, that noble king!
Painted on ivory, carried next my heart,
And given me by himself in careless hour,—
They're stealing that from me, the jailbird crew!"

But none the less for that the railroad gang
(The vault being now officially condemned)
Laugh at the outcry of the ancient skull.

* Translator: Charles Wharton Stork.

One of them gives the royal miniature
To Pock-faced Lizzie of the camp saloon
Who deals in drink and lodging for the night.
Then, decorated with the picture, she
Appears on Sunday at the navvies' ball.

The skull cries out: " I'm an ambassador,
I am a baron, and 'twas I that made
The treaty between Germany and Holland."
That doesn't help him, for the drunken crowd
Raise him aloft upon the tail-board plank
Snatched from a sand-cart as it rumbles past,
Later he serves them for a game of ball.

The skull cries out: " I'm an ambassador,
I am a baron, and 'twas I that made
The treaty between Germany and Holland."
That doesn't help him.   When at last they tire
They throw him to a dead cat in the dirt.

The skull cries out: " I'm an ambassador,
I am a baron, and 'twas I that made
The treaty between Germany and Holland."
That doesn't help him, for his voice is drowned
By the first whistle of the new express.

PRINCE EMIL VON SCHÖNAICH–CAROLATH
(1852–1908)

OH GERMANY!*

GERMAN town with gables
Upon a moonlight night —
I know not why I always
Am touched so by the sight.

Into his lamplight yonder
A youth is staring long,
He's sighing, sobbing, feeling
His first and dearest song.

There sits a youthful mother
And rocks to rest her child,
She's praying while she rocks him
To sleep with singing mild.

There rest on the moonlit gables
An old man's pensive eyes,
He holds in his hands a Bible
Where a faded nosegay lies.

The twinkling stars are gleaming,
There's rustling in the trees;
The houses all seem dreaming
In deep and drowsy ease.

The fountain is splashing, flowing
As always on Simon Square,
The watchman low is blowing
Upon the horn his air. . . .

* Translator: Margarete Münsterberg.

[298]

PRINCE EMIL VON SCHÖNAICH-CAROLATH

Oh Germany! I've had pleasure
In many a foreign land —
But to thee greatest treasure
Was given by God's own hand.

Thou living, longing foundest
Thy dreams in deepest peace.
Though thou thine iron poundest
Thy songs shall never cease.

Let no one rob thy worship —
Thy worship old and true
Of women, faith and freedom,
And keep it ever new!

Draw from the fount of story
Thy piety of yore,
And strength to fight with glory —
Today and evermore.

GUSTAV FALKE (1853–   )

A DAY SPENT*

LEANING head on hand, I muse: oh tell,
Day of beauty, have I used thee well?

First upon my wife's dear lips a kiss,
Love's salute and early morning bliss.

Faithful toil, for daily bread the care,
Men's dispute in words that do not spare.

Then I quaffed my glass with true delight,
Warded off a wicked wish with might.

From eternal stars with blessed beam
Comes to me at last the poet's dream.

Leaning head on hand, I muse and tell:
Day of beauty, I have used thee well.

WHEN I DIE*

Upon my forehead lay your crimson roses,
In festive garment from you I would go,
The windows open till the light reposes
Upon my bed — the starlight's smiling glow.

And music! While your songs are still enthralling,
And one by one the parting cup you drink,
Then I would have my curtain slowly falling,
As summer nights on ripened harvests sink.

* Translator: Margarete Münsterberg.

[300]

GUSTAV FALKE

ISOLDE KURZ (1853–   )

NEKROPOLIS*

CITY is standing in the waves
That rose from deepest lair,
There each of the houses the water laves
And kisses each marble stair;
There palaces stand in their glory's pride
And gilded is pillar and wall,
But over the battlements far and wide
Destruction is brooding for all.

No sound of wheel or of hoof is known
The lion to wake from his dream,
But low from the Lido the night-winds moan
And sea-gulls ocean-wards scream.
The moon makes silver the silent tide,
The gondolas glide their way,
And sea-weeds on the water ride —
Like storm-tossed corpses stray.

Oh pearl, thou of all in the deep most fair,
Thou beauty out of the sea,
Where are thy daughters with golden hair,
Thy sons oh where may they be?
And where is thy splendor, the gleam of thy
    gold,
That all the earth would dread?
The arts that so many a heart would hold?
Where is thy realm? With the dead.

* Translator: Margarete Münsterberg.

By night, though, the greatest canal along
Where flickering night-lights play
Rise sounds like whisp'ring and amorous song
Of shades that deserted stray.
Frolicking swarms of masks whirl round
Upon the piazza near by,
And clashing swords on the Riva resound;
The masts are dark'ning the sky.

It seems as if from the night and deep
Had risen the Venice of old.
The sea-wind wakes and the wave from sleep,
Her corpse to rock and to hold.
The sea is rising, with passionate arms
There by the canal-bed to cling,
As if the young spouse with his kisses and charms
To beauty new life should bring.

ISOLDE KURZ

RICHARD DEHMEL (1863–   )

THROUGH THE NIGHT*

UT ever you, this sombre you,
Through all the night this hollow soaring
Of sound—and through the wires a roaring:
The homeward road my steps pursue.

And pace for pace this sombre you,
As if from pole to pole 'twere soaring;
Of thousand words I hear a roaring,
And dumb my homeward road pursue.

FROM AN OPPRESSED HEART*

AND still the roses gleam for me,
The sombre leaves their tremor keep;
Here in the grass I wake from sleep.
I long for thee,
For now the midnight is so deep.

The moon's behind the garden-gate,
Her light o'erflows the lake with gloss,
And silently the willows wait,
On clover damp my limbs I toss;
And never was my love so great!

So well I ne'er before had known
When I embraced thy shoulder dear,
Thy inmost self felt blindly near,
Why thou, when I had overflown,
Wouldst moan so from a heart of fear.

* Translator: Margarete Münsterberg.

[303]

Oh now, oh hadst thou seen this glow —
The creeping pair of glow-worms' flame!
Ah, nevermore from thee I'll go!
I long for thee.
And still the roses gleam for me.

WAVE DANCE SONG*

I TOSSED a rose into the sea,
A blooming fair rose into the green sea.
Because the sun shone, sun shone bright,
After it leaped the light,
With hundred tremulous toes in glee.
When the first wave came,
Then my rose, my rose began to drown.
When the second wave raised it on shoulders tame,
The light, the light at her feet sank down.
The third snatched it up and then the light
As if in defence, leaped high tremblingly.
But a hundred leaping flower petals
Were rocking red, red, red round me,
And my boat danced about
And my shadow like a spright
On the foam, and the green sea, the sea —

MANY A NIGHT*

WHEN the night on fields is sinking,
    Then my eyes can see more brightly:
Now my star begins its blinking,
    Crickets' whispers grow more sprightly.

Every sound becomes more glowing,
    Things accustomed now seem queerer,
Paler too the skies are growing
    Near the woods, the tree-tops clearer.

* Translator: Margarete Münsterberg.

Meditating, never heeding
  How the myriad lights are showered
Out of darkness, on I'm speeding —
  Till I stop all overpowered.

VOICE IN DARKNESS*

There's moaning somewhere in the dark.
I want to know what it may be.
The wind is angry with the night.

Yet the wind's moan sounds not so near.
The wind will always moan at night.
'Tis in my ear my blood that moans,
My blood, forsooth.

Yet not so strangely moans my blood.
My blood is tranquil like the night.
I think a heart must moan somewhere.

THE WORKMAN*

We have a bed and we have a child,
      My wife!
And work we've for two all our own to call,
And rain and the wind and the sunshine mild;
We are lacking now but one thing small
To be as free as the birds so wild:
      Time — that's all!

When on Sundays through the fields we go,
      My child,
And see how the swallows to and fro
Are shooting over the grain-stalks tall,
Oh, we lack not clothes, though our share is small,
To be as fair as the birds so wild:
      Time — that's all!

* Translator: Margarete Münsterberg.

But time! We're scenting a tempest wild,
　　We people!
Eternity our own to call,
Else we've no lack, my wife, my child,
Save all that blooms through us, the small,
To be as bold as the birds so wild:
　　Time — that's all!

THE GOLDFINCH*

THE sunlight stabs; a thistle plot
Gleams in the noontide still and hot.
Above the wide and jagged mere
Of leaves the stalks are lifting sheer
Their heads of purple.

Across the foliage iron-gray
A bright bird hops and hops away
Amid the host without a fear,
Blithely, as though no thorn were here —
A little goldfinch.

He flirts his tail and whirs his wing.
Then comes a breeze with gentle swing
From blossom-spear to blossom-spear
And shakes the shadows far and near;
Off darts the goldfinch.

I too go onward free of doubt,
Behold the bright world round about,
And pass through life without a fear
As if no thorn could trouble here
Our glad existence.

* Translator: Charles Wharton Stork.

RICHARD DEHMEL

THE BIG MERRY-GO-ROUND*

(A Song for a Child.)

A MERRY-GO-ROUND is in the sky
  That's turning night and day,
Fast as a dream it whirls on high
So bright we cannot see it fly,
  All formed of light's pure ray,—
  Hark, little rogue, I say.

Listen, it takes the stars along
  That up in heaven gleam.
Through space it bears them swift and strong,
And as it goes it makes a song
  So delicate we only seem
  To hear the music in a dream.

In dreams we hear it from afar,
  From heaven with brightness crowned.
How glad, you rogue, your dreams then are.
And we turn with it on a star;
  Never too fast, we've found,
  Goes the big merry-go-round!

* Translator: Charles Wharton Stork.

ARNO HOLZ (1863–   )

LIKE ONE OF THESE WAS HE*

 N the woods is a village small
Lying in the sunshine's gold,
By the hill-side house, the last of all,
Sits a woman old, so old.
    She sits and spins no more,
    Her thread slips to her feet,
    She thinks on the days of yore
    And sinks into slumber sweet.

Noon-day steals with quiet deep
O'er the glimmering green, and now
Even thrush and cricket sleep
And the steer before the plough.
    All at once they're marching by,
    Gleaming the woods along,
    Ahead of the soldiers fly
    Drum-beats and fifes' gay song.

And to the song of Blücher brave,
" They're here!" cries the village gay,
And all the little maidens wave
And the boys cry out: " Hurrah!"
    God bless the harvest gold,
    And all the wide world too.
    The Emperor's soldiers bold
    The fields are marching through!

* Translator: Margarete Münsterberg.

ARNO HOLZ

Turning round by the hill-side near,
Where the last house seems to smile,
See, the first in the woods disappear,
And the old woman wakes meanwhile.
    So heavy her heart is growing
    In deepest reverie,
    Her tears are flowing, flowing:
" Like one of these was he."

OTTO JULIUS BIERBAUM (1865–)

ENOUGH*

KNIGHT rode through the ripened grain,
No spurs he had and loose his rein.
The horse that feasted on his walk
Snatched many a ripe and yellow stalk.
The dazzling summer sunlight's beam
Upon the black steel cast a gleam,
Upon the horseman's armor rough;
One word was on his shield: Enough.
His lance stayed cross-wise all the way,
His iron hand upon it lay.
When to a spring his course had led,
He took the helmet off his head,
He knelt upon the stony sand,
Drew water with his iron hand.
And then he let the water go,
And tenderly he watched its flow:
My heart in fight and fray was hot,
And love at all times left me not.
Now home I ride with gentle pace,
And bring a smile upon my face:
    Enough.

* Translator: Margarete Münsterberg.

OTTO JULIUS BIERBAUM

STEFAN GEORGE (1868–   )

THE SHEPHERD'S DAY*

HE flocks were trudging from their winter haunts.
Their youthful shepherd once again went forth
Upon the plain illumined by the stream.
The freshly wakened fields waved greetings gay
And singing lands were hailing him with joy.
He smiled unto himself and walked along
With wakening heart, upon the spring-touched ways.
Upon his crook he leaped across the ford,
And, as he halted at the other shore,
Rejoiced to see the gold that waves had washed
From underneath the stones, and fragile shells
Of many shapes and tints that promised luck.
The bleating of his lambs he heard no more,
And wandered to the woods, the cool ravine.
There brooks are rushing headlong down the rocks —
The rocks where mosses drip and naked roots
Of sombre beeches darkly intertwine.
In silent contemplation of the leaves
He fell asleep although the sun was high
And silver scales were glistening in the stream.
He woke and climbing reached the mountain peak
To celebrate the passing of the light.
With sacred leaves he crowned his head and prayed
And through the mild and gently stirring shadows
Of darkening clouds soared forth his hearty lay.

* Translator: Margarete Münsterberg.

[311]

THE VIGIL*

WITHIN the chapel quivers candle-light.
And there the page his vigil keeps alone
Before the altar's threshold all the night.
" I shall partake, when morning dawneth bright,
Of all that solemn glory yet unknown

When by one stroke I shall be dubbed a knight.
My childhood longing hushed, I shall not swerve
From deeds of rigor, with my spurs and might
Devoted in the good war I will serve.

For this new honor I must now prepare:
The consecration of my sword unstained
Before God's altar and the symbol there,
The testimony of high worth attained."

There his forefather's image gray and old
Reposed and slender vaults rose overhead.
Trustfully clasped his hands lay stony cold,
Upon his breast there was a banner spread.

His eyes are darkened by the helmet's shade.
A cherub spreading wide his pinions pale
Holds over him the shield with coat of mail:
Upon an azure field the flaming blade.

The youth is praying to the Lord above
And breaks the narrow bounds of prayer with feeling,
His hands devoutly clasped as he is kneeling.
Then slowly into thoughts of pious love
An earthly image unawares is stealing.

* Translator: Margarete Münsterberg.

STEFAN GEORGE

" She stood among her garden gilly-flowers,
  She was much less a maiden than a child.
  Upon her gown were broidered starry showers,
  About her golden hair the sunlight smiled."

He shudders, and he longs in his dismay
  To flee the vision that he deems a snare;
  His hands he buries in his curly hair
  And makes the sign that lets no evil stay.

The blood is rushing hot into his cheek,
  The candle-flames shoot lightnings in his face.
  But now he sees the Lady Mother meek,
  Upon her lap the Saviour giving grace.

" I will forever in Thine army serve
  And all my life no other aim will seek,
  And from Thy high commandment never swerve.
  Forgive if for the last time I was weak."
Out from the snow-white altar's covered chest

A swarm of little angels' faces poured,
  And as the organ's sacred murmur grew,
  The Valiant's innocence, the Dead's deep rest
  With tranquil clearness through the whole house soared.

LULU VON STRAUSS UND TORNEY
(1873-   )

THE SEAFARER*

German T Classics

HE ship was bursting with a mighty crash.
Ablaze were bow and deck and every mast.
The old boat pitching rose to port: a splash —
A surging of gray waves — the gale's shrill
    blast —
Thundering orders — prayers — then cry on cry —
A blow, a headlong fall — God stand me by! —
Down, down. Black night upon all senses fell.

Mate, fill my glass! This yarn is long to tell.

'T was in the deep I saw — I saw that sight.
They have no day down there, they have no night.
The sand is shimmering green. There planks lie
    scattered,
A giant mast in livid splinters shattered.
And up from pallid vines rise bubbles whirling —
From vines that evermore are swaying, curling,
Their long and wary tendril-arms unfurling.
And glistening shells among the wreckage lie
That snap without a sound when prey floats by,
And there are fish with lustre livid pale
That beat their tails transparent as a veil.

A restless host is wandering on down there,
A thousand thousand, an unnumbered band:
Their hands are stiff, their eyes unseeing stare,
With leaden feet they wade across the sand,

* Translator: Margarete Münsterberg.

Way-farers lost without a path or way—
Blue-jackets, grimy fellows, women folding
Limp arms round languid babes that they are holding—
That lived on sunken ships; forlorn they stray,
Their names are lost, they wear strange garbs of yore:—
All those who went and then returned no more.

I saw them all, like pallid phantoms pass,
As though I watched them through a blurring glass.
One beckoned dumbly as he passed me by,
And so I followed him, I knew not why.
The way was endless, and it grew and grew,
Our feet were tired and they stumbled too.
And him who fell, his helping neighbor raised.
A woman slipped and when I helped her, dazed
She hung upon my neck, a load of lead.
Deep blue abysses gaped. And overhead,
Like clouds upon the water gray and pale,
The shadows passed of many a giant whale.

One man I looked at more than all the rest,
His languid head hung limp upon his breast,
And then I knew old Peter Jens, the rover,
Who once went overboard, at night by Dover.
I gently pulled his ragged shirt to say—
And then my voice seemed strange and far away—:
" Where are you bound? "—He looked with glassy eye:
" We're seeking, seeking, seeking! " his reply.
" What are you seeking, Jens? "—He answered:
    " Land! "—
Then all about who with us crept and drifted,
Their weary, pale and anguished faces lifted.
A wailing trembled all along the sand.

Yet all at once my power seemed to gain.
I turned about with mighty voice to call
Unto this lifeless, ever wandering train:
" Now courage! Follow me! God leads us all! "

My heart was quickened and it beat again,
And ever through the void all pale and still
I was drawn onward by an unknown will,—
Behind me crept that endless gloomy train.
How long a time elapsed, I did not know.
At times the darkness fainter seemed to grow—
The gloom that hung about on every hand—
And on the hard and livid waves of sand
Something arose quite near that seemed like land—
Within our grasp! And then again it faded.
The ugly brood that lurks within the deep
Pursued us lazily. Then faint and jaded,
Lost in the mighty void, we cannot keep
Our courage, stifled all our hopes must cease—
No morning dawns! Ah, there is no release!
Wherefore this torment?

                 Faint they reeled and stayed
Worn out, beneath the everlasting shade.
Where art Thou, God? I cried, but no sound made.—
—Now, now: a point! A sudden glimmer bright!
A crevice burst—a flood of light was gleaming,
The earth and sky with golden glow were streaming!—
Salvation! Hail! A rushing for the light!
I hurled the woman up unto the strand
And staggered, with my last force crying: Land!

Here, mate! My glass is empty. Fill it, lad!
What next? Why nothing. I can tell no more.
I only know—the night was very bad—
They found me lying on the Scottish shore.
My ship? The wreck? God knows where that had
    stranded.
All those who in the night with me had landed
Were dead and cold. They've found a resting-place:
A bit of earth, a cross. God give them grace!
Sometimes at night when there's a creaking, crashing
And when the whistling winds the yards are thrashing,

LULU VON STRAUSS UND TORNEY

Against the hatches angry waves are splashing—
Then it comes over me: to wander, wander
Forever with those thousand others yonder!
Many I've seen for years, but ever more
New-comers join—each night a mighty band!
Sometimes I find one whom I knew before;
He nods and dumbly stretches out his hand.
And many a comrade in that silent throng
I've borne upon my back or dragged along.
I see them, all the sea did ever swallow;
The others too I see: those yet to follow,
Many a youth who laughs with us today,
Upon whose heart no thoughts of dying weigh.
And step for step through all the night we go,
Deep, deep down there.

      Jan Witt, ah, well you know,
No shaking then can wake me from my dream,
And should you shout to wake the dead, and scream.
But I come back at early dawn of day,
When in the east the blackness turns to gray;
Then I awake. My head is dull and weighs
Like lead. And then I cannot laugh for days.
Ho, fellows, why so dumb? A roundelay!
For what the morrow brings, who cares today?
Heads high and gay! Our sailor's custom keep!
We men, when we're at home or when we fare
On foreign seas, each day our shroud must wear.
And He above—He also knows the deep!

BÖRRIES VON MÜNCHHAUSEN (1874–   )

BALLAD OF THE WALL*

ONTETON, where is thy wall?
Chalençon, where is thy sword?
Where is thy tower, Tournefort?

Noblemen's swords, how their blades were all sharp and
    good!
Noblemen's swords grew dull in Plebeian thick blood.

Tournefort's tower is black and burnt inside,
From the crest they banished the blazoned flag, its pride.

And over the wall of the castle of Monteton
" Vive le son! "
Flutter the bloody fragments of song
" Vive le son des canons! "

This side the wall there fights a nobleman,
Rash, desperate and always in the van,—
Wherefore?—Red grows the green ground hereafter,
Bitter, bitter, bitter rings his laughter.
Beyond the wall a filthy ocean raves
In greedy and grasping and cowardly waves—
This side, that side—who guessed ere the eve was spent!
The wall lay low, then herbs gave forth a scent;
The battlement a sunken tombstone drear,
Wailing women, the clouds, into the grass wept tear on tear.

Flashing death-lights:—balcony, gable, tower anon—
Bier, too, is the cobblestone for a Monteton;
By the curs of the gutter o'ercome and wounded to death,—
Bitterly, bitterly he laughs with last breath.

* Translator: Margarete Münsterberg.

[318]

Monteton, where is thy wall?
Chalençon, where is thy sword?
Where is thy tower, Tournefort?

Our wall is the judge whom the king doth uphold,
Our sword is the army undaunted and bold,
Our tower the church — a steep tower and old!

But in Notre Dame on the altar — horrid sight! —
A naked woman performs a shameful rite,
A naked harlot bawls and screams and sings,
A wild and drunken roar through the cathedral rings.

And judges — judges too are by,
As never more vile saw the human eye!
A butcher with bloody apron presides,
And listens to lies with his fat ear — besides
His helpers: bullies and stable-boys plain,
The accuser a thief — ha, he can arraign!
And sentence on sentence the scythe whirring saith:
To death!
To death what is calm and noble still,
To death Cadore, to death d'Anville,
To death what better than they must be,
To death Clermont and Normandy,
To death!
Sentence on sentence the scythe whirring saith.

Monteton, where is thy wall? —

The dungeons of the Temple are deep, so deep,
Deeper the captives' woe till death's last sleep!
Half rotten the basket where rests the Duchess old,
As proud on this castaway seat as on throne of pure gold,
And about her are standing the Marshal and the Comtur,
The old names of the court, the Dames d'atour,
With delicate bows and smiles free and light.

Past the windows above, wheels thunder with might,
The pavement rebounds,
The singing resounds:
" Vive le son des canons! "

The howling of dogs that have torn their chains madly,
The roaring of those who celebrate badly,
The scream of the vulgar who long what is noble to blight,—

But down here all is quiet and light.
No forehead grows pale, no eye-lashes quiver,
As their lives they have lived, they meet death with no shiver!

A terrible clock is the prison-gate
Every half hour with its grating invidious,
Le Coucou, the hangman, long-armed and hideous,
Le Coucou steps out, who does not wait,
Who counts not the years of your young life — nay,
Not even the months till your wedding-day,
Comtesse de Neuilly!

Before the Duchess low she bends her dainty knee,
And with her three or four court ladies go,
And with her the cavaliers bow low,
With smiling lips she stands, and so:
" Votre bras, Monsieur le bourreau! "

The way through Paris, the way of blood,—
Red-hot now surges the song's wild flood:
" Vive le carmagnole! "

But they are not abashed at all,
They walk into death without timid delay,
They are walking with talk and with laughter gay,
What holds them together fast, they know:
The wall that into the sky doth grow,
Though the stones be falling,— the wall upward strives,
They smile in their death as they smiled in their lives.—

BÖRRIES VON MÜNCHHAUSEN

Monteton, that is our wall,
Chalençon, that is our sword,
That is our tower, Tournefort!

FAIRY TALE*

RADIANT eyes and cheeks glowing bright,
In the sofa corners, one left and one right.
And tightly clenched each little hand.

" So the king's son left the forest-land
With the princess, happy his way to wend,
And now the story is at an end! "

Two mournful sighs. Each mouth small and red
Is closed a while in silence dead,
Two sentimental voices then:
" Again, Papa, please, please, again! "

NINON! QUE FAIS-TU DE LA VIE?*

WHAT are you making out of life,
Ninon, Ninon?
A roaring farce and wild,
A play for the gutter's child,
With dancing, too, Ninon!

What are you making out of life,
Ninon, Ninon?
A tragedy will be your mirth,
The saddest tragedy on earth,
When you grow old, Ninon!

MINE OWN LAND*

THERE gleams a plough in Thuringian land,
Steered by a firm and happy hand
Through mine, oh mine own ground!

* Translator: Margarete Münsterberg.

And mine is the plough and the horses are mine,
And the silvery birch and the coal-black pine,
The herd by the forest edge found!

Is there in the world a happier lot
Than this one that I from my ancestors got?
At dawn in the saddle I ride on my round.
The gain of the mart push aside now, my hand:
There gleams a plough in Thuringian land,
That goes through mine own ground!

WHITE LILACS*

THE day was damp — the snails were out, for token —,
    But when the night above my garden hung,
See! the white lilacs into bloom had broken,
    And o'er the wall their heavy boughs were flung.

And on the wall great pearls with limpid lustres
    Were dripping from the lilac-blossoms pale,
While, woven through the fragrance of their clusters,
    Ran the gold ditties of the nightingale.

* Translator: Charles Wharton Stork.

RAINER MARIA RILKE (1875–   )

TWO POEMS TO HANS THOMA ON HIS SIXTIETH BIRTHDAY*

1

MOONLIGHT NIGHT

SOUTH German night, spread out beneath the
    moon,
    And mild as if all fairy-tales were there,
    The hours fall from the steeple in a swoon
    As if into the sea, to some deep lair,—
Now round about a rustling, calling fond,
Then silence hangs but empty in the air;
And then a violin (God knows from where)
Awakes and says quite tranquilly:
              A blonde —

2

THE KNIGHT

THE knight rides forth in blackest mail,
The rustling world to meet.
Out there he finds all: the day and the dale
And the friend and the foe and the castle's pale
And fair May and fair maid and the woods and the grail,
And God Himself doth never fail
To stand upon the street.
    But within the knightly armor yonder,
    Behind that gloomy wringing,
    Cowers Death and has to ponder, ponder:
    When will the blade come springing
    Over the iron wall,
    The stranger, freedom bringing,
    That from my hiding-place shall call
    Me forth, where I for many a day
    Am waiting, crouched and clinging,
    That I may stretch out once for all
    With play
    And singing.

* Translator: Margarete Münsterberg.

MAIDEN MELANCHOLY*

A YOUNG knight comes into my mind
As in some old, old saying.

He came.   Thus comes the storm to bind
You in its mantle, all entwined.
He went.   Thus you are left behind
By church-bell's blessing — to yourself confined
When you are praying —
You want to scream into the calm, but find
You do but gently weep, your face, inclined,
Into your cool scarf laying.

A young knight comes into my mind,
In arms I see him straying.

His smile, it was so mild and kind:
Like sheen of ivory enshrined,
Or like a homesick longing blind,
Like Christmas snow where dark ways wind,
Like turquoise stone that sea-pearls bind,
Like moonlight kind
On some dear volume playing.

AUTUMN DAY*

LORD: it is time.   The summer was so grand,
Upon sun-dials now Thy shadow lay,
Set free Thy winds and send them o'er the land.

Command to ripen those last fruits of Thine;
And give them two more southern days of grace
To reach their perfect fullness, and then chase
The final sweetness into heavy wine.

* Translator: Margarete Münsterberg.

Who now is homeless, ne'er will build a home.
Who now is lonely, long alone will stay,
Will watch and read and write long letters gray,
And in the lanes he to and fro will roam
All restless, as the drifting fall-leaves stray.

THE LAST SUPPER*

HERE they are gathered, wond'ring and deranged,
Round Him, who wisely doth Himself inclose,
And who now takes Himself away, estranged,
From those who owned Him once, and past them flows.
He feels the ancient loneliness today
That taught Him all his deepest acts of love;
Now in the olive groves He soon will rove,
And these that love Him will all flee away.

To the last supper table He hath led;
As birds are frightened from a garden-bed
By shots, so He their hands forth from the bread
Doth frighten by His word: to Him they flee;
Then flutter round the table in their fright,
And seek a passage from the hall. But He
Is everywhere, like dusk at fall of night.

FROM THE BOOK OF THE MONK'S LIFE*

I

I AM, Thou Anxious One. Dost Thou not hear
My surging senses break 'gainst Thee alone?
My feelings all, that snow-white wings have grown,
Fly round Thy visage in a sphere.
Dost Thou not see my soul now standing near,
Clad in a garb of stillness, facing Thee?
Doth not my spring-like prayer, as on a tree,
Grow ripe beneath Thy glance, that mighty beam?

* Translator: Margarete Münsterberg.

If Thou the Dreamer art, I am Thy dream.
But when Thou art awake, I am Thy will,
And then I gain a majesty sublime
And spread like star-lit heavens, calm and still,
Above this odd, fantastic city Time.

II

All those who live and move away
From Time, that city of distress,
All who their hands on stillness lay,
Upon a place where no roads stray,
That hardly doth a name possess,—
Thee, blessing high of every day,
They name, and write in gentleness:

But prayers alone are real — naught more;
Our hands are sanctified — behold!
What they have fashioned doth implore;
If one doth mow, or sacred lore
Doth paint — the very tools adore,
In strife a piety unfold.

And time in many shapes is told.
We hear of time and yet we do
The everlasting and the old.
We know that God us doth enfold
Grand like a beard, a garment too.
We lie within His glory's gold
As veins the hard basalt run through.

HERMANN HESSE (1877–)

TALK IN A GONDOLA*

HAT I dream, you ask? That yesterday
We had died, we two. In fair array —
Clad in white, our hair with flowers wound,
In our gondola we're seaward bound;
Bells from yonder campanile peal,
But the water gurgles round the keel,
Drowns the distant toll that's gently failing.
Onward, onward to the sea we're sailing,
Where the ships with masts that tower high,
Sombre shadows, rest against the sky,
Where on fishing-boats there gleam the moist
Deep-stained red and yellow sails they hoist,
Where the roaring mighty waves are swelling,
Where the sailors lurid tales are telling.
Through a gate of bluest water, deeply
Downward now our boat is gliding steeply.
In the depths we find a wid'ning range
Filled with many trees of coral strange,
Where in lustrous shells that hidden gleam
Pale gigantic pearls with beauty beam.
Silvery fishes pass us, glist'ning, shy,
Leaving tinted trails as they flit by,
In whose furrows other fish instead
Gleam with slender tails of golden red.
At the bottom, fathoms deep, we dream;
As if bells were calling it will seem,
Now and then, as if a wind that fanned
Sang us songs we cannot understand,

* Translator: Margarete Münsterberg.

[327]

Songs of narrow streets we long ago
Left behind, of things we used to know,
Songs so far, far off about the ways
That we trod in long forgotten days.
And with wonder we'll remember slowly
Now a street, now some cathedral holy,
Or the shouting of a gondolier,
Many names that once we used to hear.
Smiling then as children smile in sleep,
Moving still our silent lips we keep,
And the word will, ere it spoken seems,
Fall into oblivion, death in dreams.
Over us the mighty vessels float,
Sails are bright on many a sombre boat,
Snow-white birds in gleaming sunshine fly,
Glistening nets upon the water lie,
Spanning all, with arches high and true
Glows the heavens' vault of sunlit blue.

IN THE FOG*

In the fog to wander, how queer!
Lonely is every bush and stone,
No tree sees the other near,
Each is alone.

Once my world was full of friends,
When my life still had light;
Now that the fog descends,
Not one is in sight.

Only he is wise who knows
The steady gloom to fall
That slowly round him grows,
Severed from all.

* Translator: Margarete Münsterberg.

In the fog to wander, how queer!
Solitude is life's own.
No man sees the other near,
Each is alone.

AGNES MIEGEL (1879–   )

THE FAIR AGNETE*

HEN Sir Ulrich's widow in church knelt to pray,
From the church-yard toward her floated a
lay.
The organ on high did cease to sound,
The priests and the boys all stood spell-bound,
The congregation harkened, old man, child and bride
To singing like a nightingale so loud, outside:
" Dear mother, in the church where the sexton's bell rings,
Dear mother, hark outside how your daughter sings!
For I cannot come to you in the church — I must stay,
For before the shrine of Mary I cannot kneel to pray,
For I have lost salvation in everlasting time,
For I wedded the waterman with all his black, black slime.
My children they play in the lake with fishes fleet,
They have fins on their hands and fins on their feet,
Their little pearly frocks no sunlight ever dries,
Not death nor yet a dream can close my children's eyes —
Dear mother, oh I beg of thee,
Lovingly, longingly,
Wilt thou and all thy servants pray
For my green-haired water-sprites alway,
Will ye pray to the saints and to our Lady kind,
By every church and every cross that on the fields ye find!
Dearest mother, oh I beseech thee so,
Every seven years, poor I may hither go,
Unto the good priest tell,
The church door he shall open well —
That I may see the candle-light
And see the golden monstrance bright,

* Translator: Margarete Münsterberg.

[330]

That my little children may be told,
How the gleam of the Cup is like sunlight gold!''

The organ pealed when the voice sang no more,
And then they opened wide the door —
And while they all inside high mass were keeping,
A wave all white, so white, outside the door was leaping.

RICARDA HUCH

By Friedrich Schoenemann, Ph. D.

Instructor in German, Harvard University

RICARDA HUCH is not a poet of the people, nor for the people, but her writings have gained an evergrowing, readily applauding audience among readers who have feeling for artistic prose and a natural ear for style.

She won her reputation in three different lines: first, as the author of several valuable novels and novel-like prose works; second, as a lyric poetess of great refinement; and third, as the writer of a keen survey of older German Romanticism. Her novels are daring studies of life, and in them symbolistic romanticism and modern realism are blended uniquely. Her lyric poems are remarkable both for grace of form and for wide sweep of thought. Her work on the German Romantic School, through its deep psychologic insight, competes successfully with the best scholarly presentations of this subject. Thus Ricarda Huch combines in a high degree versatility of talent with the original quality of mind which gives to all her works a note of distinction.

The external facts of her life are quickly told. She was born in the city of Brunswick in 1864, and having lost her parents when she was still very young, was mainly educated by her grandmother, a charming woman of high spiritual gifts, to whom the granddaughter lovingly dedicated her first remarkable work, the drama *Evoë!* (1892). She lived at home until her twenty-third year, when she resolved to get a scholarly training. She went to the university of Zurich, Switzerland, one of the very first European universities admitting women to the study of

[332]

the arts and sciences. There, she studied history and literature, and received the degree of doctor of philosophy.

In Zurich she stayed for nearly ten years. After having taken her degree, she accepted, first, the position of a secretary at the public library, and then that of a high school teacher in Zurich. In 1896 she left that " town of hope and youth," as she has called it, and went to Bremen where, for a while, she taught in a Latin school for girls. In Vienna, where she afterward lived for a time, she married a dentist, Dr. Ceconi, whom she followed to Trieste and later to Munich. In 1906 she obtained a divorce from him. Soon afterward she married again, and with her second husband, a cousin of hers, who is a lawyer in Brunswick, she is living in her native town.

We have but scant information about the details of her outer life. The chief interest, therefore, will rest in her spiritual biography. And her inner history has, indeed, a special interest due to the rather abrupt change which at the beginning of her career came into her relations with the world around her. It must have been like a revolution to her when she left her North German home and went to the Swiss university town. She came of old patrician stock, one for whom life was made easy and never became " a mere drought and famine." Although imbibing readily the refinement and culture of her family traditions, from the beginning her mind was working against the limitations which she found in the life about her. Her instinct for self-development at last made her break traditional bounds, and free herself to become a woman after her own mind.

Ricarda Huch, who never takes her readers into her confidence, has not told us sufficiently what the new phase of her life in Zurich meant to her. Where even the landscape was new to her, everything must have attracted the young woman. She took part in the real student life, and met people who were congenial to her. And when she tried to grasp all her manifold impressions, and to give them adequate expression, she found herself a poet.

In 1890 she published her first volume of *Poems*, which was overlooked until she attained fame as a novelist. In 1907 appeared *New Poems*. In these two volumes of verse her poetic genius showed pronounced individuality. She is not, indeed, essentially a lyric poet, she is too problematic for that; besides, she does not like to open her heart, but rather comments on life. Only some smaller love songs and poems of nature are "pure feeling breathed in pure music." Yet even when she pours out her love, her hopes, and her sorrows, and charms us by the simple pathos of genuine lyric poetry, there still remains a certain sad touch of restraint and shyness, a marked feature which she shares with many a North German poet and, strangely enough, also with the Swiss Gottfried Keller, whom she congenially understands, and on whom she wrote an appreciative essay. But in addition to these short lyrics of rhythmic grace—and more important than they—there are dreamy fancies, sombre legends, and, above all, plastic renderings of historic episodes in her poems. These poems are like finely-cut cameos, all of a perfect art which reminds us of Konrad Ferdinand Meyer's masterpieces. Ricarda Huch surely was influenced by this master, and has quite remarkably assimilated his art.

Her inspiration, however, was purely personal. Some strong expressions of her poetic nature are to be seen in her tempestuous love of beauty and freedom, her mystic glorification of death, and her pronounced interest in history, all of which find their expression also in sundry prose works.

Her intense love of beauty, united with her acquaintance of Italy and thirst for historic knowledge, inspired her to write excellent essays on the heroes of Italy's political renaissance (*The Risorgimento*, 1908). And on those psycho-biographical sketches, poetical studies based on historical sources, so to speak, is based *The Life of Count Federigo Confalonieri* (1910), another prose work, half history, half fiction. It is the time of the Austrian sway

over Northern Italy which is pictured in this novel-like
work, a period which Elizabeth Barrett Browning, too,
described in *Casa Guidi Windows*. And like the English
woman, Ricarda Huch is intensely interested in the
struggle of the Italians to free themselves from the Austrian yoke, and to become a unified nation. Perhaps her
best tribute to the Italy of her thoughts and dreams was
paid in the *History of Garibaldi*, comprising two parts,
The Defense of Rome (1906) and *The Fight for Rome*
(1907).

But not Italy only was " a face full of remembrances "
to our author. She also undertook to revive a tragic epi-
sode of the German past, in her remarkable book, *The
Great War*, the first two volumes of which appeared in
1912–13. It gives the story of the Thirty Years' War in
the form of a prose epic.

There are very interesting chapters and passages in
these and kindred books, clever studies of human nature,
wonderful accounts of epoch-making events, interspersed
with lyric effusions and romantic ballads, but, on the whole,
we must say that the author has wasted in these works her
poetic strength on political themes too big for her grasp —
reminding us again of Elizabeth Browning in her Italian
period. Nevertheless, Ricarda Huch here as in all her work
proves herself a prose writer of fine skill and of an austere
beauty of language. To a certain degree, she is to German literature what Walter Pater is to the English art
of writing.

Although it is not seldom that the critic in her runs away
with the novelist, Ricarda Huch is no scholarly poet in
the disagreeable sense of the word. In the main, the solid
burden of her thought is steadied by her good taste and her
mastery of words. Her poet's heart lives in history. To
her, instinct for poetry must needs be instinct for history.
And from the very first of her career as an author she
showed a keen sense for historic retrospection.

It remains for us to consider Ricarda Huch's novels

which, like her poems, show her art fully. Her first printed novel was *Recollections of Ludolf Ursleu the Younger*, published in 1892. Ludolf Ursleu, the last scion of a North German patrician family, in the cell of a Swiss monastery where he has fled from the world, writes down the fateful history of his house. But the book is more than a mere family chronicle; it is the story of his sister Galeide's and his cousin Ezard's unhappy love. And the author takes great pains in tracing the psychological influence of their unlawful and secret passion on the different members of the Ursleu family. To highten the situation, fate lurks behind the scene: a horrible epidemic of cholera gives the story a gloomy background. We hear the author's constant cry: Let us obey nature, not the world, for nature is good and beautiful and brings happiness. But her characters who obey the call of nature rush to predestined ruin.

A slight variation of the same theme, that is a man of patrician family wavering between his wife and the woman he really loves, is found in another novel *Vita somnium breve* (*Life a Short Dream*), which was published ten years later. Here also, the leading motive is, "Oh life, oh beauty!" And the end of the story, like that of *Ursleu*, is chaos instead of beauty. In both of these novels resignation is the last note.

These books may be contrasted with two other novels: *From the Triumphgasse* (1902), the best known of Ricarda Huch's works, and *Of the Kings and the Crown* (1902), which is the author's most symbolic novel. In the *Triumphgasse* we are led into a totally different atmosphere of life: the slums of a large Italian town. The owner of a crowded tenement in the poorest part of the city describes the fates and frailties of his tenants. The most interesting group of figures is formed around the old woman Farfalla and her sons and daughters — all of them children of physical and moral wretchedness. Only the crippled Ricardo knows of a better life, where his soul dreamingly wanders about in blossoming gardens of eternal beauty. But he,

RICARDA HUCH

too, is no victor over circumstances, for the title of *Triumphgasse* (the street of triumph) is mere mockery. He dies "a fettered slave in the procession of life."

What the novelist portrays in these two books shows her changed attitude toward the humbler classes. In the two first mentioned novels, she is rather remote from the life of the toiling many; e. g., all the Ursleus "wear life like a beautiful garment or ornament." Then, when living in Trieste, as she told in a letter, Ricarda Huch saw what women and children had to suffer, and what it meant to be a social outlaw. Now, after this experience, she feels how a common man feels who has lost his happiness or, worse still, his self-respect and honor. And with subtle observation she pictures wildgrown human beings, men blinded with passion or even raging maniacs. She does not, however, raise her characters from the despair of drudgery and brutality to confidence in life. She is no Jane Addams, nor does she want to be more than an objectively observing bystander. She sketches life as it is, and her method is more analytic than intuitive. Yet she must not be classed with the naturalists, because she is too refined and tasteful. The plots and structures of most of her stories deserve unstinted praise, and delight lovers of artistically organized and well-proportioned novels. And over all her books there plays that symbolistic spirit of neo-romanticism which spreads a veil of beauty even over the ugliness of life.

It is impossible to sum up Ricarda Huch's life and message to our generation in a few sentences. All her books from first to last command our respect. She is not afraid of life as so many old and new romanticists are, nor is she ignorant of it. She has lived on terms of sympathetic contact with primitive people as well as with representatives of an overrefined civilization. She has thought honestly and does not shrink from declaring her criticism of life. But her characters are no winners in the fight of life, because her self-centred philosophy is a humane scepticism and even materialistic determinism. She does not lead us into the land of heart's desire where there has been given "beauty for ashes, the oil of joy for mourning, the garment of praise for the spirit of heaviness."

Ricarda Huch's prose has breadth and repose and calm development, and is, at the same time, full of variety and of admirable clearness. Her style possesses delicate precision, felicities of word and cadence, superb lines — in a word, an atmosphere of art which belongs only to the highest order of prose.

RICARDA HUCH

THE RECOLLECTIONS OF LUDOLF URSLEU THE YOUNGER (1892)

TRANSLATED BY MURIEL ALMON

CHAPTER I

F Martin Luther, who had the qualities necessary to become great, we learn that he was one day forced to see a man who was walking and conversing with him suddenly struck dead by lightning. This occurrence is said so to have shaken his spirit that he turned from the world, became a monk, and went into a monastery where he, unfortunately, did not remain. I have had the same experience, although the bolt which I saw blindly descend did not belong to the external world; but it was not less destructive.

All at once I saw, as I will now fully describe, that there is nothing, absolutely nothing in life that stands firm. Life is a bottomless and boundless sea; doubtless it has indeed a shore and sheltered havens, but we do not reach them alive. It is only on the tossing sea that there is life, and where the sea comes to an end life ceases too — just as a coral dies when it comes out of the ocean. And if we take the beautiful, iridescent jelly-fish out of the water, we find a hideous mass of gelatine in our hands. Now I think men and life are such that it is indeed possible to obtain peace and security, but only by renouncing life with its joyfully rippling waves, its changing colors, its wild tempests. Many people, particularly the young and the old who have experienced nothing, think that divers eternal rocks are to be found in the midst of the irresistible turmoil where the first wave merges with the second in the very moment of its formation, and so on continuously, and the last and the next instant are so closely united, like twins, that no splinter of " now " or " the present " can be wedged in between them. By these rocks they mean love and friendship and other feelings of the heart; for these make us feel happy and therefore good, and so people consider them sacred. But now, what eternal anything can come out of that childish thing, the human heart, that madcap that never learns to sit still in the school of life? That constantly flutters back and forth as if it hung on too long a stem like the leaves of the aspen-tree? It floats about like a skiff on the mighty sea of life, now shipping so much water that it sinks and despairs, now borne by the waves so high in the air that it approaches heaven, and then it shouts jubilantly and triumphantly. But it must come down again, and when down go up again. It may also run a smooth course or be becalmed so that it lies as still and anxious as if it were before Lodestone Rock. But whatever happens, it finds no haven at sea; havens are on land — that is the Other Shore.

My boat, after a fairly uneventful passage, ran into a great storm, was shipwrecked, and hurled upon the strand. I did not run easily into the bay, I was thrown up by the sea like Robinson Crusoe. My desert island and my Other Shore is the cloister of Einsiedeln. Here I abide now, and life lies forever behind me. But it has gone so well with me that though I no longer live, still I am not dead, but can look back from the shore over the broad waters that I crossed and think of my passage. I have always found that looking on was the most beautiful thing in life. He who marches in a magnificent procession swallows the dust, and sweats and chokes behind his mask; what good do his own splendid costume and the festive scenes all about do him? He sees nothing of them, except perhaps the nearest things, and even those imperfectly. But if one stands above on a high balcony or has simply climbed up on a garden gate, or even laboriously peeks out from a roof-gutter, has everything in sight as if he were God and it were all paraded before him just for his pleasure. So it amuses me to let the days of my bygone life pass before me like a procession. There will be strange figures to look at, gay flags, pictures, symbols, and spectacles. I can bid them move faster or slower, as I please, and can call the fairest and strangest ones up to me, to observe them more closely and to touch them. It is in this spirit that I write my experiences, hidden from every one; for it is no pious tale that I set down.

I will also tell something about my childhood and early youth; for if one does not know the cunning chick he judges the fowl unjustly, and one thinks less of the noble swan if he does not know that it was once an ugly young duckling. Those who have grown up with us continue to see in our faces the good, tender features of the child, and whoever has seen in a museum an old Viking vessel looks at our steamers with double curiosity and richer thoughts.

Chapter II

I was born in one of the Hansa-towns of Northern Germany, a town which I never can recall without execrations and never without tears. My father was a prosperous merchant; such men compose the respected portion of that community. They have usually seen many countries and peoples and have thus been able to acquire the polish of men of the world. As one cannot be as unrestrained abroad as at home, they have habituated themselves to a refined bearing and pleasing manners such as are not found in many circles; thus they make an impression, and it still fills me with pleasure to think myself back into a gathering of such men. Though they have many cares, yet everything is done on a large scale, and as long as they play any part in life, they have money and spend it freely. They do indeed lack a genuinely thorough education and do not care for it, although on no account would they appear to be without it. Life was fair and splendid in my youth, as among the Phæacians. This mode of life prevailed in our house too, and yet much was different from other houses. Possibly this was partly due to the fact that my family on my father's side had not always belonged to this Hansa-town, my grandfather being the first to settle there. My ancestors had been clergymen, whereof nothing remained in the family but an inclination to scholarliness and to what is above this earthly sphere.

The Ursleus of former times had perhaps been religious enthusiasts; those whom I remember no longer clung to religion, as indeed accords less with the genius of our times. They occupied themselves with poetry, the fine arts, and the sciences, to be sure only superficially and amateurishly, but for that very reason with all their hearts and full of enthusiasm, and not at all like the rest of the Phæacians, so as to be able to make use of their attainments in society. For we lived mostly by ourselves, that is to say in our own family, which was indeed large enough.

My father, Ludolf Ursleu, Sr., unfortunately had to waste his splendid powers on mercantile affairs and cares. But out of consideration for us and from a certain estheticism he bore this silently and alone. For in his heart he looked upon his occupation as a necessary evil for the purpose of acquiring money, and despised it; in our house it was considered the real business of a human being to wear life like a beautiful garment or an ornament, to carry one's head high and to be cheerful. Perhaps my father considered that the most dignified conception because my mother seemed to be made for the realization of it.

How beautiful she was! When one looked at her, one did not indeed think first of her beauty, for she was perfect and for that reason far less striking than a woman who lacks something. But it made one cheerful and glad to look at her countenance, and as far as I know it never occurred even to women to envy her this distinction. She never showed off her beauty, although she took a great

pleasure in it; for she was childlike in the way that we
read of savage peoples being childlike, and like them she
could have draped herself with bright beads and laughed
at her reflection in the water, without ever thinking that it
was she herself who looked out so charmingly. Everything
she said and did was as pure and simply original as a
spring at the spot where it bubbles out of the earth high
up in the glorious wilderness. As a boy I often used to
look at her and try to think how she would look in old age;
that made me pensive, for I could no more imagine it than
one can think of the Venus of Milo as an aging woman.
She seemed in truth to belong to the light-hearted, immortal
gods. My father too was a strong and handsome man, but
thought and worry and years did not pass over him without engraving their furrows. When I heard the myth of
the goddess of dawn and her mortal husband, how he continued to wither in her rosy arms, I always thought of my
parents, less as they were then than as I imagined them in
the future. Such a comparison would never have occurred
to my mother herself, for she seldom thought of herself
and she was not in the least sentimental. Nothing, neither
love nor hate, could have burned into a passion in her.
To a certain extent her happy nature was in league with
her beauty; what she felt was never so violent that it could
have injured the latter.

I, the eldest child, was named after my father. I resembled him little, however, inwardly or outwardly, yet still
enough to feel my affinity with him strongly in the presence
of other people. I had hotter blood than he. That was the
cause of my living a wilder youth than he would ever have
desired or allowed himself; and it was also the reason why
later on my youth left me sooner than his had done, and
that I became a morose old man at an age when he had still
been a stately figure.

After me came my sister Galeide, of whom I shall have
most to say in these pages. Because she was far from
being as beautiful as my mother we never thought of her

appearance. Yet she was really a delightful creature, with soft round limbs, comfortable and cosy to have on one's lap like a young kitten, quiet and contented. Hence she was petted and spoiled and she accepted it all calmly and rewarded it with but little tenderness. I must say, however, that she could be very fond and loving when once she had conceived an affection for any one; she was never actually cross with anybody. She wanted people to let her go her own way and did not dislike being alone. Then she would lie in the sun and play theatre with the clouds, or perhaps she would merely dream, and generally she had a kitten, a rabbit, or some other animal with her, and she seemed in general to prefer animals to people. It was remarkable how animals would always seek her out and how tame they were with her. She was usually so gentle and peaceable that our relations all got into the habit of calling her " the good child " or " good little Galeide." I never called her so, for I always said to myself, " she is not really good, she does what she likes and it happens to be just what others like too."

She was always very loving toward me and, although I was several years older, often in a maternal way. Altogether it was peculiar how she could be at once so childish and so motherly; she continued to be both as long as she lived, and she was much else besides, of which I will speak later.

Chapter III

Whoever calls my native city beautiful loves wide and straight streets, large and clean houses, and rectangular squares. I abhor all that. There are old quarters there too, but their age is evident only in dirt, narrowness, and closeness, not in a dignified aspect full of memories. Suabia is the place to live, in those ancient free towns where one walks about as in a lovely fairy tale of bygone days. In my boyhood, to be sure, I understood nothing of this charm, partly because I was not acquainted with it, but in those days I should have lacked the necessary knowledge and experience.

It is different with nature; the understanding of her language is born in us. Indeed, she is the oldest, faithfulest, and truest friend of man. A curse lies on the man at whose cradle she does not stand and over whose youth she does not watch; his soul is never set free, his bosom can never wholly unburden itself, he is like a seed that lacks the sun. And I should have been a different man if I had been born in Switzerland, for I believe my genius was of no bad quality and but little was lacking to make me really amount to something. But little or much, if anything at all is lacking the man fails and amounts to nothing.

When I was a boy of thirteen my parents took me with them to Switzerland. At that time I was still passably good, diligent, and sensible. Now after I had looked at the mountains for a time and become accustomed to them, a truly heavenly feeling of happiness, such as I had never dreamed of, came over me. I loved the woods and the white peaks with tempestuous affection, humility, and dread. I can still recall my innocent and blissful feelings at that time, and cannot do so without emotion. I think I see the friendly little boy under the kind, mighty fir-trees and among the boulders with their weather-beaten faces. Galeide was with us too and without showing any great astonishment she rushed into this beautiful landscape with wild joy, as if she had never known anything different. While I loved to wander about the beautiful woods in the valley, she constantly desired to climb the high mountains, in whose ascent she showed amazing strength and skill for a child of her age. Whenever we reached a summit, she would run ahead, give a Bacchanalian shout of triumph, and shake her locks in the wind.

This annoyed me, for I thought it Indian-like, unesthetic, and altogether unmaidenly. When I think of it now I realize that it was at any rate characteristic of my sister Galeide.

Once while we were in the mountains she was presented with a marmot, whereat she showed an absurd joy which also annoyed me. And still more so the silly way she behaved with the animal, as if it were much better than any person. Later, when we were at home again, the mountain animal was out of place in our city life and our parents took it away from Galeide. As soon as she found it out, her grief caused a violent fever; I can still see her crouched down in a chair covered with gold-colored plush, singing strangely in a low voice in her delirium. Her condition was so disquieting,— and by no means simulated — that the animal had to be given back to her. The most curious thing was this: when it died, just while she happened to be out, the whole family was seized with serious apprehension of her wild outbursts of grief. No one wanted to be the bearer of such terrible news (at which all the sensible and cleanly inmates of the house really struck up heartfelt and joyful songs of praise). With the utmost gentleness and consideration she was finally told of the death, but lo and behold, not a single tear reddened her mild eyes. She stroked the furry little body lovingly and pitied the tiny animal in the most graceful terms for having had the thread of his merry life cut so early. She also kept him in truly faithful remembrance and was always glad to tell little stories and anecdotes about Urselino (her name for the unfortunate creature); and she never wanted to have another. But I always suspected that she was glad of the pretty picture that she had been able to add to her store of memories and recollections.

While my younger sister was still putting all her time into such perfectly simple and childlike hobbies, I was entering upon my first love affair. I cannot refrain from telling this pretty little story here; it was so innocent and proper,— for the first and last time, unfortunately. If I had only always been content with the soul of that thirteen-year-old boy! Many things would not have occurred which gave me little happiness at the time and of which I am ashamed now.

Well, then, we were at the Wallensee, that inexpressibly beautiful lake which is accused of treacherous ferocity. I loved it the more for its hostility to the people that sailed upon it, and was confident at the same time that it would know I was not to be reckoned among them, but was a special kind of man who understood it and held it sacred. Moreover, I thought it would be a blissful lot to be buried beneath those green wave-mounds and to be able to look up motionless through the moving emerald glass into the blue sky above it. But my parents never allowed me to go out on the lake alone. I felt deeply insulted by this at first and thought myself eternally disgraced when the boatman once sent his little daughter, who was to all appearances younger than I, to accompany me. This child, Kordula, nimbly grasped the big oars and began to row, and I watched with utter amazement her thin but very graceful brown arms as they worked so bravely and untiringly. Her hair was a little tangled, but this, contrary to my usual taste, I soon found very charming; her dark eyes were not large, but fiery and not without a certain good-humored cunning in their expression. When she began to speak, however, my sense of beauty was outraged and I began to criticize her irritably for her native dialect. But she resented this greatly, saying that that was beautiful and patriotic; but we Germans had to serve kings and bow down like slaves — in short, we were not free and could not do as we liked. That irritated me to the utmost and I remembered with pleasure that I too was a republican, which, however, I could not make her understand. Soon my arrogance died down entirely and resolved itself into admiration of the daring Swiss girl. In the shadow of the gigantic Chur-firsten mountains, on the clear water of the mountain lake, it was not difficult for me to think of my country as shamefully enslaved, and the more vigorous character of the Swiss, the strength and hardiness of the mountain people, I thought to be simply the result of their fortunate state of freedom. In this way the brown-skinned girl Kordula merged for me with the noblest thought a man can think, with the vision of freedom, and my heart grew so full that it was actually heavy to carry; but the fuller the heart, the more light-heartedly does one live.

In spite of her well-intentioned patriotic boasting, Kordula had no little respect for people from far-away cities, with their more refined habits, so that her admiration for me was about equal to mine for her, and it was this that made our love so delightful. My parents looked upon it as a charming idyll and did not interfere with us at all, nor did they even betray the amusement we afforded them.

One evening we were out in the boat as the sun was going down. A train sped past with a snort. A feeling of cosiness and content came over me as I saw it rushing away without my having to go with it; for that would have to come some time, but not yet. After it had passed the stillness seemed deeper than before. The ice-gray of the mountain tops gradually took on a warm violet color in the light of the sun. The lake was perfectly calm and seemed itself to be looking breathlessly at the miracle about it. While I felt unutterable infinite emotions, Kordula's feelings formed into something quite definite, and she suddenly began to repeat a sentimental patriotic poem which she might have learned at school.

I was affected by it beyond measure. Hot despair possessed me at the thought that I was not a Swiss and could not call these mountains and this beloved green water mine. Now I too began to make verses, addressed them all to Kordula, and gave them to her. Whether she understood them or not, she saw at least that they rhymed, and so to her I was a poet; for she could not yet distinguish between good and bad verses. Thenceforth she regarded me with increased respect and liked particularly to look at my eyes. Once I asked her what she saw in them; she answered with a very pretty simile, " I see your thoughts swimming about in them like little fishes twinkling in a lake, many, many of them.'' I blushed and was ashamed, and yet I was proud and glad as never before.

In the end we had to take leave of each other after all; that was heart-breaking. But it was worst of all when we were at home again. My enjoyment in going out was spoiled, and on my way to school I would obstinately keep my eyes on the ground so that I need not see the hated stone houses and the bare horizon. I liked best to sit in the house and cry and cry with unconsolable homesickness, and the greatest bliss that I could imagine was a grave in Lake Wallen beneath the crags of the Churfirsten. It was great misery and, on the whole, I was not so wrong to cry. When we leave nature we leave the good and the beautiful, and above all, happiness. I should have been born a shepherd-boy in the Alps; then I should probably be sitting there still yodeling and shouting, instead of checking a creeping tear when a sound from the mountains echoes across into my bare cell here in the monastery.

Chapter IV

I have so far said nothing about my great-grandfather. If, as I later realized, our whole family did not fit into this century, my great-grandfather, Ferdinand Olethurm, my mother's grandfather, was still more out of tune with the present generation; as indeed he had actually sprung from another time, when nothing as yet was known of the new German Empire, gallophobia, and the social problem. His patriotism recognized only his Hanseatic town, which he cherished in his heart as lovingly as if he himself had carried stones to build it. Although to this extent he was a true patrician of the old style, yet he possessed such a remarkable mobility of spirit that nothing new, however far it might lie beyond the horizon of his youth and his maturity, was incomprehensible to him, still less indifferent. What young people found so extremely refreshing and comforting in him was that he never considered an event or an idea primarily from the standpoint of morality, as many would perhaps expect of such an old and venerable man. If any one pleased him, that person might later have turned out to be a footpad or a pirate, and still my great-grandfather would have found an explanation. So great was his sympathy for the life of the heart; for after all, everything that happens in the world is in the last analysis explicable, even necessary. But otherwise Ferdinand Olethurm could have dispensed with an explanation and would have gone on cheerfully loving and hating as his heart dictated. For this reason the impression he made was less that of clarified wisdom than of inexhaustible youthful strength and indestructible individuality, and thus he dominated men and held them captive under his influence.

He loved Galeide and me beyond measure, her even somewhat more than me; partly perhaps because she was a girl, and then because, with all her softness, she could at times display an iron inflexibility and firmness which may have seemed as pleasing to him as a raisin in a rice pudding. Altogether she was considered a remarkable child, although I could not say for what reason. Just as little could I say why every one in our house felt such an insistent desire for her presence, since it sometimes happened that you were quite unaware of it, even though she was in the room with you for an hour. My parents could not make up their minds to send her to boarding-school, as is customary; instead of that, and in order to conform somewhat to the prevailing principles of education, they decided to take a Frenchwoman into the house, from whom Galeide should learn the timidly admired language of our otherwise hated neighbors.

Among the young girls who answered the advertisement there was one from French Switzerland, called Lucile Leroy. It was now several years since I had been in Switzerland, but the mountain land still dwelt in my memory, beautiful and spotless in the brilliant sunshine, and it pleased me uncommonly that a girl from that wonderful country was to come to our sad North. My parents always had a taste for something exceptional, and to us a Swiss was as rare as one of our oysters or a Pomeranian goose-breast was on his mountains. Galeide said little about the project, although it concerned her especially; but she seemed rather sorry than glad. It was settled that Lucile was to come to us; all went so smoothly that not the slightest sign could be observed of how fateful this choice was to become for us. For with the girl's dainty feet, destiny set his brazen sole on our untroubled threshold and came, disguised and fearful, into the midst of our comfortable Phæacian life. Not that any evil proceeded from Lucile herself, nor did it make itself apparent for some time to come. My parents received her with an open-hearted kindness such as is not offered to many girls in similar positions. But the manner in which she accepted it soon showed us that she well deserved it. Clever and active as she was, it was easy for her to do what was expected of her and, conscious of this, her behavior in other ways was that of a welcome guest; she made no one unhappy by a demeanor of forced and obtrusive humility, but enjoyed the friendship she received and repaid it with ardent love and devotion. She was vivacious, always could bring up things that lent zest to the conversation and — what my parents most desired — she discussed them in a foreign way and generally from a point of view which we were in the habit of overlooking, for she had grown up in very different circles and circumstances from ours. Relegating nature to the second place and underestimating it, she strove consciously and methodically for the things which we had absorbed unconsciously, the manifold educational influences of a large city. She respected a highly cultured mind above everything, and sought with admirable zeal and diligence to acquire such culture herself. Everything she saw in our home delighted her: the high, spacious rooms of our house, its arrangement with a view more to beauty than to usefulness, and our whole manner of life, of which much the same could be said. But enchanted as she was, she still remained, more than she knew, herself, and could never break completely through the wall that surrounded the well-cultivated flower, fruit, and vegetable garden of her soul. Consequently she disapproved of some things that were done in our house and expressed her opinion with a freedom which pleased my parents the more because they were not obliged to conform to her views. They enjoyed hearing her lay down her principles in an eloquent sermon, and even began to regret that Galeide lacked such a manner of speech and thought, for Galeide spoke little of principles, nor had she any, or if she did sometimes remark that she considered this or that good or bad, that she would or would not do this thing or that, she said so brusquely and bluntly, often using shocking expressions — though it must be admitted that when uttered by her gentle voice they did not sound as objectionable as if another girl had used them. Nevertheless this habit of hers came to irritate me.

Although Galeide was grieved to feel how much our parents appreciated this strange and interesting creature, yet she did not make Lucile suffer for her jealousy; I must mention this as a proud and admirable trait of her character. The two girls felt the difference of five or six years in their ages relatively little, and I remember, anyway, that people talked to my sister, who in some respects was still a wild and most unreasonable child, as they would have to a mature person. Lucile and she were like sisters together, or rather far more intimate than sisters commonly are. Galeide even vied almost imperceptibly with Lucile and overwhelmed her with tender, loving marks of her affection. Lucile returned this love with no less wrapt intensity, indeed, perhaps, she even outdid Galeide in this respect. She showed me that sometimes, when I accused Galeide of having too little desire for goodness, which, by the way, I not only did not possess myself, but, at that time, considered actually objectionable in a man. "She does not want it," said Lucile, "and why should she? She is good. You know, the essence of genius is that it does not have to follow existing laws, but itself gives the world new laws by what it does. So it will be with Galeide and that too is the secret of the irresistible charm that she exercises." This seemed to me to be an immensely exaggerated remark.

Lucile and I said "thou" to each other. She sometimes treated me very much as a boy, which, however, I refused to stand. And I did succeed in swinging myself up onto a higher plane in her estimation, thanks to my having read a great deal and to the passable liveliness of my mind, which enabled me to be her welcome partner in those discussions of *belles-lettrse* which she loved. Before she came I had imagined that she must look like Kordula of Wallen Lake, although that would have been an incomprehensible freak of nature. This notion stirred my spirit agreeably, although I had already begun to tread other and less edifying paths of love. But I soon got over the fact that Lucile was not Kordula, for she made an impression on me and I was flattered to find that she was not unwilling to talk to me. Her presence kept me within beneficial bounds, at least to the extent that I sought to suppress the consequences of my recklessness. If I appeared at home with the slightest suggestion of intoxication, or in the miserable mood that follows the excessive revels of young people, she did not hesitate to show me her disapproval and contempt in the sharpest manner. I did indeed resent this with presumptuous and disagreeable sensitiveness, but still I feared such disputes and took pains to avoid the causes of them. At bottom, to be sure, I did not really improve; her influence was not strong enough for that. And how could it have been? I yielded to every impulse, good or bad, provided it could be carried out in a way that suited me. I wanted to be a man of the world, and was a fool; I wanted to be one who knows how to live, and learned nothing but how to die early. I was like a dog that in snapping at the reflection of his bone lets the bone itself fall into the water and cannot find it again.

Chapter V

I can scarcely await and yet I dread to see approaching, in the course of my recollections, the shadow of the man to whom my soul clung as to no other. I speak of my cousin Ezard Ursleu, the only human being I should like to have been, for he pleased me better than myself. His father, my uncle Harre, was a prominent physician in my native town. But as far back as I can remember he no longer practised except in a few friends' families, where he had been the family physician for years. For the rest, he constantly sought, and with success, to explore and advance his science, and had not only an enormous knowledge of his profession, but also in other fields, for, after the manner of our family, he occupied himself with many things which by rights did not concern him. To a complete man there is indeed nothing that does not concern him, but our earthly conditions do not allow the growth of such: for earth showers infinite plenitude, and the dish we use to catch it is shallow and tiny. Harre Ursleu, however, was more justified in following this course than most people, because he grasped more than they, and he could not be accused of knowing many things rather than much. His good health and moderate habits enabled him to work and think for hours. He was no book-worm, however, but on the contrary displayed such brilliance of mind that people often unjustly doubted its depth; he enjoyed life, too, and more than many a strict moralist thought permissible. But just as little as he listened to them, just so attentively did he obey his nature, never undertaking more than he could bear without harm to himself, and considering it a disgrace to miss any scientific meeting or to neglect any piece of work for the sake of a material pleasure. Thus he was a man of mark and an acceptable example to young people, since he represented the two things they consider worth striving for: famous distinction in one's profession and the ability to appreciate and enjoy the tidbits of life.

His son, although very different, was his greatest pride. He intended him for a great career; and where could better prospects of that be found than in the old Hanseatic town? As a transatlantic merchant he might direct the current of gold in a magnificent way to his own and his fatherland's benefit, or, as a member of the government, enjoy, in a small circle, the standing of a prince. It is well known that the rulers of an aristocratically governed republic often think more of themselves than do the kings by the grace of God, to which opinion they may indeed be entitled; for our princes today are all descended only from vassals, whereas of the families in the old cities some rightly call themselves descendants of the free people under the Germanic conquerors. After considering and discarding other plans, my uncle thought it best for his son to study law, as he might thus most easily reach the head of the government.

I was not yet twenty years old when Ezard came back from the university and I really made his acquaintance for the first time. He came just on the day of Galeide's confirmation and was at the dinner given to celebrate it. From the real heroine of the day, who looked very slender, pale, and mournful in her black gown with a train, attention soon wandered entirely to him. Is it not like Odysseus coming among the Phæacians I thought, for it was thus that I had imagined that divine sufferer, not perhaps bearing in his face the traces of sorrows endured, but betraying in his appearance the opponent and conqueror of fate. And there is no antagonist whose overthrow fills us with such a feeling of strength and satisfaction as fate. Yes, indeed, he moved with the step and bearing of a victor. One began to feel secure when he was near, because he inspired the confidence that he could overcome all the disagreeable things of life. How did he do this? For a man he was not tall; he was slender and well-proportioned. His beauty was moderate though noble, and rendered highly impressive by the fact that it fused with his spiritual expression; one might have thought that his face owed its beauty entirely to the nobility of his expression, and again that it was only the outward harmony of his features that brought out the appearance of spirituality.

I felt all this at that time without fully acknowledging it to myself, for I was just at the age to be presumptuous, and besides was *too highly gifted* and endowed to be content with the rôle of an admiring satellite, without trying myself to be somebody. My cousin Ezard possessed the grace of innate, natural modesty which may well be called the twin sister of beauty; I mean the beauty that reveals the gleam of the fine spirit that fills and animates it; comparable to a green goblet of Venetian glass which does not disclose its true soul till the deep gold of mellow Rhine wine illuminates it. Scarcely any one, I imagine, had ever refused my cousin Ezard love and recognition; thus he had no reason to be vain. It is said that shepherds have a peculiar knack of taking hold of their animals, so that they patiently submit to the shearing. Ezard had such a happy knack in the treatment of people, who always showed him the best that was in them, as much, to be sure, to their own advantage as to his.

It soon appeared that Ezard was particularly attracted to Lucile. After the manner of highly developed men who possess a few feminine qualities in addition to the advantages of their own sex, he admired chiefly those women who were distinguished by independence, individuality, and energy. For on her part, Lucile was instantly enchanted with Ezard. But she concealed it under a graceful coyness, contradicted no one as much as him, whereby she could be exceedingly diverting and provoking, and so to speak built a fortified wall about herself, giving him, with his youthful strength and love of action, a new incentive to win this girl.

Uncle Harre loved to measure swords with her in conversation. She admired him; the restless activity of his mind, which would rush forward like a waterfall, break up every beam that fell upon it into all the colors of the rainbow, and play with the many colored jewels, dazzled and delighted her. And he was amused by the assured intrepidity with which she attacked and rebuked him, now in this, now in that. Religion was frequently the subject of their disputes. Lucile, following the traditions of her family, was a Roman Catholic. This led my uncle to banter and tease her about what he considered monstrous excrescences of that faith, things which a clever talker can easily represent as fantastic and irrational, but she did not dislike this, as it gave her the opportunity to defend her belief in eloquent effusions. On such occasions Galeide felt ashamed that she was not drawn more to one party than to the other, and would gladly have lighted a tiny flame of sincere faith in her innocent breast. My great-grandfather usually supported whichever party seemed to be the weaker, or he would form a new one for himself by extolling Buddhistic or, it might be, Parsee doctrines as the treasure-house of Divine wisdom.

Uncle Harre favored his son's affection as long as he considered it merely a flirtation, but he declared emphatically that it must never develop into anything serious. A marriage with a Swiss governess was not what he had hoped for Ezard. Nevertheless this prejudice might have been overcome, for Harre Ursleu was no ordinary seeker after worldly advantages and still less a barbaric father who would have refused to let his child's heart have its own life. But Lucile was not the woman to make a really significant impression on him. "She is a clever little thing," he said of her, "her mind twinkles continually like a fixed star; but I prefer the quiet, steady radiance of the great planets. And I ask myself, what could she pose to a sculptor for? A witch? Absurd! A Venus? Impossible! Diana? God forbid! She is too small. She might most easily be imagined as Minerva if, again, it were not for her inadequate size. Her body is too small for a grand woman, and her mind is too big for a pretty little doll. I enjoy sitting beside her in company, but I do not want to have her in my family.''

Ezard was not in the least shaken by his father's opinion. Many qualities may have pleased him in Lucile which Uncle Harre himself possessed and therefore could not see or could not appreciate in others. Ezard wooed her, and in the light of his love, as in that of Bengal fire, she was prettier, more fiery, stronger, than before. Galeide's loving attentions began where Ezard's had to come to an end. She bore her happiness joyfully, as a great wave carries its proud, glistening crown of foam. Life was merry at that time in the house of the Ursleus; the way was beginning to lead uphill and every one was still conscious of such a supply of strength that he was quite ready to spend it freely.

CHAPTER VI

I HAVE given up wishing wholly and altogether, for should I have gone into this cloister if I had still cared to wish? I have often looked on and seen that: he who wishes is like one who shakes an apple-tree; the fulfilment falls on his head and makes it bleed. Still I cannot shut out one wish, that my student days might come again, the time in which one chooses the style in which he will build the house of his life. God above, how immature and ill-advised I was when I stumbled into that task! I looked on aspiration and striving as sentimentalities of past ages. Work, I thought, is slavery and the fate of the unfit, as potatoes are the food of the poor. The people who impressed me most were those who ate only the tips of asparagus stalks and the soft part of oysters. So I must learn to consume life, I thought, just nipping the tidbits, so as to get the enjoyment and the taste without the burden of digestion. If I had applied this principle to the actual process from which I borrowed the figure of speech I should at least have come out of the struggle of life with one trophy: a good digestion. And I should not count that little. But I did not merely nip and skim off the cream, rather I took active part in all carousals, and wanted to lead in this more than in other things; in no regard was such an ambition as difficult for a student of that time to gratify as in this. I wanted to be a good fencer too, and with much practice succeeded pretty well. I think I never devoted so much industry and perseverance to anything as to the use of the rapier; nor did I do so, like those godly athletes at the beginning of the century, in order to toughen the body which was to fight for my fatherland, but for the sake of winning the esteem of my comrades, of whom scarcely one in ten could judge of a man's real worth, much less amount to anything himself.

I might fitly say nothing about my studies, for they took up the very least part of my time. I studied law, principally because Ezard had studied it and because I cherished the unreasonable conceit, without indeed being clear about it in my own mind, that if I only roughly imitated his conduct, I should quite automatically become like him.

I had my love-affairs too, but there was none among them that it gives me pleasure to remember. Still, here and there, there were a few little things that are worth setting down. Although I had resolved not to retrace these paths of my life, yet one or another of them entices me with its graceful windings or wooded hollows to turn meditatively into it. For after all it is errors that make us wise. The fire burned St. Augustine too before he came forth purified. Even though I do not presume to be a saint, yet it seems to me that my nature did not seek reprehensible pleasures merely for enjoyment, but to train itself for the better by experience of the worse. This is the distinction between a wild, profligate youth and a quieter but more corrupt rake.

In a university town where I spent several semesters there was a girl in a little cottage who sold sweets and all

sorts of beverages. It was a mark of distinction among
the young fellows there to have once possessed this girl's
favor. Hence all the students liked to appear at her shop,
although they disdained the dry, stale goods she displayed.
They paid for them without eating anything, and that made
it all the grander. The girl's name was Georgine; she had
a white skin and was noticeable for her reddish hair. By
nature and from habitual sitting in her shop she was very
lazy and slow in her movements, which prevented her from
appearing vulgar. I was head over heels in love with her,
and I must say that she had a beauty that is usually met
with only in fairy tales or dreams. When she drew herself
up to her full height, raised her heavy eyelids a little, and
indolently moved her full lips, one expected to hear something like this: " I am the queen of the sea and have a
palace of mother of pearl and chairs of coral; swear to
be true to me and you may go with me." She wore her
shining hair like a crown and every polished glass bead in
it like a priceless diamond. Every one knew that she
lavished her favors on the highest bidder, but this did not
enter the mind of the man to whom she would grant a kiss
as if he were a beggar and she were tossing him an alms
from her abundance. She was sluggish in feeling too, and
had let herself be loved, as a lapdog lets itself be stroked
by many hands. She was the same before and afterward.
Altogether there was something about her like a beautiful
animal or a half-human being, like a nixie with a fish's
tail. It was no trick to win as much of her favor as she
gave to every one who was not actually displeasing to her.
But that was not enough for me. It became clear to me
that nothing could give me such a tremendous prestige as
to win Georgine altogether for myself alone. To this my
thoughts and efforts were now directed. I may say that
ambition was not my only motive; my heart was still fresh
and unspoiled enough not to be satisfied with scraps. I
did not want to buy a pig in a poke, I wanted not only a
body but a soul as well, though to be sure I demanded of

it nothing more than that it should be able to love me. And Georgine really had such a soul, as now appeared. She was like the leaf of the wig-tree, which does not smell until it is rubbed and bruised; up to that time no one had ever tried to press out the essence.

I used to tell her about my parents and my sister and the way we lived. She did not understand much of that, but this at least she did grasp, that I loved her, if not more, at least more worthily than the others. And without doubt that was the principal reason why she gave me more than all the others. A man's nature shows itself not only when he does great deeds, but just as well when he comes into a room and says good morning. An exceptional man kisses and lets himself be kissed differently from a very ordinary one, and so Georgine may have seen that her prey was rarer than usual, one that she could not get again any day. Then she began to love me more and more, to be anxious and jealous — so ready are most creatures to mount higher, if only a ladder is held for them. This took her somewhat out of her own nature, and with her serenity she lost also something of the splendid decorum of an Oriental harem queen; but as I was already at the height of my passion, this no longer disturbed me, but, on the contrary, strengthened my feelings.

For my sake she now gave up all the others and became unapproachable because I wanted to have it so. This did indeed gain for me the hoped for prestige, not without its own disagreeable features. It was traditional that beautiful Georgine should lean back in her chair, pour out lemonade, and smile sleepily with her green eyes. How were the young fellows to treat the beautiful woman now? They would willingly have rocked on their knees before her, but to feel a little respect and esteem for a soul that was forsaking the worse for the better, that was beyond them. On the contrary they felt the change to be a grievous insult. Georgine, however, paid no attention to that, but continued to lay bleeding hearts at my feet by way of love-gifts, as an Indian gives his beloved the scalps of slain pale-faces. This pleased me immensely and her not less. She treated the rejected ones more disdainfully than was justifiable or advisable after what had gone before. So it went so far that a low-minded wretch took a most fiendish and unworthy revenge on her by pouring sulphuric acid over her beautiful white face and thus destroying forever that wonderful work of nature. It was misery to look at her. Her golden hair shone above her disfigured countenance like the sun above a desolate, smoking battlefield. She was not only no longer beautiful, she was hideous. I sat there and wept as a father weeps over the ravished body of a lost child. Unhappy Georgine was completely crushed. With trembling hands she took down her hair and pressed it to her eyes. "Oh, my beautiful face! My beautiful face," she groaned, and I never heard another word from her. She moaned these words with such terror of soul and pleading lamentation that it wrung one's heart, although they concerned only an external, transitory possession. But one felt that her heart had every reason to break; for she was now entirely bereft, denuded, disgraced, and poor. Pitiful wretch that I was, I was afraid that she would beg me to go on loving her as before. But that did not enter her mind; on the contrary she vehemently sent me away and would not even take any money from me. I did not wait to be told that twice, and immediately went on a long trip to be able to give myself up to my thoughts, which I felt to be very deep and significant.

In the meantime the wretched woman drowned herself. She had written her last request on a scrap of paper in large crooked letters, asking that when she lay in her coffin they would cover her face with her hair. This was done, and it seemed quite symbolic; for as the mantle of gold covered the disgrace of her face, so her beauty, while she was alive, had spread its divine wings above her poor, disfigured soul, so that she was gladly forgiven for the sake of her noble intercessor. And her strange misfortune touched all hearts, so that every honor was shown her at her funeral: people unconsciously did homage to nature, which rules above all, pouring out her horn of plenty where she pleases, solely at the dictates of her own whim; but the whims of nature are law.

I no longer know whether I tried to pretend to myself that I was the hero of this sad adventure. At any rate, I came out of it in a state of deep-seated depression and imagined that fate was blighting my well-earned pleasures and showing me the most beautiful fruits only to snatch them maliciously from my outstretched hands, like another Tantalus. In reality it was quite otherwise and I, or rather the mixture of my soul-forces, was to blame for everything. Among the birds there are the swallows that sail hither and thither, the warbling larks, the wag-tails that trip up and down and dip their tails, and the waddling, splashing ducks. The proud and sure flight of the falcon, who flings himself into the air like an arrow and seizes what pleases him, and then again hovers above the earth as if he were hanging from the sky on a golden thread, is not bestowed on every man.

Summary of Chapters VII–XI

[Ezard and Lucile Leroy fell in love, and Uncle Harre's attempt to prevent the match by requiring Lucile to change her faith was frustrated by Lucile's consenting to do so.

A few weeks before the wedding Lucile went home, accompanied by Ludolf and his mother. She concealed her change of faith, and the visit was pleasant, as Mrs. Leroy, though living as proprietress of a large farm, had the cultivation of a city woman. Ludolf found Lucile's brother Gaspard, a boy of twelve, less congenial. Mrs. Leroy had allowed Ludolf to pick the roses, but there were some which Gaspard wanted for Lucile's bridal bouquet. Once Ludolf pretended he was going to pick these, and Gaspard thrust his clenched fist through a window-pane and picked them himself with his bleeding hand.

The marriage ceremony was performed in the village church, and the next day Ludolf went home and returned to the university, where he passed his first examination without particular credit. Then he went home to begin his career as an unpaid barrister in the law court.

He found Galeide much changed. She spent much time with her great-grandfather and with Lucile, who had become absorbed in her husband. Ludolf reflected at times that Ezard and Galeide would have suited each other well, and on one occasion Lucile even told Ezard that when she died he must marry Galeide.

A boy was born to Ezard and Lucile called Harre, after his grandfather. Galeide almost lived at Lucile's and the baby soon took a great liking to her, so that it often seemed as if she were his mother.]

Chapter XII

After little Harre's christening we never again had a family festival, no family gathering I mean that could really be called festive. For although care had already taken hold of us even then, yet each hid it from the other, and though we knew each other's feelings, no one had as yet spoken of it, and so for hours we could act as if nothing were the matter. Then too, at that time we were still at peace among ourselves and felt ourselves to be a unit, so that we felt comforted and encouraged from the very fact of being together; for, as a whole, we were a sturdy group and might well trust ourselves to withstand the shock of a contrary fate. But now a new and sudden attack in the rear of our troop took us so unawares that neither shield nor sword was at hand for defense, and we were driven apart.

As little Harre continued his healthy growth, he conceived a deep love for Galeide and she for him, so that she neglected everybody and everything else. That was her way: if she once grew fond of anything, her love was so

strong and whole-souled that it carried her away and
engulfed everything else.   Little Harre was full of her
waking and sleeping, allowed himself to be guided by her
eyes which were in no way remarkable, laughed when she
came, and dropped the corners of his mouth piteously when
she went.   Lucile tolerated this without jealousy, chiefly
because it concerned Galeide, whom she idolized, and also
because she loved the little girl who was born to her afterward more than the boy.   Perhaps she would have loved
him better if he had not been called Harre, but as it was
she looked on him as belonging entirely to his grandfather,
whom she did not particularly like; for she was influenced
at times by such trivial, superficial things.   My cousin
Ezard, on the other hand, was not satisfied that the child
should be so entirely in Galeide's power, although he was
the only one who reigned almost equally with her in the
little boy's heart.   He probably feared that she would
spoil him too much; what other objection he could have I
do not know, for with my sister the little fellow was on the
whole in good hands, and Ezard was too just not to realize
that.   Moreover, the courtesy that underlay his intercourse
with her prevented his ever speaking seriously to her on
the subject, but his feeling was noticeable here and there
in his behavior and may occasionally have caused a little
discord.   My father, who grew more and more melancholy
and distrustful as his worries increased, watched this situation with a close attention of which all the rest of us
thought it quite unworthy.   He yielded to the strange idea
that Ezard and Galeide were conscious of a forbidden
affection for each other, and that this was the cause of the
change in their behavior (which existed far more in his
imagination than in reality).   He tormented himself and
all of us with this extraordinary delusion and even considered it his duty to go to Lucile with this Job's news,
as he thought it to be.   Lucile, however, laughed at him
and took the whole thing as a delicious joke, like a person
who is himself afraid of ghosts but no longer feels any

fear of them as soon as some one else begins to tremble and says: Look, there it squats in the corner!

She repeated the conversation that she had had with my father not only to me but to Galeide, when we all three took occasion to deplore the unfortunate man's increasingly unhappy state and to pity ourselves no less for having to suffer under it. Whether Lucile also told her husband I do not know or have forgotten; one thing is certain, however, that he and my sister showed utter unconstraint, or, as one might also say, that same constraint which had always been for Lucile a matter of regret and astonishment.

Something else, however, came up to strengthen my father in his delusion. At that time two young men were courting my sister, of whom one would have been very acceptable to him as a son-in-law. He was a citizen of our town, not bad looking and with an adaptable mind, so that, although of a different stamp from ourselves, he was soon at home in all our ways and always knew how to meet my great-grandfather and my parents in the manner that pleased them best. This was not the result of politic motives alone, it was rather owing to his natural friendliness of feeling which enabled him rightly to understand other people. Both Galeide and I enjoyed his society very much, as in conversing he could display and unchain in others a kindly and at the same time delicate wit, which we particularly liked. The gloomier the atmosphere in our house threatened to become, as soon as we were alone, the more we rejoiced in the distraction and diversion that he brought us, and we encouraged him to visit us very often, without thinking what the consequences might be. He was musical, too, and that was enough to make any one welcome and popular with us, for we all loved and cultivated music passionately. In fact he was a cellist by profession and had a good and respected position in our opera orchestra. His name was George Wendelin. Galeide was visibly attracted to him, but she showed just as clearly that she felt nothing for him that could have justified any ex-

pectation of love. She was also his superior, highly clever
and talented as he was, in that she had a stronger and more
pronounced character than he, as soon appeared; for he
allowed himself to be blindly ruled by her, without being
able to claim the slightest reciprocity in this respect.

The other suitor, a Rhinelander, was still further from
her heart, but he occupied her more with the foreign ideas
that he brought into our circle, for he was a youth of the
latest pattern, had read everything and thought about
everything. He disapproved of everything that existed,
presumed to be able to improve everything, and was also
inclined, as may readily be imagined, to the socialistic doctrine, carrying his passion for innovation into all spheres,
such as poetry, music, painting, and so on. Such things
had a great power of attraction for Galeide, but as she
never took other people's word for anything — and I say
this in her praise — but wanted to examine and experience
everything herself before she adopted it as her opinion,
she began by meeting the young man's arguments with
her old views, which were, for the most part, nothing but
inherited household goods, and which she had scarcely once
tested in respect to their usefulness. On account of his
views the young Rhinelander inspired me with unendurable dislike; my mother, on the contrary, was well pleased
with him and much edified by his extravagant utterances.
You see her mind was so original and fresh that nothing
conventional clung to her or influenced her; hence she was
never disturbed by the fact that an idea was unusual, but
always derived from it at least the pleasure we find in
wandering through an unexplored region, even if it does
not please us in itself. It goes without saying that my
great-grandfather was altogether for the agreeable Rhinelander, who, incidentally, was half a genius; all unawares
he went on educating himself to be a Socialist and iconoclast, and he managed to reconcile such views with his
aristocratic prejudices so magnificently that it would have
been a psychological treat for me if the young man — Philip

Wittich was his name—had not been so utterly puffed up at this success. Consequently I was only disgusted. Galeide got much enjoyment out of the society of her two admirers; for she was never averse to attentions, which she received very gracefully, especially if the men concerned knew how to pay them in an entertaining and not in a silly manner.

At the same time she was perfectly sure of her heart, for that remained as cold as marble, and she troubled herself little about what the feelings of the unfortunate young men might be, when she treated them in such a familiar and sisterly way. In that respect she reminded one of the children who cheerfully pull off the legs of frogs and beetles and watch them struggle, for which cruelty, though it fills us with horror, the children cannot rightly be blamed, as they act with no bad intention and, as one may say, unconsciously.

We tried to avoid having Wendelin and Wittich meet each other in our house; for their rivalry and then too the difference in their natures and views made them intensely antagonistic and brought a note of excitement and hostility into the conversation which dispelled all sociability. My cousin Ezard did not like either of them, and it was just that which supported my father in his opinion that Ezard did not wish my sister to marry any one, and in fact intended, so long as he could not have her himself, that at least she should not belong to any one else. Now as my father, with the terrible state of his fortunes always in mind, desired most ardently to see my sister married and well provided for, he was much in favor of a marriage with the cellist, though he was far too delicate of feeling to try to influence her even by the slightest hint.

Ezard's dislike of the Rhinelander was due more to the difference in their natures than in their views; for although he disapproved of the passion for innovations, particularly violent ones, yet, with his great love of justice, he always tried to separate the person from his opinions, and often sought to appreciate a man while he disputed his views. But because of the Rhinelander's youth, his assertions, made like revelations, often bordered on presumption, for he could scarcely have thoroughly experienced and tried them, but had simply picked them up out of the streets. It was evident that as one born and raised on dry, sandy soil, he aspired to the unusual and the extravagant without having any corresponding element in his nature, just as deformed persons often have a passion for adorning themselves with gay and glittering ornaments. It is more difficult for me to understand why Ezard was so reserved with Wendelin. The most probable explanation seems to me that a certain lack of force and a certain mediocrity in his nature moved Ezard to say that he did indeed like to joke with him and to hear his music, but that he did not consider him a desirable addition to the family.

My father not only imagined that Ezard's feeling for Galeide was the cause of his speaking and acting thus, but also that Galeide herself scorned her suitors for Ezard's sake; even if she did not love him, although that was probable, she could not make up her mind to act contrary to his wishes. This erroneous opinion took complete possession of him, and with the love of their own suffering that some people have, he purposely drove himself deeper and deeper into his misery, by unceasingly observing Ezard and Galeide wherever he could and believing that he constantly saw fresh corroboration of his supposition. With his dark fears and predictions the unhappy man made himself as unwelcome to us all as the prophets of the Old Testament were to the people of Jerusalem, and like them he suffered twofold torments, grief on the one hand at the approaching misfortune in which he himself firmly believed, and on the other the cold-heartedness of those who were associated with him and who now, disturbed in the comfortable course of their life, became more and more estranged from him.

Chapter XIII

DURING a period of great heat Lucile had gone with her little girl to stay in the country; little Harre stayed with us, principally in Galeide's charge, lest the presence of both children should interfere with their mother's recreation. I, too, was fond of him with his defiant eyes; but at home they fretted and fussed too much about him, and that spoiled him for me. My cousin had been kept in town by business and was frequently at our house, on the boy's account if for nothing else; he nearly always had his midday meal with us. Once when we were sitting at the table, Harreken, as we called the child, grew naughty and instead of eating his soup, hit it with his spoon so that it splashed. He was sitting between Ezard and Galeide. Ezard may have been annoyed that day by business matters, for whereas he usually did not correct the boy except for serious naughtiness, he now forbade the malefactor such conduct in the severest manner. The child was frightened at this unexpected attack from his father, generally so kind, and began to cry; Galeide reddened with annoyance and fear for her favorite and drew him to her to quiet him as quickly as possible and prevent the paternal wrath from rising further. On his part, Ezard grew red when he saw Galeide 'behaving as if her relation to the child were, to a certain extent, closer than his, and ordered his sobbing son to be quiet and eat his soup. Galeide threw a cold glance at Ezard, for she was too wise to argue with him about training in the child's presence. The impression that the little incident made appeared, however, in the behavior of the others; my great-grandfather smiled somewhat mockingly and looked knowingly at Galeide, and my father cast gloomy glances from one to the other. I was just about to divert the general attention with some innocent topic and turned to my mother, on whose lips a whimsical speech seemed to be trembling, when Ezard rose, picked up the sinner, who, clinging close to Galeide, was still crying quietly, carried him into another room, and then came back at once and went on eating. My mother now laughed aloud; Ezard took it pleasantly and also answered my teasing remarks in the same spirit. But Galeide had grown quite pale; she still remained sitting at the table, however, and took part in the conversation. After the meal was over, Ezard went at once to his little boy, made peace with him, for he never was angry for long, and came back into the room with him in his arms, while the child held him tight round the neck and his merry twinkling eyes showed that all trouble and strife were forgotten. As it was now time for Ezard to go, he put Harreken on Galeide's lap and held out his hand to her to say good-by; she took it, but her nostrils moved as they always did when she got on her high horse and made fun of some one. Full of anxious thoughts, which all of us except Galeide saw through and smiled at, my father went to his room. In the meantime my great-grandfather discoursed at length on the insignificant incident, regretted that Ezard had been so unfavorably influenced by Lucile, as he would not otherwise have been so childish as to try to reprove such a small child by solemn strictness instead of smiles and playful wisdom, and so on. He also spoke to Ezard himself about it afterward and pointed out how much Galeide was doing for the child, taking almost better care of him than his own mother, and that now her soft heart was hurt, although she did not show it. To be sure this was wholly false, for Galeide was not easily hurt, and all she thought was that Ezard understood nothing about bringing up children; perhaps she also triumphed a little in her confidence that she would keep the child's affection even though Ezard should intend to rob her of it. On the other hand she did suffer under my father's strange manner, which she did not exactly know how to explain, and that may have made her look sad on that day, which always showed with such disproportionate clearness in her soft, mobile features, that she looked like a Niobe when she was merely annoyed at a drop of rain. After what my great-grandfather said to him, Ezard could not but think he had caused her sorrow, and he was immediately quite ready to make it good again. But as their intercourse, though pleasant and courteous, had always been rather formal, he did not know just how to go about it, and postponed it until after Galeide had put the little boy to bed and was still sitting beside him, while he clung tightly to one of her hands as he fell asleep. When Ezard came to our house at this hour, he was wont to go to the bedroom and kiss his son good night; on that day, after he had done so, he sat down beside Galeide on the edge of the bed, took her free hand, and drew it to his lips as if he would thus ask her forgiveness. They were alone, but long afterward I heard them tell what happened; they still remembered exactly how at that moment a delicious content had come over them, sweeter they thought than anything they had ever felt before. They remained sitting together till my mother went in to see to the child, and she reported to us that they had looked at each other radiant with happiness, so that they must have become reconciled and now everything was in order again. She told this in my father's presence, and not without a purpose; for it was her opinion that his unnatural delusions must be met by setting before him with complete unconcern the true and normal relation, as it was and might rightly be. But she only succeeded in making my father start as if he were hearing just exactly what he feared and what fitted in perfectly with the scheme of his forebodings. Now, for the first time, his fears agreed with the reality, which, however, none of us as yet suspected, so that we still regarded him as deluded and afflicted by a painful desire for self-torment.

Soon, however, this strange and fearful fate became apparent to us all. During the days that followed this unhappy day Ezard and Galeide were extraordinarily joyful; happiness beamed from their eyes, whatever they did

and whatever they said.   We yielded to the agreeable
influence that radiates from happy people, and enjoyed
the golden mood without inquiring into its cause.   But the
two unfortunate beings could not help gradually coming to
themselves and realizing what had happened to them.   At
first, perhaps, they simply felt an unsuspecting joy in this
affection, as in a flower that has opened in a warm night
and stands there in the morning in all its beauty, or as
a child stares with wonder at the Christmas presents which
unseen hands have spread out beside his bed while he slept.
But love can truly be compared to a fire, in that it is never
satisfied, but constantly demands more food, strains upward, and expands gigantically to fearful beauty and to
the destruction of everything that stands in its way.   Lucile
soon came back from her visit, like a swallow that seeks
its old nest in spring and finds it destroyed by bad weather
or hostile hands.   Ezard did indeed receive her happily
and heartily, and at once told her that at last his eyes
had been opened to Galeide and her beauty, and that, in
accordance with Lucile's often expressed wish, he was now
her friend and brother, just as Lucile formerly had regarded herself as Galeide's friend and sister.   The poor
woman realized better than Ezard the nature of this supposed friendship; even if it had been no more than friendship, she would not have borne it calmly and without envy,
and she had wished for it simply because she was all too
sure of her happiness and could not imagine it; but it was
her nature to play in imagination irreproachable, even
sublime parts, which in reality were beyond her.

[Outwardly things went on as usual.   All that the family
felt at first was great uneasiness.   Ezard and Galeide were
the only ones who knew what had brought about the change.
The others mostly blamed their father's gloomy suspicions
or Lucile's jealousy.   They persuaded themselves into believing that Ezard and Galeide were merely friends.]

Chapter XIV

Of us all my mother was the most to be pitied, for because she had the soul of a child she suffered as children suffer, who are unable to help and advise themselves, and are disconsolate and silent. She also possessed that clairvoyance of children which often suddenly and unintentionally revealed things to her that escape the brooding observer. Like Mignon she lived without care or effort, but, like her, she had sorrow enough. Much of it I never knew, but now I can vaguely and painfully feel it.

She was never ill as long as I can remember, but we knew she had a defect of the heart which to be sure she did not feel very much, but which under the strain of excitement or any unsuitable mode of life might lead to her sudden death. Hence we were accustomed to keep everything from her which could disturb the usual course of her life. But as all our circumstances were shaken in these latter years it was unavoidable that she too should be affected. My father and my great-grandfather, to be sure, watched over her as if she were a sacred treasure of brittle glass; but my father's anxious solicitude only oppressed and burdened her, just as a young bird misses the light and freedom when its mother's wings shield it too closely and incessantly. She seldom spoke of what had come to pass with Ezard and Galeide, and then she usually emphasized only how perfectly evident it was that their relation was proper and innocent. But one could see that she was repressing a secret anxiety that it was not so. She was like a child that thinks it perceives something uncanny near its bed at night and has not the courage to reassure itself, but buries its head in the pillows. Several times she asked me in a manner that was intended to be jesting, whether I did not think that Ezard and Galeide paraded their newly formed friendship a little too ostentatiously, and the like; but as I saw well that she merely wanted to allay her anxiety, I had not the courage to answer seriously, and

Permission Amsler & Ruthardt, Berlin   MAX KLINGER

APHRODITE

simply replied in the way that I knew would be most beneficial to her.

It was on a cold day in January that my mother was
taken with an indisposition, and as the doctor advised rest
she went to bed. My father had already been in England
for some time and we concealed from him this slight attack,
which seemed to give no cause for alarm, the more willingly
because my mother was usually visibly relieved when he
was not there to drag the burden of his melancholy and his
worries through our rooms like a black mantle of mourning. Each of us pursued his work and his pleasures as
before. At that time my custom was to dispatch the most
necessary of my professional duties with indifference or
dislike, and then pass the rest of my time, particularly the
evenings, with mostly rather superficial acquaintances in
rather shallow merriment.

I distinctly remember one winter evening when the snow
fell steadily from a whitey-gray sky so that everything
was veiled by an immeasurable moving cloth and it made
one weary and sad to look out. My great-grandfather,
Galeide, and I were sitting by my mother's bed, Galeide
and I all ready to go out, she to a concert, I to a jolly
festivity arranged by my comrades. I had offered to
accompany her to the concert hall, which suggestion she
did not seem to welcome, so that I concluded she had reckoned on meeting Ezard. She accepted my escort, however,
and we had gone together to my mother's bedroom to wish
her good night. She lay there smiling and looked at us
contentedly, glad that we were going out for our own
pleasure. As we knew that she always felt happiest in
the company of my great-grandfather, we left her without
concern, although it was gloomy beyond all measure in
the dusky room, where each knew that the other was hiding
secret anxiety in his soul. My great-grandfather, to be
sure, had no suspicion of anything in respect to Galeide;
but, accustomed to examining my mother's features with
regard to her condition, and familiar with the slightest

change in the countenance he loved, he had perceived something in it that seemed strange, new, and worse to him than anything that her former temporary sufferings had caused. When we came into the room my mother's face seemed peculiar and unrecognizable to us too, but we attributed it to the pale light of the snow that shone through the window. Nevertheless I felt as if we ought not to go out, and Galeide also hesitated to start and stroked the yellowish, marble-like invalid hands that lay motionless on the counterpane. In his restlessness, however, my great-grandfather urged us to go, and Mama nodded slowly in assent to his words. I asked if I should not light the lamp, for I hated to go and leave her alone in the dark, but Mama refused because she wanted to watch the snow and the ravens that flew past the window. So we rose, bent over the invalid, and kissed her, while she looked at us with dull eyes, thoughtfully and yet as if from a remote distance, so that it made us uneasy and we at first walked in silence through the snow. As I had expected, we soon met Ezard, who greeted us without embarrassment, and told us that he, too, was going to the concert and without Lucile, who had wanted to stay at home with the children. He asked after Mama at once, and said that, in accordance with a promise he had once made my father always to watch over her in the latter's absence, he had been to see the doctor; he had, however, found nothing serious in her condition, and declared it to be a sick headache that in his opinion would pass in a few days. The conversation cheered us and dispelled the anxious impression we had received; yet during the first part of the evening I had to keep banishing from my eyes the vision of the dark sickroom and the high window past which the snow and the ravens flew. Gradually it ceased to return, and the night passed like many another, full of that noisy merriment that, however loud it may be, leaves no echo in the soul that we care later to awaken in order to listen to it. I came home long after midnight, not intoxicated by any

means, but still immoderately stimulated; two friends
accompanied me and we strolled through the streets in
loud and merry conversation.   At our garden gate we
parted, promising to meet again the next morning in the
restaurant which we frequented.   I was surprised to find
the door of the house unlocked, and thought that Galeide,
who must have got home before me, had carelessly left it
open.   I went quietly to my room and lit a light, but I
could not keep my eyes open and threw myself half un-
dressed on the bed, my limbs felt so heavy.   Immediately
after Galeide came into my room, as pale as death, and
said: "It is a good thing that you are here, Ludolf; Mama
is much worse."   I stared at her and my senses, dull as
they still were, perceived that she was clinging to a bed-
post with one hand, that tears were ceaselessly streaming
down her face, and that she was still wearing the white
dress and golden girdle with which she had adorned herself for the concert.   I turned very sick, although I could
not quite remember what had happened during the day.
I wanted to ask but could not, and so staggered silently
after Galeide.   When we came into the sickroom I knew
that Mama was dead even before I saw her.   In an arm-
chair in the corner sat my great-grandfather, crying softly
to himself and sobbing at intervals: "My child!   My
sweet one!   My little girl!   My darling!"   As for me,
I felt not like crying, but like bawling, for well I knew that
in all my life, and if I should live to be a hundred, no one
would ever love me again as my Mama had; in the most
neglected and wildest days of my godless youth she had
been all that I knew of heaven and truly my love, and my
senses almost left me when I saw her lying there lifeless,
no longer herself.   Kneeling by her bed I hid my head
against it in that state of numbness in which, though alive,
we are as dead and without power over ourselves, yet conscious of the external world.   I heard Galeide ask Ezard,
who also was present, to shut the window, and I knew
it was done on account of my loud lamentation; but it was

not possible for me to stop nor to moderate my voice, although I seemed to myself like a whining animal and was ashamed. At last I simply moaned and moaned and scarcely knew why, and I could not calm myself till my great-grandfather came up to me, stroked the hair off my forehead with his light, tender, aged hand and tried to dry my hot and streaming face with his tear-soaked handkerchief. At that I felt as if I were still a little boy and I willingly allowed him to take my hand and lead me into another room, and finally I fell asleep with the old man sitting beside me watching. He was never benumbed by any blow of fate or showed himself to be weak as long as any one near him was weaker and more in need of help than he.

Next day I learned that not long after my great-grandfather had left my Mama, and had fallen asleep, he was awakened by a heavy fall in her room; hastening to her in terror he found her lying unconscious on the floor near the window, which she must have opened shortly before. One of the servants, hurrying to get the doctor, met Ezard and Galeide in the garden, and this might explain to some extent what had happened. None of us doubted that my Mama, who had perhaps not yet gone to sleep or had been awakened by their returning steps or voices, had opened the window in order to see them, moved by some feeling of anxiety. The window looked out on the back of the garden; it is possible that Ezard and Galeide, believing themselves to be alone, were still walking up and down there, lost in their unfortunate passion, and perhaps they gave expression to it in their bearing and gestures and Mama saw it; it was a bright moonlight night. The icy winter cold struck her directly as she stood there in her thin nightdress; but doubtless it was especially the phenomenon of this criminal love, appearing fearfully fateful at dead of night in the snow-covered garden, that had gripped her heart so that she lost consciousness. But these were only unexpressed and painful conjectures; the only certainty that Ezard had accompanied my sister home after the concert, was perfectly natural and in no way unusual. The two attended to all the formalities that follow a death; they also notified my father of what had happened, at once and as gently as possible, and they did all this with great composure and in such a considerate way that it seemed to go on of itself.

My father arrived home in the night before the funeral, and his presence at once settled down on the slumbering house like an incubus. Whereas up till then we had felt the natural and therefore bearable grief at the death of an adored mother, there was now added to it an uneasy gloom, for every misfortune was reflected in my father as in a mirror that magnifies and distorts, and since everything centred about him as the head of the family, the terrible reflection could not but impress itself on us more sensibly than the reality. Galeide felt this most, for he would not let her leave his side, and during the first night, when he felt incapable of sleeping, she had to stay up with him, though he asked it of her only by an appealing glance, or by his whole disconsolate and thoroughly shaken demeanor. On the following day the house was astir early and there was much to attend to on account of the funeral, as well as guests to be received, and as all this fell principally on Galeide, she was in such a state of overfatigue when evening came that her look filled us all with pity. My father, however, overwhelmed with his sorrow, seemed to notice nothing of this and sat constantly beside her, holding her hands in his as if they were something that the departed one had left him for a keepsake and as her sole dear legacy. I had noticed during the day that Ezard was vexed at this and often sought a pretext on which to call my sister from her father's side. He also told us that, in his opinion, our father was yielding to his grief too much and more than became a normal man, and was giving way to flabby sentimentality. Galeide contradicted him and thought it unjust to count up my father's tears so soon.

This seemed to excite Ezard even more, and when in the afternoon Lucile went home on account of the children, he could not make up his mind to go with her, but stayed with us; which was also not unnatural, for as our near relative it was certainly his right and his duty to stand by us.   We ate our supper in silence, and Ezard constantly regarded Galeide, who again sat beside Papa, with a burning, penetrating gaze, either unable or without the will to control himself.   It struck me then for the first time how much he had changed, and how his passion had come to show itself in his features, his bearing, his whole person. When it grew to be so late that he could not well remain with us longer, and our father still made no move to let Galeide leave him, he decided to interfere himself, and my great-grandfather encouraged him in this with approving glances.   As he turned to my father and suggested that he retire, since it was his duty to think of his health and above all to spare Galeide, who had scarcely slept since our mother's death and who besides was worn out by the unbroken excitement, a sudden fright seized me, he looked so handsome and so terrible, much as we imagine Lucifer, the fallen angel.   I asked myself: is it possible, can the feelings in our house have become so barbarous that Ezard is fired with wicked jealousy of Galeide's father and can no longer bear to see the expression of her childlike love? Even before that, during the day, I had been tempted by similar thoughts, but had hastily banished them.   But what was stamped on Ezard's face could not be misinterpreted, and my father recognized it at once, as one could tell from his eyes, which he moved slowly and meaningly back and forth between Ezard and Galeide.   He rose and brought his powerful frame close to Ezard who was not much shorter but not so broad: " You shall not have to reproach me with lack of self control, my nephew Ezard," he said. Then he turned to us with a curt good night and walked heavily to his room, without taking particular leave of Galeide.   Galeide looked after him and then rose and said

good night to us in an expressionless voice, without looking
at Ezard; but he called her name when she was already
at the door and held out his hand to her with a despairing
gesture, whereupon she quickly and vehemently gave him
hers and then left the room immediately, in order to hide
her tears, as it seemed to us. My great-grandfather pitied
her tenderly and indulged in disapproving remarks of our
father, who he said always yielded to his feelings in a
selfish and, as he expressed it, Oriental way, and was now
crushing poor little Galeide with his love as he formerly
had her mother. Ezard now also took his leave, but from
the window of my bedroom I saw him wandering about the
snow-covered garden as if he were trying to master his
wild passion before he went home to his wife and children,
and the thought of him restlessly driven about out there
kept me long awake. At last — it may have been after
midnight — when I heard the garden gate move quietly, I
thought he must have gone, and fell asleep.

Summary of Chapter XV

[A distant cousin of Galeide's age, named Eva, came to
the funeral. Ludolf thought her doll-like and childish, and
Ezard did not care for her. She accepted Uncle Harre's
attentions all the more eagerly and they were soon engaged,
Lucile alone approving. The wedding was not very joyful,
and the couple soon came home from a short trip, already
disappointed with each other. Uncle Harre took refuge
in work, but Eva had no resource, and her unhappiness
soon won the sympathy of the rest of the family. Meanwhile Ludolf had found out that Ezard and Galeide sometimes met secretly, but was not quite certain how intimate
they had become.]

Chapter XVI

What my father must have suffered in solitude is beyond
expression. It is said that physicians in dissecting a
corpse can sometimes estimate the degree of pain that the

sufferer endured; similarly it is only now, in looking over the entire past, that I realize how much more wretched he must have been than we were inclined to suppose. For it is impossible that he did not foresee the fall of the good old house that bore his name long before it occurred, but he went on working in spite of it, untiringly and to the point of exhaustion, and, bitterest of all, without hope. He said not a word of this to any one and therein he was at fault, but it would not become me, his son, to reproach him with it. What kind of beings must we have been that he did not dare to test the endurance of our love in the fire of suffering! Did we seem to value him solely as a provider? I shudder and am shaken to the marrow when I put such questions to myself. At that time, however, we lived and thought only from moment to moment. Galeide and I breathed more freely when our father went on long business trips. At such times we were as good as alone in the big house and did as we liked. Galeide attended to the household in a rather superficial way and read a great deal, but she had taken a special fancy to learn to play the violin, and in this she displayed a strikingly intense and persistent zeal. Our father was forever besieging her with offers of presents, by which he tried, if not to buy her love, at least to give expression to his, and he was more than happy whenever she uttered a wish. Generally she would accept nothing, or only trifles, for she was sensible enough to wish to avoid unnecessary expense; but when it came to the violin and the lessons that went with it, she condescended to ask, even to beg, anxiously and bashfully, like a child. At that Papa would not have hesitated to fetch her such an instrument out of the blazing fires of hell if he could not have procured it elsewhere.

Almost every one in our family was musical, and I may say in a better sense than that in which the word is generally used. I do not know why it had never occurred to any of us to choose this art for a profession, unless it was that we loved it too much to want to drag it down into

our everyday life. Ezard played the piano so beautifully
that he would undoubtedly have attained to greatness in
that direction if he had been able to devote time as well
as perseverance to it, and although my indolence and carelessness kept me from any finished performance, yet to me
music was the most beautiful thing in life, the friend and
comforter to whom I kneeled, and in whose lap I laid my
head without shame. At first it annoyed me that Galeide
was learning the violin, for I heard nothing but abominably
discordant tones, and beautiful songs that I loved, arranged
for beginners, laboriously played with defective bowing.
But it cannot be denied that she rapidly reached a point
where her playing was not so distressing, so that I was
not unwilling to accompany her on the piano, when we were
always deeply joyful and contented. We had a music
room in our house, in the middle of which stood the grand
piano, lighted in the evening by a chandelier which hung
above it. The walls were divided into windows and mirrors as high as the room, which reflected us when we were
playing. I remember that I frequently looked at Galeide's
fiddling reflection because it pleased me much better than
the reality. The first piece that we played together was,
"Long, long ago." As her bowing was still very timid
it sounded somewhat as if some one were singing while
he wept, which was not inappropriate for this song and
was the reason that I never could hear her play it without
being deeply touched. At this moment it seems as if that
melody, so often heard, were coming in to me through the
open window in the long-drawn, sad tones of a violin; yet
it is probably nothing but the shawm of a shepherd boy
on the mountains opposite.

During this time Ezard and Galeide were slipping deeper
and deeper into their amorous passion, which, however,
I only felt vaguely then and was far from knowing as
certainly as I now unfortunately know everything. At
times it seemed to me as if Galeide were waiting for me to
go out, so that she could be alone with Ezard, but I did not

inquire further because I was afraid. So they were often alone in the big, almost empty house, at times quite openly, when music brought them together, at times without any one's knowing it. In the meantime they lived fairly well controlled lives and tried to behave like everyday people, by which Lucile gladly allowed herself to be soothed, so that outwardly a better relation was established. But it was only the most cruel dissimulation and constant, torturing self-restraint that made this possible for Ezard and Galeide, and in their despair they sought every kind of expedient to lighten the burden.

At that time an epidemic of typhus had called attention to the bad drinking water in our city, and the senate resolved that a careful investigation and thorough improvement should be carried out. To this end a commission was appointed whose first duty was to study and compare the water systems of other cities; Uncle Harre stood at its head. At the same time he suggested that the old sanitary regulations, now no longer adequate, ought to be replaced by new ones which should conform closely to those used elsewhere in the German Empire, as far as they seemed to be efficient. Thus Ezard hit upon the idea of taking from his father some of the necessary work; he was especially attracted by the need for acquiring a great deal of new knowledge, since that seemed to promise him interesting activity; but he intended more especially to take the trips this project would necessitate and make use of them for his own criminal purposes. For he told himself that they would give him an excuse for being away at any time, so that he could often see Galeide when he was thought to be out of town. As this motive was hidden from every one except Galeide, it seemed peculiar and capricious that Ezard should want to undertake matters which must interrupt so seriously his present occupation. On the one hand people admired his versatility and on the other they blamed his lack of steadiness, but however they judged him, they all considered him a striking and incalculable person.

Ezard paid not the slightest attention to all this, although he was, as a rule, modest enough to listen to other people's judgment even in matters with which he was better able to cope than they. But his peculiarity was that his will usually slept, and never, on any occasion, appeared as disagreeable stubbornness or a whim, but when once it was roused, he went at his aim irresistibly with both passion and wisdom. Like an experienced runner who never overdoes, but keeps up a steady and moderate pace which he can maintain for a long time, and thus finally leaves his short-sighted and quickly wearied competitors far behind, Ezard acted calmly and with assurance, moved to act by passion, it is true, but acting without passion. It was just that which always made him appear superior and great, even when he did wrong, so that people admired him even while they censured him.

In connection with this undertaking Ezard became friends with the engineer who had been engaged to approve the water-works. Technical science had a peculiar charm for Ezard's love of action, because it leads to visible and useful results, and also because it requires a certain manual skill which alert, vigorous people usually enjoy. The fact that the engineer could introduce him to this science and teach him was sufficient to make him attractive to Ezard. Moreover he had fertile and happy ideas in his professional work and this impressed my cousin, who thought himself lacking in imagination and was easily inclined to overestimate in others that charming fertility of mind which grows poppies in the workaday grainfields of life. In reality the engineer had so infinitely much less imagination than Ezard that he could not even realize its value and its beauty, but found it a disturbing element wherever he came across its traces. It was only in his profession that he was ingenious, simply because he was logical and allowed nothing to divert or distract his attention. He came from Norway and his name was Karlsen. He wore a long, forked beard which he could throw back over his shoulders, a trick that made him popular with Eva and Galeide, both of whom displayed at times pronouncedly childish characteristics. Ezard had soon introduced him into the family, where he was well received, and in fact he gained an almost unexampled popularity there, and acquired such an influence over Uncle Harre in particular that in many things he positively dominated him. As people were then beginning to take interest in things Norwegian, which the famous writers of that nation had made familiar to us, we regarded him as a welcome acquisition and greeted with joy every trait in him that seemed to correspond to Ibsen's or Björnson's types. He utterly failed to understand more than one of the ideas that are native to us and claim universal validity, such as Noble Womanliness, Ideal Poverty, and other supermundane conceptions. Brains and energy in any individual, man or woman, pleased him most, and for that reason he evidently disapproved of Galeide, whom he regarded as a condemnable article of luxury, whereas he was well satisfied with Lucile, who was constantly busy about the house, subscribed to a lot of daily, weekly, and monthly papers in order to study all the questions of the day, and, in short, was aflame with eagerness and industry, and even preferred Eva, who had at least produced a child. Galeide was always overjoyed with his society, as his opinion of her amused her; I think I see her sitting comfortably in a rocking chair like a kitten basking in the sun, and asking him with a pleasant laugh to show her the trick with his beard. This behavior called forth Lucile's disapproval, while Ezard and I could scarcely suppress our merriment. I have forgotten to speak of Karlsen's eyes, which were not unimportant in that they expressed the greatest honesty as well as intelligence, and gave him the appearance of incorruptibility. It would have been impossible to entertain the slightest doubt of any of his words, and this was strengthened by the fact that he never gave his judgment on any matter with which he was not thoroughly familiar — a quality which also characterized my cousin.

With this Norwegian Ezard now spent a great part of the year in traveling. This unsettled manner of life was in thorough agreement with the state of his mind, and it did him good to be able to 'yield in bodily reality to the storms that pursued his soul and let himself be driven from place to place. For physical and spiritual harmony always does us good, and a struggling, wrestling heart beats more contentedly in an actively moving body than in a resting one.

SUMMARY OF CHAPTER XVII

[LUDOLF was a frequent visitor in Uncle Harre's house. Eva treated him quite familiarly, but Ezard quite formally. She appeared to admire him greatly, and this annoyed Ludolf, and he tried to pick quarrels with Ezard. On one occasion he was unusually aroused and upbraided him for his conduct to Lucile and Galeide, for his whole manner of life. Ezard calmly admitted it, and rejoined with the hope that Ludolf might never have to accuse himself of similar things.]

CHAPTER XVIII

IT often happens that when a man loses his property and with it the external embellishments of the world, he thus learns to know what is really valuable in life, namely, the faithful love of those nearest him, which then finds the opportunity to prove its splendor, like the stars which shine the more golden the darker the night. My father, however, saw the support on which his heart had built falling with the outward props of his life. To some extent this was probably his fault, as he had not the courage to grasp this support, that is to appeal to the loyalty of his children and friends. But who will presume to say that he would have acted otherwise if he could know and feel everything that my father knew and felt. In his distress he clung to the miserable hope of being able to retain his spiritual goods by means of his material ones, but they too were just then slipping from him. Like a will-'o-the-wisp the vision of wealth danced before him and lured him on into ruinous regions. Hoping to delight Galeide, he brought her one thing after another, now a rare flower in winter, now a beautifully set, sparkling precious stone, and the poor child tortured herself to thank him and to smile, without being able to prevent his feeling the artificiality of her joy. It was pitiable to see. Although my father had not the strength to adapt his conduct to the state of affairs in another, and as many may think, more worthy manner, yet he did gather courage and resolved to leave our home for a lengthy period. The condition of his business moved him to take a trip across — it is thus that we speak of going to America in our ocean-wonted sea-broken Hansa towns. He wanted to try once more, to make a last effort, to avert the ruin of his house — or he may have thought he could better endure the awful wreck while standing at the wheel.

When he first spoke to us of his intention, but without mentioning the very threatening condition of his business, he watched Galeide with self-torturing attention to see what impression the news would make on her. She did look at him sadly, but it was not a child's unaffected expression of sorrow at losing its father, revealed in unabashed lamentation; for his absence meant a relief to her, in fact it would enable her to see Ezard, who had grown to be the only thing on earth to her, oftener than usual. But the very consciousness that what her innocent childish heart would have liked to feel as a sorrow, really filled her wild brain with happiness, caused her a pang comparable to the sword that pierces the breasts of the abandoned lovers in Dante's poem and adds unceasing pain to their infamous bliss. At the same time my father was too weak in his love for Galeide not to enjoy the softer mood of parting. He would not let her leave his side, and to me too he showed more tenderness than usual. Since my great-grandfather hailed and admired the resolution to make this

journey as a courageous attempt to break away from the
melancholy brooding of the last few years, we were all
contentedly harmonious, and the last days that my father
spent with us have remained in my mind as bright and
soothing. One evening my great-grandfather's powers of
persuasion even induced my father to sing us a few songs,
which he had not done for years. His voice was a tenor
of medium range that affected the heart by its soft quality
and melting tone, and he sang according to the old, simple
method, bringing out strength and expression less by the
artful rise and fall of his voice than by the soulful feeling
that audibly permeated all his tones. I accompanied him
on the piano and from my place could see my great-grandfather sitting in a corner of the sofa, listening and thinking, while Galeide, leaning back in the window-seat, gazed
out into the long, dark garden. Among others my father
sang an old-fashioned song beginning, " I fain would know,
when soon I shall be buried," the idea of which is that a
man, feeling the premonition of his approaching death,
puts the melancholy question whether the only one on earth
whom he loves will keep him in faithful remembrance and
come to visit his grave. After minor chords a joyful rise
in the melody accompanies the final words, in which the
doubter comforts himself with confidence in her faithful-
ness. When my father had sung this song, Galeide leaned
forward from the window-seat and begged him to repeat
it, remaining in that attitude while he did so, and her eyes
stared at us so fixedly out of her soft face that one might
have thought her a wax image.

On one of the days that my father had spoken of as the
last before he left for America we all assembled at Uncle
Harre's. He knew more than any of us of the business
misfortune that threatened, and was full of real concern,
even full of fear, for he could not save my father and yet
was too closely united with us not to feel our fortunes as
his own. He concealed his mood under an excited manner
to which his natural vivacity easily led; yet for moments

at a time he would suddenly lapse into brooding, looking
fixedly ahead, with the bearing and face of an old man.
Then he would seem to recollect himself, toss back his
heavy, gray-white hair, and jump up to begin a lively
conversation with some one of us. My father also made
an effort to appear composed and cheerful, and even con-
versed with Ezard, seriously, it is true, but in a kind way,
which I thought especially to his credit, though Ezard
seemed to bear it not without inward pain. Most of all I
pitied unhappy Lucile, who doubtless felt as if she were
now losing her last stronghold, to be left alone among
hostile powers; she kept close to my father's side and
nestled her dark head gently and confidingly against his
shoulder. When we separated, late in the evening, and my
father bade farewell to Uncle Harre, the brothers threw
themselves into each others' arms and sobbed aloud; much
affected, we others turned away and strove to suppress
our own emotion. When he said good night, my father
kissed us several times in quick succession, and Galeide
especially he pressed closely to him as if he wanted to keep
a piece of her and take it with him. We were too over-
tired, however, to attach any unusual significance to his
behavior. But I awoke in the morning from confused
dreams, maybe about four o'clock, and when I could collect
my senses I heard Galeide calling out of the open window,
" Papa! Papa!" I dressed in haste to see what was the
matter, and hurried into the garden, which looked bleak and
gray; the chill that usually precedes sunrise was in the
air, and I shivered. Galeide, who was leaning out of the
window, did not seem surprised to see me and said, " He
has gone! You go after him, I cannot!" With these
words she burst into tears and dropped her head on the
window-sill, so that her loosened hair hung out.

It was now clear to us that my father had wanted to
spare himself, and still more us, the pain of saying good-by,
but still we decided to go to the harbor at the sailing time
of his steamer, to wave a last greeting to him from the

shore. We carried out this plan, and when we caught sight
of him he seemed to us more composed than on the preceding evening. He nodded to me seriously and gently, as
if he were advising me to bear everything that might come
with manly courage, yes, and as if he were confiding to my
keeping not only Galeide but also himself and his memory.
But when he turned his gaze on my sister, his face assumed
an entirely different expression which I cannot describe, it
was so full of sadness and mild reproach. Galeide returned
his gaze unwaveringly as long as he was still discernible
on the slowly receding ship; she looked as I had never
seen her before, more like a stone sphinx than a living
person, as if the soul in her bosom had become soulless to
be able to bear the unbearable.

To some it may seem incredible that she could not put
away from her, for the sake of her father and Lucile,
the passion that was making these two loved ones so miserable, that she did not even try to do so, and had not, even
at this moment, the courage to give up the man whom
heaven and earth refused her. Nor will I try to palliate
this crime of her law-defying spirit, but I must say that,
at times, it seemed to me more worthy of her that she did
leap into the abyss with open eyes and conscious will. She
scorned to yield to the emotional mood of a moment, and
the pleasure of being able to gratify, by a comforting
promise, even if only temporarily, those who are pleading
and suffering, never tempted her to deceive herself; she
always knew that she would be able to suffer or to do
anything except to give up Ezard.

When the ship had become a dancing speck before our
eyes, we turned away from the water, walked on together
for a time in silence, and then separated, Galeide going,
as I could not help thinking, to meet Ezard.

[Ludolf and Galeide were now left practically alone in
the big house. Ezard was at home much more frequently
than before, hoping to see Galeide oftener. One night

when the moon shone brightly Ludolf was awakened by steps in the music room. There he found Galeide looking strange and ghostly in her white nightdress, and they both started on seeing each other. It had seemed to her as if she had heard her father singing, " I feign would know, when soon I shall be buried.'' Ludolf told her she had been dreaming and they both laughed and went to bed.]

Chapter XIX

I could not bring myself to speak frankly to Galeide about her relation to Ezard, for I was one of those people who are afraid of excitement and who, if a crime is committed near them, will perhaps turn quickly into a side street to avoid being called as witnesses. I did, however, tell Eva of all that I observed and thought, and that was far more comfortable and might, after all, gradually lead to something. I was also human enough to find a certain charm in being able to show Eva that Ezard lived and moved entirely in some one else and did not care a pin for her, though, to be sure, she knew this well enough without my help.

I was not, indeed, in the least in love with Eva; on the contrary, my feelings for her were so good and noble that it still does me good to recall them. She entered into my conversation with admirable courage and spoke of Galeide with much affection, which I thought particularly to her credit, as even under ordinary circumstances it is usually as rare as it is pleasant for women to say kind and nice things of one another without ulterior motives. With gentle consideration she then told me that this unhappy passion was already the talk of many people in town, as Ezard and Galeide allowed themselves, with incomprehensible carelessness, to be seen together in public, and that she herself had already recognized it to be the duty of their relatives to do something to prevent greater mischief. At this I flushed hotly, for one never realizes an unfortunate or improper state so thoroughly as when people have gossiped about it and it has thus become an historical fact that can be looked at objectively. But neither of us thought of any thorough and systematic measures which should settle the whole matter, but intended to go to work in a round-about way to check and patch it as far as possible. We thought it was particularly to be regretted that Galeide was so much alone, and that it would be a good thing if there were some one else in our house to whom she would have to give her attention, so that she would thus be gently compelled to give up her meetings with Ezard. Eva had already thought it all out and had a plan that her elder sister, Anna Elisabeth, should come to visit us, for which many reasons or pretexts might be found: she might come to see our great-grandfather or Eva, and take advantage of our almost empty house, or even to look after our household a little, for it was Galeide's unalterable reputation that she knew nothing about housekeeping. How true that may have been, by the way, I cannot say definitely, but I must confess that I was, on the whole, well taken care of as long as she had the supervision, and I thought it praiseworthy that she never made a great to-do when something was not in order, but calmly and pleasantly corrected the omission, or somehow set it right, so that one felt each time that it was intended to be so, or even that it was much better thus.

I had only seen Anna Elisabeth once, many years before, and my memory of her was of some one very aristocratic, even queenly, so that the idea of her coming was by no means disagreeable to me. At the same time I was much exercised to know how I should tell Galeide of the plan, for, although it might have been something perfectly harmless and natural, still the consciousness of its purpose embarrassed me, so that I did not believe I could lay it before her without blushing.

It was then late autumn. I remember this because at that time I was once present at a scene in the garden and can still vividly recall the foggy atmosphere, the falling leaves, and the melancholy of disintegrating nature which impressed me on that occasion. At the far end of our garden there was a sort of grotto under the sylvan shade of broad chestnut-trees, although their branches were bare on the afternoon of which I am now thinking, and through them could be seen the spires of the town and the high chimneys of the factories. Coming back from a walk, I was strolling through the garden to see if I could still find a ripe plum or green-gage, when I caught sight of two figures sitting there whom I recognized as Galeide and Lucile. Galeide was sitting on one of the projecting stones of the grotto and had Lucile, who was considerably smaller, on her lap, so that they sat there in an intimate embrace. Full of annoyance I thought, '' Galeide has got hold of her again!'' For, dear as they had formerly been to each other, yet in the years just past Lucile had had a hatred of my sister, which was comprehensible and pardonable enough. I now came nearer and could distinctly perceive the expression of grief and love in Galeide's face, which was looking up at Lucile. Lucile turned round toward me when she heard my steps, and I saw that she had tears in her eyes; she turned back again to Galeide at once, as if I were not there at all, and said: '' I have made your dear hair all wet,'' and tried to dry it with her hands, smiling at Galeide. I had already got into the habit of behaving as if many things were perfectly natural which I really thought very unusual and strange, and so now I nimbly lugged in some indifferent subject of conversation, which the two immediately took up in the same spirit.

But afterward, when Lucile had gone, I did ask my sister whether anything had happened between them, to which she replied, '' Oh no, we were speaking of former days, and Lucile complained that I was not as tender to her as I used to be then.''—''And why aren't you?'' I asked. '' She wouldn't believe me if I told her, neither now nor later,'' answered Galeide, looking disconsolately off into space. "But you seemed to be very loving with each other when I came into the garden," I continued. "I could not do otherwise," said Galeide, as if there had been something to excuse. I also inquired whether they had spoken of Ezard, and at that Galeide's face immediately took on the stony expression that I already knew, and she said coldly and calmly, "She asked me whether I loved him."—"And what did you say?" I asked. "I said no," she returned. I tried to understand why she had said no and what Lucile might have planned to do if the answer had been different. When I asked Galeide's opinion on this, she said, "Perhaps she had made up her mind to say, 'Take him, he shall be free, I will give him up!' But she never could have actually done it; so what good would it have done?"

[Ludolf could not imagine nor did he ask what Ezard's and Galeide's wishes and plans really were. When Christmas came he had still not told his sister of the proposed visit. They bought a stately Christmas tree, and on Christmas Eve, after everything was ready to be hung on the tree next morning, Galeide seemed disinclined to go to bed.]

I went and left her alone, but I was surprised and could not help thinking that she hoped to see Ezard that evening. The situation was such that even while we had just been chatting together peaceably like children, a word, a breath, could suddenly stir up the whole mess of suspicion and torment, so that it threatened to descend and destroy us. Anger rose in me that this obstinate passion should thus recklessly ruin our life, and I thought this was the occasion when I could speak frankly with Galeide, telling her that I had provided against her longer being able to yield to the outrageous impulses of her frantic heart. I continued to work myself into a state of wrath, standing at the window so as to see whatever should happen and no longer be a stupid dupe.

All at once I saw Ezard's strong figure coming down the street with such a light step that the snow scarcely squeaked under his feet; he looked up at our house. He must have caught sight of Galeide, for he nodded slightly toward the drawing-room and then entered the garden. There was a cold, dead silence far and wide; but still such a venture was recklessly bold, and if by chance a late reveller should pass, it might lead to the most cruel ruin for us. My heart beat with rapid throbs as I saw him approach the house and begin to swing himself up the wall. Now it all seems to me as if I had dreamt it, for it appeared strange and incomprehensible enough in the icy winter night. In my indignation, an exciting scene just suited me, and I hurried downstairs and into the drawing-room.

It was lighted only by two little Christmas candles, which Galeide had undoubtedly fastened to the Christmas tree and lighted in the meantime. She and Ezard stood close to the window, still glowing and trembling from the tempestuous embrace out of which my entrance had startled them, as I could easily see. At the same time their bearing was by no means that of discovered sinners; on the contrary they stood there erect and majestic, somewhat like the helmsman on a sinking ship, who sees the engulfing waves coming and yet remains steadfastly at his post. Doubtless I felt this, but it angered me doubly to see them standing there so resplendent with joy of life, yet reckless of the poor life that they were treading under their feet, and I did not hesitate to say all this to their faces, although I began to feel more like a troublesome marplot than an ordained avenger.

Galeide came swiftly up to me, laid her hand on my arm, and said: "Don't speak so loud, Ludolf, or great-grandfather will hear you."

She did seem to be much excited, but at the same time quite unembarrassed, and the same with Ezard, whom I thought I had never seen look so handsome.

He said to me: "If you wish, let us talk about this

tomorrow, Ludolf. I shall go now, and you need not worry, for I shall take care that no one sees me. But let Galeide sleep now, I demand that.'' Galeide smiled at him and said: '' Don't trouble about that, but go now.''

At that they looked once more into each other's eyes, steadily and with strange power, as if there were some secret magic in their gaze, but they neither shook hands nor kissed, and Ezard swung himself up onto the window-sill and went down the wall. Galeide watched him and after a time, probably when he had reached the path unnoticed and unhurt, she turned round to me with the words:

'' I want to tell you, that this is all soon coming to an end now, for after Christmas I am going away.''

I was utterly astonished and disconcerted. '' You?'' I said. '' Going away? Where?''

She said, '' Either to Vienna or to Geneva to study music at the conservatory.''

I did not know what to think. '' You alone?'' I asked.

She looked at me half smiling and half fearful, and I think my terror increased her own dread, but she tried to suppress it and said: '' Yes, it must be, and I must be able to do it!'' She threw back her head with a quick gesture, like one who tries to suppress his rising sobs, then she gave me her hand and said: '' Good night, Ludolf,'' looking at me so peculiarly and sweetly that I could not help kissing her, although I had come with very different intentions.

I remember distinctly that as I was about to go out of the door I saw the two candles burning and went back a step to put them out; but then I thought: What for? let them burn on as long as they can, and went upstairs. After I was in bed I could not help thinking constantly of the two candles burning all alone in the big, empty room, and as I was very tired and at the same time excited, my thoughts became confused, and I no longer knew whether they were candles or people, and began to cry with pity and cried myself asleep, as I had sometimes done as a little boy when the world seemed to me so sad and incomprehensible. Now I need no longer tell Galeide anything about Anna Elisabeth and now Anna Elisabeth would not need to come at all. Yes, but who would do the housekeeping? Everything that I thought brought me back again to the great empty house and to the long table about which a numerous, joyful company had formerly assembled, and at which in future my great-grandfather and I were to sit opposite each other alone. I had never before felt how fleeting everything is that to children seems sacred and eternal, and one moment I felt as old as the hills and tired of life, and the next I felt so tiny and helpless that I should have liked to cry aloud till some one came to comfort me.

All at once it seemed to me that Galeide was the fairest and dearest thing on earth to me, although we were far from being as confidential and intimate as some brothers and sisters. I never entertained the thought of trying to dissuade her, for in going she did what was right and sensible, and what else ought to have been done? It was a disconsolate night; I can scarcely remember another like it. When we stand amid events, our hands are full, and we bear much without knowing it; but there come lulls and moments when we see as it were the gray ghost of future misfortune beckoning us from the distance, and they are the worst; they are united to those in which we again suffer in retrospect what we lived through and suffered long ago. And now the page on which I write, like the pillow on which I lay that night, is wet with my tears.

SUMMARY OF CHAPTER XX

[GALEIDE has to tell her great-grandfather, but decided not to tell her father. In the meantime Lucile had learned part of the truth, and there was a terrible scene when she told the old man, but he became reconciled and helped Galeide pack up. Lucile had learned the truth in part, and reproached Galeide, who felt herself to blame and could make no defense. Ezard did not go to the station with Galeide.]

Chapter XXI

Meanwhile Anna Elisabeth had arrived and occupied Galeide's room. Her presence at once made itself most pleasantly felt. Where she was it could be neither sad nor monotonous. Indeed, she could be enchanting, although she was much too indolent and too dignified to devote herself to that end. She reminded one of my Mama and of Galeide more than did her sister Eva, but all her proportions were slighter and she was more ethereal; her hands were the whitest, slenderest, and daintiest that can be imagined. She was several years older than I, and loved to tease me gracefully by treating me like a boy, which would probably have irritated me very much if I had really been one, but as it was I found it highly charming and willingly submitted to it. She knew how to take each person as suited him best and displayed a temperate benevolence toward all; unlike so many women, she was never jealous of the advantages of others, but sincerely admired them, which she could well afford to do, for she herself made a fine impression even among the most beautiful and amiable women, and that without the slightest apparent effort on her part. Thus she caused life in our house to assume a more pleasing aspect, especially after the removal of the Christmas tree, which had continued to spread about it an atmosphere of sad remembrance. After it had been taken away, my great-grandfather said: "Now the child no longer sits under the tree," by which he meant Galeide, whom his mind's eye had probably still been seeing there.

We seldom saw Ezard any more; our house no doubt seemed dreary to him now that Galeide had left it, and moreover Lucile had conceived the plan of diverting him by a varied social life. She herself enjoyed it greatly, though she would have no more confessed that to herself than to any one else; my cousin, on the other hand, had now entirely lost his former moderate fondness for society, but he was as cheerful and entertaining as was proper, and in general continued to live outwardly as if Galeide's departure did not concern him, or at least had no effect on him. He still went away on business at times, although there was no longer any real reason for it; that is to say, a conclusion had gradually been arrived at, as regards the water-works, which was of great importance for us all.

The Norwegian, of whose popularity in our family I have spoken, had sketched the plan of a water supply in which a system of his own was to be used, which he promised would be more efficient and serviceable than anything hitherto known. He succeeded in so thoroughly convincing Uncle Harre of the value of his invention that the latter allowed himself to be drawn into a risky undertaking.

In spite of all the preparations that had been made, the senate still hesitated to do anything thorough; but especially it balked at the fact that Karlsen was a foreigner, whereas they would rather have directed the honor and profit of the work into the hands of a native. Moreover, Karlsen had not concealed the fact that large sums would be needed before everything could be put in proper working order, and our council was too excessively cautious and diffident to dare to make the necessary appropriation. On the other hand, it proposed to the Norwegian that he should undertake to carry out his plan on his own account, in which case the senate would agree to take over the works at a considerable sum and to refund the cost as soon as the system should prove its usefulness.

Ezard was the only one of us who could at all judge the technical part of the enterprise, but he fully realized that he owed the greater part of his knowledge to the Norwegian himself and was scarcely competent to supervise him. Hence his attitude in the matter was one of reserve, whereas Uncle Harre, sight unseen, transferred his faith in the young engineer's personality to his invention, which he really no more understood than the "thing-in-itself" or the Trinity. Without asking any one or listening to any

Permission Theo. Stroefer, Nürnberg   MAX KLINGER

PSYCHE AT THE SEA

one, he threw the greater part of his fortune into this
enterprise, for the success of which he had no security
but the confident attitude of the Norwegian, whose own
means were not sufficient to enable him to carry out his
invention, but who declared most positively that in a few
years Uncle Harre would get back many times his in-
vestment.

After my uncle had once taken this step, Ezard thought
the only right thing to do was to make every possible effort
to further the rapid progress of the work, so that it should
not come to a standstill owing to negligent management.
To this end he not only himself purchased an interest in
the undertaking, but from then on threw aside his other
professional work entirely, and devoted himself solely to
the advancement of this splendid enterprise. The ener-
getic activity into which this led him satisfied him for the
time and filled him with hope for the success of the plan
and the profit to be gained from the capital invested in it.
But as often as delays and difficulties appeared, he too
showed signs of inward disquietude; in fact, more and
more frequently he displayed an absent-minded restlessness which was far from being in accord with his true
nature. At such times he reproached himself with not
having forcibly restrained his father from risking his fortune; for if that should be lost, then indeed an incalculable
calamity would arise.

As to Uncle Harre, he had aged so perceptibly within a
short time that even we who saw him almost daily were
struck by it. We were glad to see that he did still retain
his upright bearing and the elastic step with which he
strode along like a youth, but his capacity for work had
decreased, and the exuberance of his former view of life
had subsided equally. Whereas he had formerly liked to
tease my father about his pessimism, he himself now often
seemed unable to shake off a deep depression, and not seldom even worried his young wife with such attacks. There
was this difference, to be sure, that what was my father's

natural disposition appeared to be abnormal in him. Also, he laughed at himself and struggled manfully against it, and when he did not succeed in any other way he tried medical treatment. It is often said that the most skilful physicians are blind where they themselves are concerned. This was not quite true of my uncle; at least he had moments when he recognized his own condition most distinctly. But he had a theory according to which physical ills should be combated and could be conquered by the will better than by medicine, a view to which his strong and able nature had led him and which may also contain certain grains of truth, but which may sometimes become dangerous for a doctor if he adheres to it on principle. It actually did occur that, with this theory in his mind, he neglected the early use of those means which are supposed to cure the sufferer by the effect they have on his body. Now as it gradually became clear that his will no longer did what he required of it, he inwardly despaired wholly of ever being able to regain his former health and strength, but began nevertheless to submit to the most various cures, visiting now this watering place, now that; but as he was without any real confidence and therefore did not adhere at all to the prescribed mode of life, he always returned with more shattered nerves than before. Perhaps his theory really fitted him better than any one else, and the fact that his mind was no longer able to master his illness simply showed that the mind itself was no longer sound, whether it was old age or some other ailment that was weakening it. This realization came to my uncle much sooner than he showed and opened up to him the fearful possibility of lapsing into mental disease with increasing age. He now even spoke of this at times, but only when he seemed to be in a very merry, even exuberant, mood, so that one could think it a part of his other jokes and nonsense. At such times he used to say such things as, " You young people, Ezard or Ludolf, show yourselves to be truly free and liberal minded men when such a moment comes, and put a weapon in my hand, so that my physical can follow my mental death immediately. For it is the duty of a man who has sons and daughters to leave them not only a good name, but also the image of a strong and able father, so that they may rejoice in him and he may be a beneficial memory to them, not a bogey that makes them fear for their own future.''

Such speeches shocked innocent Eva and also Lucile, who found them all the more criminal and rash that she believed them to be mere words without any deeper meaning, but my great-grandfather still more, in whose opinion suicide was a deadly sin which he could not bear even to hear discussed. For he liked to believe in a Christianity embroidered with philosophy, and regarded God, so to speak, as the highest wisdom and the epitome of all good, to whom full power over the lives of men must be reserved. Hence in my great-grandfather's eyes a suicide was an iniquitous rebel who encroached upon the rights of the Almighty, a Prometheus who stole a spark from the giver of light and life, and for whom no punishment hereafter and no judgment in this life is too ignominious.

Anna Elisabeth had a much keener glance than her sister Eva and far fewer prejudices than her grandfather, and hence on the one hand she took Uncle Harre's insinuations more seriously than Eva, and on the other she judged them less harshly than my great-grandfather. But she avoided everything ugly and depressing and was very skilful in turning such discussions into mere light conversation without betraying anything of her deeper thoughts. At the same time, she concerned herself greatly with Uncle Harre's and Eva's financial circumstances, with an understanding of money matters that compelled my astonishment and admiration, and she represented to Eva that she ought to take an interest in these things, as she could not expect that her husband would live to see his children entirely grown up (to be sure she had only one child at that time and never had another), and she would then have to be answerable for their further education.

To me Anna Elisabeth once said, " Dear Ludolf, it was very unwise of your family to ally itself to ours. For we Olethurms represent the feminine principle, you Ursleus the masculine. Now it is said that man must earn and woman must take care of his earnings. But what good can come of a union in which both understand least of all the very thing that is their part? At real acquisition, which is understood to mean the untiring and industrious addition of one well-earned dollar to another, you Ursleus are incompetent; and we, as I willingly confess, should have spent the first one long before the second was added to it. In short, we can do nothing but play directly into each other's hands to our mutual destruction. If I had known you all before as well as I do now, I should never have consented to letting Eva be bound to you by her husband."

Then Eva would try to defend herself and proudly lay before us the principles on which she had arranged her housekeeping; and to me they seemed quite worthy of respect, but Anna Elisabeth laughed and said:

" You dear child, every one of your words simply confirms what I say. So that is what your innocence thinks is saving and economy? If any one should say to you, but this, and this, and that is really superfluous, you would answer just like grandfather, Oh, we have to have that! That is only decent and respectable! That is simply necessary! "

I could see that Anna Elisabeth had observed well and was right, on the whole, but still her words hurt me and that because, as I now clearly see, they seemed to prove how little she thought of still another union between our families. I said it seemed to me that recognition of these weaknesses would be equivalent to laying the foundation for their correction and that if one only knew he was going astray, some effort on his part would bring him back to the right path. At that Anna Elisabeth looked at me with an indescribable smile in her fine gray eyes and said: "My dear boy, if you ever prove able to earn and accumulate money like a good citizen, you have hidden your finest talents from me till now with more skill in dissimulating than I should have believed you possessed. As to myself, I must acknowledge that I feel better able to squander the treasures of the king of Siam than to distribute the income of our above-mentioned citizen over the cycle of the year; and I take credit to myself for this knowledge of myself, for it alone distinguishes me from the other Olethurms and keeps me from imprudent and ruinous acts."

It increased my admiration for Anna Elizabeth that she was so extraordinarily right, but with the mental reservation that I should some time prove to her by my deeds that she had not fathomed me as thoroughly as she believed, and in imagination I already enjoyed the modest pleasures of a simple and industrious life. I was satisfied, however, with this anticipation, and put off the real beginning of an improved mode of life to a day which, curiously enough, I always thought of as removed from me by a constant interval of time. But at the same time I was convinced that some day I should astonish the world by the sudden development of the most excellent civic virtues, and looked forward to this with as much delight as the people of Schlaraffenland looked forward to the ready roasted and seasoned pigeon that should drop from the sky into their mouths.

Chapter XXII

[GALEIDE wrote gaily about her new surroundings in Geneva. When Ludolf's father returned from America and found that his child had been torn from him, it was a sad homecoming. He said little about the success of his journey and no one asked about it. So he faced alone the inevitable ruin of his family. He and Ludolf went to the Harz Mountains, taking with them little Harre, who prattled incessantly about Galeide. After a time Lucile came and took the boy away, much to the old man's grief. Much as he loved the little fellow he could not be reconciled to Ezard, and it was like a farewell for life. Ludolf went out into the woods after leaving the station, heartsick for Anna Elisabeth.]

When I came out of the wood, as weary as an old man, I felt myself drawn to my father, whose solitary suffering all at once seemed very comprehensible to me, and I was inclined to be surprised and to blame myself that we had lived side by side for so long without ever becoming real friends. When I asked after him at our rooms, I was told that he had gone out. I no longer remember what impression this tidings made on me, or what moved me to go into his room. My eye fell at once on a sealed letter addressed to me in my father's large, clear handwriting. In a flash I knew everything that had happened and that would now follow — all in an instant — and I trembled so that I had to wait some time before I could open the letter.

There were many things in it which I did not read at that time and was too agitated to understand; the only thing I grasped was that I should find my father dead at a spot in the woods which he described. If I remember aright, it seems to me that at first I felt nothing but blind horror that I was alone. I sent a telegram to Ezard at once, telling him that my father was critically ill and asking him to come immediately. But when once I had left the village behind and was in the woods, I found myself again, my awakened heart grasped everything, and all my fear was lost in boundless, overwhelming grief. The more I collected my senses, the more I hastened my steps, in the hope that I might perhaps still come in time to prevent the hand I loved from carrying out its dreadful intention. I raced forward through the trees like a fugitive, and suddenly, all out of breath and covered with sweat, I stood at the spot where I was to find him. And at the same moment I caught sight of the motionless body lying there in the moss, and as my blood was already coursing wildly from my frenzied running, I grew dizzy, everything faded before my eyes, and I dropped beside my dead father. Thus I remained for a time, only half conscious of myself and of what had happened, till the longing to see my father became so strong that I roused and dragged myself up to him. But his face still showed so many traces of the life that had scarcely left it that I was struck with horror and watched timidly to see whether the body would not twitch. Gazing fixedly with pain and dread at the beloved features, I noticed that dusk was falling rapidly and I hastened away to fetch people, so that the body should not have to lie in the woods over night.

At the inn where we were staying I said that my father had taken his life in a moment of insane depression, and the people were quite ready to believe me, for his constant melancholy and silent manner might easily have been taken for a mental affliction, and moreover the respect that his appearance awakened prevented any suspicion among the common people of what they would have considered wrong and reprehensible. At the same time they were averse to disquieting the other guests by the presence of a dead body in the house, which I could well understand. I therefore agreed to the proposal that my father should lie in a little house which had been lightly built of wood for the comfortable enjoyment of a view, and which could be locked with a key in the possession of our landlord. At first it was my intention to watch by my father after he had actually been carried there, but I was almost ashamed of my purpose, as excessively sentimental, and since it was already rather late at night I went home. Thus, with the soughing of the dark firs about him, he lay alone where we had stood side by side a few days before, looking at the undulating country round about and the gently waving tree-tops just below, he with the unutterable secret in his soul that his frozen lips had now betrayed to me.

Chapter XXIII

I HAD also notified Galeide at once, and it so happened that she and Ezard first saw each other again by our father's dead body. This gave me a strange feeling, when I thought how the dead man now lay so still between them, nor prevented them from looking full into each other's eyes, though that had been his bitterest grief while living. It was impossible that the two should not have had similar thoughts, but the idea did not seem to move them to shame or remorse; on the contrary, when they looked at each other there was a lofty consciousness and a proud light in their eyes as if they had won a victory. Whether they were intoxicated by reading in each other's looks the confession of a love that had been not lessened but intensified by separation, or whether they looked on my father's death as a sign that fate was on their side, I will not venture to decide, but I believe they were moved by both feelings.

I felt deep resentment of their assured bearing and, turning to them, I said bitterly: " It seems to me, you feel less that he has been torn from us than that he was in your way and has now been removed."

They let this remark pass without defending themselves, indeed they seemed to let me talk because after all I could not know what was in their minds. But my words had started Ezard on a train of thought which was so extraordinary, in fact so uncanny, that even now I cannot write of it without asking myself whether this is not a dream or some other hallucination of my own fantasy. After he had gazed at my father for a time, as if he were trying to remember or think of something, he said, half to himself and half to Galeide:

" That is the first! "

I waited to see whether he would add anything to these words, which in themselves were incomprehensible, and, as he did not do so, I was forced to think that he meant my father was the first of several who must die before something that he had in his mind must or might happen. I searched his face for some confession or betrayal; how symmetrical it was, how nobly harmonious! But at the same time there was an expression of determination in it which I felt obliged to call now superhuman, now inhuman. I should have liked to ask him whether a dream or some other supposed omen had tempted him to lie in wait for the death of his blood-kin, so that his damnable passion might have full sway. But I could not bring myself to do it, just because I felt more and more certain that it was so. And Galeide, who had perhaps understood the meaning of Ezard's words better than I, had turned pale and looked at him with wide-open, frightened eyes; she seemed to feel a sudden horror, but probably as much of herself as of him.

As far as I noticed, they made no effort to see each other alone without my company; Galeide declared her intention of returning to Geneva that same day, while we should be taking the coffin with the dead body back to our native town. The trains which were to take us in different directions stood opposite each other; ours left a few minutes earlier. I watched Ezard and Galeide constantly, less like a faithful Eckart who should restrain them from evil, than from jealousy on my father's account, whom I felt they were defrauding of the tribute due him every time they had a feeling that was not for him. Nevertheless, again I could not help admiring their stern strength in their passion, for at parting they offered neither hand nor lips (as, indeed, during the whole day they had not touched each other even lightly or accidentally), but said good-by merely with a glance and a kind, comforting smile, which I thought particularly touching and striking under the circumstances, as if one should find, in the burning sand of an African desert, a fragrant violet or an anemone in bloom.

When we arrived at home, Anna Elisabeth had already gone, which did not surprise me, but on the contrary seemed only to confirm my presentiment or calculation. She had left a very kind, sympathetic letter for me, and I did not doubt at all that she felt earnest and sincere pity for us. But she could not bear gloom, just as some people cannot bear the atmosphere of a church; I knew that well and could not be angry with her for it; it even pleased me, unhappy as I was, that she did not want to appear other than she was.

She had been quite right. Truly miserable days now came for us, for the meanest of all cares, with which my father had so long wrestled breast to breast, now that he was thrown, stood before us with its great, gray body, and stared boldly into our faces. In mine it could not read much but infinite contempt of its insolent harlot's glance, contempt which was far stronger than my fear; but there was no spark in me of courage or joy of battle, if for no other reason, then simply because it disgusted me too much. It was about the same with my great-grand-father. He had had the greatest part of his fortune in my father's business and now had lost it. But he bore this calmly and did not trouble much about what was to happen now; his concern was solely for Galeide and me, for, and he said this not without pride, we were by nature absolutely unfit to enter into practical life and make our own way. The house in which we lived, however, still belonged to him, and he had always intended to leave it to Galeide and me, because he knew that we would cherish it with reverent love; families that live long in one place are wont to honor their houses as they would a temple.

Although there could be no question for any intelligent man that the house must now be sold, yet at first no one dared to speak of it till one day Ezard quietly explained the matter to us, saying at the same time that he had already taken steps to bring about an advantageous sale. For a single moment he seemed hateful to me, for he spoke without any appearance of sorrow or sympathy; my great-grandfather, on the other hand, at once agreed with him and even thanked him for his trouble, which of course he deserved. To my inexpressible wrath I now had to see strangers fingering and belittling our home. I hated and despised them all in advance, if only on account of the miserable money that gave them the right to take possession of our good property and drive us from our threshold. My only consolation was to ridicule and make fun of them, together with my great-grandfather, who displayed no little talent and inclination in this direction, although we really knew nothing whatever about them and they were doubtless all respectable and good-natured people. For hours at a time I could sit first in this room, then in that, and lose myself in tears as I thought how it had formerly been there, how I had imagined it some day might be, and how different it had now become.

In the meantime I let Ezard go on caring for us and acting for us, which he did without asking or saying a word, and I believe that in his simple heart, so full of strength and kindness, he really took it as a matter of course and scarcely blamed me for my remissness or for indulging my grief overmuch. He arranged my father's affairs, too, and settled with the one creditor who could not be wholly satisfied out of the proceeds of the wind-up for a sum which was very considerable for Ezard's circumstances at that time. For the progress of affairs in regard to the water-works was now beginning to be very uncertain and dubious, causing him serious worries, of which, however, he said not a word; nor did I learn of the above-mentioned sacrifice, made for us and for my father's memory, until long afterward.

We were in such need of money that the house had to be sold hurriedly and below its value. My great-grandfather, who was always very changeable in his moods and views, now overwhelmed Ezard, who had arranged everything, with irritated reproaches.

"Naturally," said Ezard without showing any sensitiveness, "I should not have hurried the sale if I could have provided for you all in the meantime out of my own means; but my own affairs are in a bad state. The water-works do not yet run as they should; if we do not soon obtain more capital, to enable us to make the necessary improvements, the work will come to a standstill, and I don't yet know what will happen then."

We saw how serious the condition of affairs was from Ezard's depressed face better than from his words. My great-grandfather's mood immediately veered about, and he tried to persuade my cousin to use the money gained from the sale of the house for himself, although as grand-father himself could not be exposed and left to the care of the Great Spirit like an aged Indian, this would not have done much good. He also managed in his consoling speeches to put all the blame on Uncle Harre, who, as every one knew, had drawn Ezard into such a mad and risky undertaking. Ezard sadly shook his head.

"It is just that," he said, "that troubles me most. I knew my father. I should have restrained him by force, should never have allowed it to go so far. Instead of that I went into danger with him, so that now neither of us can stretch out a saving hand to the other. If I were the only one concerned, my heart would be lighter, as I could manage to provide for my family alone even if I had to begin all over again. But my father has a young wife and a little child and is aging day by day; he feels and I see his powers diminish. If he should lose everything now, how could he think of retrieving it again in the short time that is left to him? Every day I have only bad news to give him; he starts at the familiar sound of my steps. I am often so weary that I should like to say: I can do no more! if I did not keep saying to myself unceasingly: I must!"

In his endeavor to comfort the unhappy man, my great-grandfather, as nothing else was of avail, finally began to speak of Galeide, brought out her letters, and read some passages in them which told of her activity and her prog-ress. One of them ran something like this:

" My dearest Grandfather, I work like an ant or a bee, my arms ache in the evening as if I were a washerwoman. But I shall really be a success some day, I can tell you. (Don't rely too firmly on that though!) At times I am so sure of it that I should like to throw my violin into a corner for sheer ecstasy. But don't be afraid, my heart, in reality I don't do that, but let my reason rule and put it carefully into its case every evening and make you say to me: What a good child you have grown to be, you naughty Galeide."

My great-grandfather looked on Galeide's letters as something precious and a rich source of treasure, read twice as much into them as there was there, and answered them as regularly as if he were engaged in forming a correspondence of famous contemporaries.

Although generally Ezard neither spoke of Galeide nor could bear to hear her talked of, yet this passage from her letter clearly had a good effect upon him. He rose and said with an easy glance at us:

" Yes, I believe she will be great. It was good that she went away. In the meantime let us see to keeping our heads above water."

When we were alone my great-grandfather said: " Did you observe him while I was telling about Galeide? He isn't particularly anxious to hear of her, but still he is glad to know that she is well off, and he thinks a great deal of her talent, which, of course, must strike every one. Under the influence of distance and the hard blows of fate, his morbid passion is turning into a noble and permissible friendship. It is the same with her. Every line in her letter utters a healthy joyousness and the assurance of a spirit that is free from guilt and at peace with itself."

I let my great-grandfather weave together such threads of thought, though they seemed to me to flutter unsupported in the air like summer gossamer. Keenly as he observed details, yet the picture he drew of things or people as a whole was often fundamentally false, because he measured all phenomena by himself; and there was absolutely no standard of comparison in him for Galeide's nature, which, with all its softness, was yet extremely rough and violent. He adored her and did not himself know why. In the same way he saw of Ezard only the side that best agreed with himself and which was usually expressed in his fine, amiable personality. Of the splendid and terribly irresistible demon that was in Ezard he knew nothing; but could my cousin himself, through the long years preceding a certain fateful day, have suspected what kind of a companion dwelt in his breast?

The time now came when we had to move out of our house. Not many things in my life have caused me such enduring pain, though sometimes a greater one. It is a true saying that no one should seek to comfort a man for the death of his beloved, as long as the body remains unburied before his eyes. The house in which I had spent my youth, the stone corpse of my childish dreams,—no one bore it away and buried it in the earth, so that my heart might forget and be soothed. Stately and kind it stood on its old site, and seemed to be waiting for the lost children who had forsaken it. Once more before my death, if it should not take me suddenly and unawares, I have planned to go back to my native town, not to revisit any person, but merely the old house. I want to walk along the broad street under the ramose lindens till I see the iron garden-gate and, through the fence, the round bed with its wreath of white lilies, and the lawn luxuriant with yellow dandelion; and perhaps the window will be open out of which floated so many a time the playing and singing that we loved, sweet and sublime, into the quiet summer nights.

It was on a damp day in late winter that we emigrated. The snow slipped under our feet and my great-grandfather, never used to walking, clung firmly to my arm. But even now he still tried to make life interesting to himself.

"Look," he said to me, " now we are being transplanted like trees out of our old garden into a new soil. You are

still young and can take root again, but what the gardener's intention was in digging up me, rotten old trunk that
I am, I don't know; it is a daring experiment.''

Always inclined to assail my great-grandfather's religio-
philosophic opinions, I said resentfully: "Yes, it is so
ill-considered that I don't see why you should credit the
gardener with any intention; his name is Chance and he
pulls up whatever happens to get under his hands."

For the first time in my memory my great-grandfather
did not take up this challenge, probably less for utter lack
of a reply than for general depression and fatigue. At the
same time I noticed, as he walked so close beside me, that
he had grown a good bit shorter in the last years, for now
he scarcely came up to my shoulder. I felt touched and
ashamed when I thought that he neither made use of his
great age to overrule us by the multitude of his experiences, nor to force a deferential sensitiveness upon us by
mental or physical frailties, gloom, and premonitions of
death. As we had in the meantime reached a corner where
we had to turn into another street, he stopped and looked
back once more at our house.

"Now I will not go this way again, Ludolf," he said.
"Life is over for me, and I am moving into the garden
of memory, where the plants are watered with tears.''

Yes, thought I, but who will have to shed them? You
or I? For I did not believe that the sojourn among the
graveyard foliage he mentioned would agree with him
long. But I said nothing of the sort, because I too was
much affected at that moment, and besides, because I had
just resolved to treat my great-grandfather with no less
veneration than any educated person shows for antiquities
of another kind, for ruins, parchments, or other witnesses
to the past.

SUMMARY OF CHAPTERS XXIV AND XXV

[THINGS now went from bad to worse. Work on the
water system stopped for lack of capital and much bitter
controversy between the senate and the promoters took

place, in which of course the Ursleus were involved, although Ezard strove to keep aloof from public dispute and to convince the senate of the real merit of Karlsen's system.

Going to visit his parents' graves, Ludolf encountered Ezard and little Harre, the former looking so strange that Ludolf guessed Galeide as the cause. From Eva he learned that Ezard and Galeide had recently met, and soon after Ezard admitted that he had not given up his love for her, nor ever would.]

Chapter XXVI

THE senate had finally declared itself ready to invest a liberal sum in the construction of the new water system, so that the work could now be resumed. This was undoubtedly due to Ezard's untiring activity; he worked under the most unfavorable stars, like Hercules, without at the time being strengthened and stimulated by visible successes. Now, to be sure, that I can survey the whole past from my observatory, I can see that our general circumstances were improving, thanks to Ezard's efforts. But at that time we could not know whether it was not perhaps merely a casual, temporary rise in the road. Moreover, a dreadful time was still to come, which seemed about to accomplish our ruin, and of that I will now try to speak.

Cholera had broken out in the East. We read the accounts in the papers, not without pity and shuddering, much as we tremble at dreadful scenes on the stage, with the comfortable certainty that they can never strike and never reach us. When we heard that the disease had appeared in the port of Marseilles — carried by Egyptian ships — a chill did run through us; it was as if the spectre had now set foot on European soil, sending out its poisonous breath before it. Some people thought they must ridicule any premature fear, or they really did so. Among the latter was Uncle Harre. For, in accordance with his aforementioned views, he used to attribute the customary

ravages of certain diseases largely to people's unreason-
ing fear of them. He disapproved of the detailed accounts
and descriptions in the press, as increasing the popular
dread and anxiety: but aside from that, it was mischievous
to speak of cholera in such an entirely different way from
any other disease. People acted as if there were something
transcendental and ghostly about it, a curse or a destiny
that could not be escaped. They crossed themselves and
turned pale at the very name of cholera, as if it were an
incarnate witch who could poison or pardon any one that
displeased her.

I distinctly remember all the circumstances with which
it began. It was June and so hot that even the nights were
unbearable. One day toward evening I had crawled over
to Eva's house and was eagerly breathing the air of a
fairly cool room in which the shutters had been closed all
day. The child Heileke was sitting in front of a little table
on which stood her favorite plaything, a kind of music-
box with metal keys, on which she produced little, ringing
tones by striking them with a tiny hammer. Quite fair
and white in her short frock, she looked to me like a flower-
elf, making music by striking with its stamens the walls
of the bell-like blossom he inhabits. Suddenly Uncle Harre
entered the room in a way that immediately betrayed the
fact that he was in a state of no little excitement. Without greeting me, although he had seen me, he began to
speak vehemently.

"In the harbor quarter," he said, "a death has occurred which is attributed to cholera. That fellow Wittich
(the socialistic Rhinelander) came and reported it to me;
after the manner of such fellows, who want to bring every
cough of a fly before the tribunal of the people, he demanded that the case should immediately be published in
the newspapers. That would be the way to make sure of
having cholera in town tomorrow, even if we haven't it
yet."

Pale terror had struck my very marrow, for I had an indescribable dread of repulsive diseases, and I must confess that I should not have been unwilling to take a ticket immediately for the farthest pole of the globe. Eva was frightened too, but she controlled herself and asked whether it was really proved that the death in question was due to cholera. Uncle Harre shrugged his shoulders and said that he could not rely on Wittich, for those social democrats were so accustomed to exaggeration and distortion that they might proclaim intoxication or a "holdover" to be cholera; he would first convince himself. At that Eva turned pale and begged him to give up that intention, at the same time casting an anxious glance at the child, Heileke. Uncle Harre laughed and said: "There you have it." I should not have spoken even to you two about it. The fear of it makes every one imbecile. Just think how often I visit patients from whom I might catch the germ of a deadly disease. There are a hundred deaths in every mouthful of air that we breathe. We must keep our bodies in such a condition that they can digest them."

With these words he sat down by the little girl on her narrow child's sofa, took her in his arms, and danced her, at which she laughed happily, for she loved her father with particular tenderness. I was annoyed at this inconsiderate way in which he tormented Eva, but, on the other hand, I could not but admire her so much the more; not a word or look betrayed her inward agitation, on the contrary, she now took pains to discuss and consider the matter calmly. Uncle Harre, however, was not willing to talk much about it, but insisted more and more obstinately that the whole thing was merely an attempt to terrorize people, which always afforded the social democrats particular enjoyment.

*   *   *   *   *   *   *   *   *

The number of deaths now increased so rapidly that concealment was no longer possible. As a fire that has smouldered on unseen for a long time suddenly leaps into sight in flames of astounding power, so did the dreaded disease seem all at once to appear in overwhelming power, because its insidious beginnings had not been observed. A mad fear of death now seized every one. No one knew what to do. Many took to flight. Some of those who remained scarcely dared to eat enough, for fear of taking something harmful, while others, in boastful foolhardiness, lived still less cautiously than before, as if they were facing a personal opponent, before whom they must not allow themselves to be caught in any act of cowardice. As people were unable to explain such a sudden and universal calamity all looked to the authorities, and reproaches were soon heard, as if they, bribed by the uncanny guest, had let his flying ghost vessel secretly enter the slumbering harbor in the dark and fog.

Uncle Harre, in his position as head of the department of sanitation, felt these reproaches especially. I remember one evening when he visited us at a late hour, which was the more surprising as he was not in the habit of coming to see us frequently. My great-grandfather sat dreaming in the sofa-corner, while I played the piano in the dark room adjoining. We both received him with sympathy for his present difficult and distressing position. I can still see him, his tall, slight figure as upright as ever, it is true, but it impressed one as if this were due rather to a strong effort of will than to natural elasticity.

Before he sat down Uncle Harre asked if we had no fear of infection, as otherwise he would leave again at once; it would be groundless, however, as he always took sufficient precautions. My great-grandfather denied being afraid and asked him to stay, and he actually was as fearless as the Wandering Jew who, it is said, could go to bed with the pest and never sicken. Aged men are always wont to regard the phenomena of the world with a lofty composure, easily explicable by the fact that they have already seen so many calamities approach and even the most frightful pass them by. As for me, I sat down at a not too noticeable distance from Uncle Harre. He then began to talk with extraordinary clearness of the conditions in the city, of the origin and course of the disease.

The chief evil, he said, was the bad water supply, which carried the infection into every house. Everything would be different if the new water system were already finished and in use; the epidemic would now make the city expend and lose much larger sums than it would have cost it to take over the new water system at the proper time. He went on to speak of the lack of all the necessary things: of houses where the patients could be isolated, of nurses to take care of them, of practical regulations which could go into force at once, so that private individuals might also know how to act, and have their measures duly supervised. For all this, he said, he himself was partly to blame, but still more the excessive economy of the senate, which had generally approved regulations for the public welfare only when they made a good outward showing, and had put them off from year to year, especially if no immediate advantage could be seen in them. He told all this with a calm, seriousness, and simplicity that was rare with him. My great-grandfather listened willingly and with sympathetic attention, and inquired what my uncle now intended to do to make up for what had been left undone in the past.

Uncle Harre said: "I do little, but all I can. I myself stand at the most dangerous post. The people are saying that the upper classes think only of themselves and their own undisturbed luxury and leave the poor to perish in their miserable quarters. And who cannot understand their thinking this, poor unfortunates, who really are the first, most helpless victims? I can save but very few. But I spend the whole day in the hospitals; I go home only for moments and force myself not to see Eva and the baby, so as not to put them in danger. Eva did not want to have it so, but she yields to me because she sees my anxiety. Many, in fact, most, things I leave to Ezard. For I lack the superiority that comes from inward calm, the assurance in deciding what can be done with advantage, and, what is more, the assurance in doing it. I have grown old. Formerly antagonism was to me a welcome prod that spurred me on to fresh action; now it paralyzes me. But then this is another matter. Now I feel a constant, never ceasing pressure on me, and when I stop to think what it is I hear the word ' disgrace ' ringing in my ear. I need all the strength that I still have in me to keep on bearing this unaccustomed burden — as far as may be.''

A boundless pity took possession of me, which increased when I saw my great-grandfather's touched expression and his kind friendliness toward Uncle Harre, overcoming for the first time in years the old antipathy.

'' There is good as well as evil for men in such events,'' said my great-grandfather gently. '' In the common round of life every one gives himself up too much to daily routine and indulges himself, for what is daily required of us demands only moderate strength, which a man can easily muster in sufficient quantity. But when extraordinary fatalities arise with their extraordinary demands, a man reaches deep down into his breast and brings out the treasure which perhaps no one would otherwise ever see. Every feeling and every ability is intensified; and, after all, is it not the highest thing in life for a man to come to a realization of himself and to be able fully to unfold his inmost powers ? ''

Uncle Harre's eyes flashed for a moment as in the old days and he said with fire, '' Yes, that is beautiful and true;'' then he added slowly, '' But for me it is too late. A tree may feel as I do, when the warm winds and the strong sun come in March, and it can no longer leaf and bud like the others, because the winter has treated it too severely. I have grown old.''

He sank down wearily after he had said this and rested his head in his hand. My great-grandfather moved nearer and nearer to him and laid his hand on his shoulder.

'' Harre,'' he said with emotion, '' the Creator equipped

you so extravagantly with such great and such brilliant gifts. If you realize, or think that you realize, that you have not always used them as wisely as you might have, you acquire at a stroke what you perhaps still lacked. You are not yet too old to be able to rise up once more after a defeat and look forward to better days."

"Not too old," answered Uncle Harre; "I am only sixty-five, so I am more than twenty-five years younger than you. But I am different from you and have lived differently. You know us. We are an abundant, brilliant family, but we lack something. What shall I call it? Is it moderation? Modesty in our demands on life? Yes, that is it. That made us value common, everyday life too little. We wanted to be always on the heights; we did not want to begin at the bottom. Thus I have overstrained and worn myself out; I have made poor use of my head. My goodness, with what hopes I rushed into life! And as long as I was still vigorous, I never noticed whether they were being fulfilled or not, I kept on hoping and rushing forward. And now I see them and myself collapsing simultaneously. How did my brother end? How will my son end? Nothing but ruins lie behind me, and I shall leave nothing but ruins."

My great-grandfather pondered silently in his chair after Uncle Harre had finished speaking. He seemed to be gazing into that fountain of the remembrance of all things, which, according to legend, springs eternally murmuring from the roots of the Ash-tree of the World.

"Yes," he said after some time, "fortune is no longer with you or with us. And as it is my sacred conviction that there is a justice ruling over us, incomprehensible it is true but incorruptible, we ourselves are probably to blame for our ruin."

I had risen while my great-grandfather was speaking and went to the open window in the next room to hide a great agitation. From there I heard the two continue talking in low tones, but without understanding what they said.

Outside it was perfectly still; for weeks not a breath of air
had stirred; the heat brooded heavily over all. After a
time there sounded the slow rolling of one of the ambu-
lances that constantly drove hither and thither through the
city to carry those who had been attacked by the pest to
the barracks assigned to them.

*   *   *   *   *   *   *   *   *   *

The ambulance stopped in our street, which naturally
caught my attention, for after all the cases in our quarter
of the town were still very rare. I heard a door open and
the sound of wailing voices. Uncle Harre, who must also
have heard it, suddenly came to my side and leaned out
of the window to see what was happening. I said:

"They seem to be fetching a child; perhaps its mother
does not want to let it go away from her."

His face had grown quite livid; without saying a word
he went back into the other room, gulped down a glass of
wine which my great-grandfather had poured out for him,
and then took his leave. It was clear that, in consequence
of the accusations raised against him and perhaps also of
his own secret reproaches, he was beginning to feel in a
way like an accomplice of the cholera, so that every sound
of grief it caused pierced him to the heart as if he himself
were to blame. Perhaps, too, he had thought of his own
child, delicate little Heileke; for he seemed to have conceived the unhappy idea that this being, whom he loved
most, would be taken from him by the disease as a pro-
pitiatory sacrifice. I watched him as he walked down the
street, as upright as he had come, and followed by a long,
dark shadow.

Summary of Chapter XXVII

[Ezard was appointed to superintend the fight against
the cholera. Though this resulted in a separation from
his wife and little girl, Ezard found consolation in the work
which he performed superbly, and looked happier and
stronger than for some time before.

Ludolf, who had resolved to join in the campaign, despite his horror of the disease, made a strange acquaintance during this time: Flora Lelallen, daughter of a merchant who had married a foreigner. Her parents had both been stricken, and the girl conceived the singular idea, perhaps suggested by Boccaccio's tale, of gathering lovers of life about her in the big, empty house. Night after night they came, each wearing a red rose, and Ludolf among them. When the news came that her parents had died, Flora knew it by some intuition, and at the same time prophesied her own impending death. She and her aunt sailed the next day for America, for she longed to be on the sea.]

Chapter XXVIII

MANY of the inhabitants of our town, unable to master their fear, had fled, but some of them, their power of resistance weakened by excitement and change of climate, had succumbed to the germs they took with them. In this way the epidemic spread farther and farther afield, though it nowhere showed such power as here. Whereas in the beginning other places had pitied our misery, their interest in us now became hostile, since we threatened others with our own calamity. In the newspapers which hitherto had only sought to arouse sympathy for our fate, our circumstances were now investigated, so that it might be seen to what extent we ourselves were perhaps to blame for such heavy misfortune. There appeared many things that were not to our credit, in particular the condition of our water system (for the new one could not yet be used), which was said to be, and probably was, the principal cause of the great headway made by the disease. When the investigators then sought the blame for this, our senate, although it might have admitted that its own remissness was partly responsible, was all too ready, in its human weakness, to throw off all blame, as others too seemed to deserve it. As my uncle and my cousin had headed the commission on the construction of the water-works, it was convenient to declare that they were responsible for everything that was connected with it, even though they on their part had been very active and had not shirked great sacrifices. In the meantime the Norwegian's project had proved to be practicable; but another plan, they said, could just as well have been used, and with less expense. In short, as the undertaking had once been in Uncle Harre's and Ezard's hands, all the blame now fell on them, and the senate appeared in a favorable light, the more so as the enterprise was progressing most successfully ever since the senate had taken it over.

But this was not enough. Two new grave charges were made against Uncle Harre: first, that he had not replaced the old, inadequate sanitary regulations by new ones, and second, that he had intentionally and knowingly concealed from the public the first signs of the cholera that had been observed. As for the sanitary regulations, Uncle Harre had insisted on several points which the senate did not understand, and my uncle with his hot temperament had laid ever greater stress on these particular points, and had refused to take up the matter at all, unless the senate yielded to him in this essential question, which he understood and was able to judge. So the affair had dragged on for several years, as had been the case with many another; but in this particular instance events had revealed the dilatoriness and had pronounced it guilty.

If in this matter my uncle's consciousness that he was but slightly to blame might have consoled him, whatever the outcome, yet the second accusation was a very different thing. Although he had had no evil intention in concealing the beginnings of the disease, yet the immediate consequences proved to him that at least he had not calculated the best course for the public welfare as correctly as his position obliged him to be able to do. Besides, he knew he had been sufficiently urged, and was too clear-sighted not to acknowledge that it was just Dr. Wittich's warning which had confused his judgment, and consequently, that either this or his character was not as incorruptible as the city might rightly demand of one of its chief men. Far from trying to gloss over his acts, he condemned himself with such cruel justice that he would immediately have resigned from his office, if it had not seemed to him that such a course, at a time when the pressure of worry and work so far outweighed the honor, would be shameful flight. In the meantime the unceasing, wearing activity had lost for him all its usual power of stimulation. There was no sign of success or improvement, and he felt that he was merely reducing the mountain of his guilt, not creating anything new. This together with his anxiety for the life of his child and the future of his young wife, as well as the imagined scenes of open disgrace with which he tortured himself, shattered his mental and physical health more and more every day.

The people, who knew nothing of his spiritual states and sufferings, had no sort of sympathy for him, and while my cousin was the object of every one's increasing admiration and gratitude, the hatred of his father grew stronger, and gradually the opinion took firmer and firmer root that he had had the power to avert the calamity, but had used it to bring it about. In all domestic and foreign newspapers his conduct was described and condemned; fear of the disease and the despair that reigned in the places where it had already broken out found a certain satisfaction in being able to vent themselves on some guilty person. Under these circumstances the senate, which could not have taken Uncle Harre's side without the greatest disadvantage, thought it necessary to represent the newly awakened demand for justice among the people and to oppose him and institute a formal investigation. It is true, the entire procedure was in the bosom of the senate. In conformity with an old custom provided for such cases, Uncle Harre was to appear before the assembled members to receive a solemn reprimand, and to be condemned to pay

a considerable fine, whereupon he himself was to resign.
This procedure, though not excessively humiliating in form,
inasmuch as he would be judged and blamed only by his
equals, he felt to be the most painful that could have been
prepared for him.   His nature was such that he would
rather have stood accused before a wild mob, where, speaking from a full heart, he could in part have confessed himself guilty, in part have defended himself.

The gravest feature of his condition seemed to us the
fact that he never spoke of what was going on within him.
Whereas formerly, with the fearless one-sidedness of a
child, he had stormed at any kind of hostile demonstration
from his opponents, and had thus worked off his anger, he
now refrained from any expression of sensitiveness.   His
bearing was such that we also did not dare to say a word
in his defense or of reproach against others, for fear that
from our sympathy he might draw some humiliating conclusion in regard to himself and his position.   Ezard was
the only one with whom he talked about these things, and
in answer to our questions my cousin told Eva and me
something of these conversations, but by no means all, I
thought.

Just at the time that these things were happening, the
first faint abatement of the epidemic was observed.   As
in any case people were beginning to grow accustomed to
constant peril, they became more negligent of precaution-
ary measures, hitherto so strictly observed.   Eva also
and the little girl Heileke were no longer as careful in
associating with Uncle Harre as at first.   This may have
been partly because Uncle Harre was so absorbed and
beset by torturing cares that one thing made him forget
the other, and then because in his depression he longed
more than usual to have these two bright beings near him.
Eva felt all the more deep-seated affection and admiration
for her husband, the less the rapid decline of the youthful
vigor which had graced him so long made him a suitable
object for the romantic love of a woman of her age.   In

our eyes his suffering, silently and proudly borne, endowed him with a greatness which had certainly always been in him, but from which the exceedingly restless mobility of his versatile mind had formerly detracted too much. The fact that he felt himself to be guilty, that he took upon himself the consequences, patiently, without defiance but also without whining, now gave him the dignity which formerly one had regretfully missed in him, particularly because the remarkableness of his mind had seemed to require it. Eva and I, deceived by his outward calm, sometimes yielded to the hope that he might regain all his former vigor, and who knows whether things might not really have taken a turn for the better, if a fresh misfortune had not entirely overwhelmed him: his child Heileke was taken with the disease.

On the morning of that day I was with Eva, and as we were talking earnestly about Uncle Harre, who was to resign from his office before the assembled senate on one of the following days, we did not pay any attention to the little girl, who was also in the room. But she was particularly restless and desirous of our notice, perhaps because she was already sickening with the disease; she climbed on my knee, nestled her little head against me and whispered into my ear a request to play her something. I hesitated to humor her, not knowing whether Eva was in the mood to listen, and bade the little one to make music herself with her little hammer. At that she shook her head again sadly and said, "You play, you play!" Finally I yielded to her, lifted her onto the top of the grand piano, and began to play. The music seemed to do her good, for she breathed deeply several times like one who is about to cast a heavy burden from his heart, and her features expressed increasing contentment. When I noticed this, I slipped into some merry dance music, at which she suddenly hopped down from her high seat and began to dance in a curious fashion, not according to any familiar measure, but now gliding slowly up and down, now whirling round and round so that her long fair hair flew out all about her; and all her movements were executed with as much passion as grace, so that I repeated the melody several times in a different way, to be able to enjoy the pretty scene longer. Eva, however, interrupted me, thinking perhaps that Heileke was overheating herself; she caught up the dancing child in the midst of her graceful turns and seated her on her lap. But the little girl unexpectedly broke into tears and sobbed as steadily and vehemently as if some great misfortune had happened to her. I hated all such scenes, as I never knew what to do, so I speedily took my departure, notwithstanding that I had lately sworn to watch over Eva and her child, and this would have afforded me an opportunity to do so.

As chance would have it, I found a letter at home from Flore's aunt, telling me of the girl's death. She had developed cholera soon after they sailed, and in such a violent form that she had succumbed to it in an hour. " She was buried at sea," wrote the aunt, " but although I am not so imaginative as my niece was, whenever I see the seabirds sweeping along close above the waves, I cannot help thinking that her soul is sailing there in the wind, getting its fill of life."

Until then I had never used the key to the deserted house, for the Lovers of Life had been spoiled for me and none of the others seemed inclined to continue the rather questionable league, as indeed the spirits of men seldom remain so uniformly high-strung that a notion born of exuberance can be made permanent. Now I again entered the big Lelallen room where we had reveled so madly, and as there had not been time to clean it thoroughly before their abrupt departure, I found a few utterly withered, malcolored roses on the floor, as well as empty glasses on the table. I looked at everything and then went to the cellar and brought up a bottle of wine at random. It proved to be a heavy white wine, with which I filled two glasses so that I could clink them. They emitted a very deep, pure tone that rolled wonderfully through the empty room, followed by an echo in a higher key. While I slowly emptied the glass, lost in dreamy retrospection, dusk was falling; and when it suddenly occurred to me that I was all alone in the dreary house I shuddered and would not stay longer. I drained my glass to the last drop and threw it against the marble shelf of a mirror, so that it smashed into several pieces; I left the other glass standing full on the table. If at midnight her restless spirit had come hovering through these rooms, it might have sipped warmth and life from it. As I was leaving, my eye fell on the little apple-tree, but the late blossoms of misfortune had withered in the meantime and it looked as drear as a senile old woman who has adorned herself with tattered finery because she cannot forget the beauty of her youth.

When I got home I found that Ezard had been there and had brought the news of the child's illness. She had been taken to the hospital at once, and Uncle Harre himself had insisted upon it, as every one without exception was obliged to go. I went to Eva immediately and found her alone, for Uncle Harre was constantly with the little girl and only came home from time to time to bring news of her condition. Eva was standing in the middle of the room when I entered; she did not move, quietly allowed me to embrace and kiss her — for I did not know how else to greet her — and then began restlessly to walk up and down the room. I begged her to tell me how it had happened, for I thought it better for her to speak, even if of something that must tear her heart; and she clearly took pains to do so, but she could not finish, suddenly breaking off to say urgently:

"Were you ever in the hospital, Ludolf? Tell me what it looks like. I can stand hearing it, for she has to be there. Oh, Ludolf, think of my blossom, my little bud, my soul in that grave!"

I tried to make her see that she had an exaggerated and too horrible idea of the place, gloomy though it was, but she did not listen to me.

" He is with her, and he won't let me go," she mur-
mured to herself; " if I were only a man! "

Little as I could do or say to comfort her, yet it seemed
to me that she was glad to have me there, and I stayed,
which she seemed to take as a matter of course or at least
as nothing unusual, though night had fallen.   When Uncle
Harre's steps broke in on our silence, I was sick with fear;
Eva, on the contrary, managed to control herself to such
an extent that she went to meet Uncle Harre with a smile
on her white face, which to be sure looked more like that
of a wandering spirit than of a living person.   He said
nothing but the words, " She is alive," and they did not
sound like a message of joy, for he spoke them as hope-
lessly as if they merely meant that the anxiety and torment
were prolonged.   Neither of us said a word at first; Eva
brought Uncle Harre something to eat and drink, but he
did not touch it.   At last Eva ventured to plead, " Tell
me something about her! " at which he turned his burning
eyes on her with an indescribable glance and replied,
" What shall I say?   She does not know me any longer."
Immediately afterward he rose to go; when he had already
reached the door Eva went after him, put both her arms
about his neck, and raised her face' for him to kiss.   He
caught her to him and then rushed from the room with a
stifled sob.   I stayed over night with Eva who lay back on
the cushions of a sofa as lightly as the plucked petal of a
white lily.   I could imagine that I saw her restless fears
trembling and beating behind her big, blue eyes and pale
forehead.   As she could not think of sleeping, she begged
me to play to her.   As it was late at night, however, I did
not dare to strike the keys loudly but muffled the tone so
that it seemed to come from far away, and though it made
one dreamy and sad, yet the subdued sound lured us away
from the hard reality.

I do not know how we were able to stand that state of
agitation almost without sleeping or eating, although the
following day passed in a similar manner.   But the most

terrible time was the third day, when Uncle Harre brought the news that the danger seemed to be over. For however we may be tortured by the fear of a coming calamity, yet the most unbearable suffering only begins when a new hope steals into our hearts and keeps them eternally trembling between the heights and the depths. After a short rest Uncle Harre had hurried away again, promising to return with news as soon as possible. While hitherto Eva had generally been as still and motionless and white as a dead person, a feverish red now flushed her face, and, now rubbing her hands together, now stroking back the disheveled locks from her forehead, she walked up and down all the rooms, then went to the window and back again, or knelt beside a chair and buried her face in the cushions. Her agitation did not decrease, but grew every moment, until at last, not knowing what else to do, it occurred to her to pray; she herself felt probably too confused and insensible to do so and she turned to me with the plea, " Pray, Ludolf, will you? Please, let us pray! " At that moment I simply could not think of any prayer except " Our Father," which I believed I could still say fairly well, but I could not over-come a decided antipathy to it. At the same time, Eva looked at me with a beseeching glance and plucked humbly at my sleeve in support of her request, so that I felt I would have given the world to do what she wanted. Then it occurred to me that I knew by heart the beginning of the book of Genesis, for which I had always had a particular prefer-ence and attachment, and as it might pass for a prayer, being a part of the Bible, I made up my mind and began to repeat one verse after another: In the beginning God cre-ated the heaven and the earth. And the earth was without form and void; and darkness was upon the face of the deep. And the Spirit of God moved upon the face of the waters. And God said, Let there be light: and there was light. And God saw the light that it was good: and God divided the light from the darkness. And God called the light Day, and the darkness he called Night.

As I noticed how fervently Eva's eyes hung on my lips,— for presumably she heard only the biblical intonation without understanding the words in the least,—I did not stop at all, but kept on going back to the beginning when I did not know any more: In the beginning God created the heaven and the earth. And the earth was without form and void. And she continued to listen in the same state of ecstacy.

Thus absorbed, we did not hear Uncle Harre come upstairs, and so, although all the time we were in a fever of expectation, yet at the last moment we were completely unprepared when he pulled open the door and laid a formless bundle on the floor: the child Heileke, wrapped in many big shawls which now fell apart, so that she lay open-eyed there before us, as white as snow. Eva gave a loud cry and threw herself down beside the child. With unsteady steps Uncle Harre had immediately made for a chair and burst into tears, probably the consequence of the excessive excitement and exertions of the last few days. I found it hard to master my emotion as I looked at Eva, who half lay and half knelt beside her child, now looking at her, now pressing her to herself with reverence and timidity, as if the little body were something holy; and as Eva, always of a dainty and ethereal build, had grown pale and thinner in the days past, just like her little girl, there was little earthly about them, and they could well be compared to transparent, sisterly angels, floating on equally light clouds in starry space, and embracing each other after a sorrowful time of separation.

Chapter XXIX

[On the day his child's life was despaired of, Uncle Harre resigned from his office.]

Several days passed after Heileke's recovery, during which Uncle Harre now sat absorbed in absent thought, now tormented those about him, and most of all himself, with his unbearable irritability and excited manner. As ill-luck would have it, a pamphlet fell into his hands, written by young Dr. Wittich as a report on the origin of the cholera in our town, and done in a way that made it a personal attack on Uncle Harre. It contained nothing untrue, to be sure, but it absolutely distorted Uncle Harre's personality, as if he had been a coldly smiling, cynical tyrant, growing fat at the expense of the long-suffering poor — such a picture as the socialist likes to draw of a man of property. This was bad, just because it could not be refuted, although entirely incorrect; for the facts themselves were not perverted, and it was only the writer's words that threw on my uncle this ambiguous light — which could not be caught and defined. We saw well enough that Uncle Harre had read the paper, and among ourselves we thought it best to talk to him about it, but we could never bring ourselves to do it when he was present with the unapproachable dignity of his grief in his face.

Outraged to the uttermost by the Rhinelander's hateful attack, I went to Ezard with the inquiry whether we could not do something to defend Uncle Harre and the honor of our name, as it was not always dignified, but sometimes cowardly and indolent, to allow an insult to pass in silence. He replied that his father had expressed a definite wish that nothing of the sort should be done. He did not add more, but I seemed to detect in him particular feelings and thoughts which he might not or would not tell me, but which wholly absorbed him.

A few days later, Uncle Harre invited my great-grandfather and me to spend the evening with him, to celebrate his child's recovery. We saw with amazement and delight how different my uncle seemed that evening: with the same elasticity in his bearing that had charmed me when I was still a boy, the same intelligent gleam in his eyes that so charmingly accompanied his brilliant words, even the same habit of brushing his thick, white hair from his brow with a rapid gesture of the hand, he was again the enchanting

personality, overflowing with life, that he had been at the
zenith of his manhood.   But now that he seemed to have
regained it by conquest, as it were, and we all knew what
a tremendous burden he must have exerted himself to shake
off before he could appear thus to us, he not only delighted
us but compelled our admiration, and I was gratified to
see that Eva too received a similar impression, and perhaps felt again, for the first time in months, what had
attracted her to a man so much her senior when she became
his bride.   Heileke greeted the change with unaffected joy,
which, as she was still weak and obliged to keep quiet, she
could not utter aloud as well as she could express it in
the blissfully radiant eyes that followed her father wherever he went.   From time to time she called him to her in
her piping little voice, whereupon he always hastened immediately to kneel beside her chair and let her hug and
kiss him.

Every one was in good spirits and I was disturbed
only by the seriousness that I perceived in Ezard's face;
which despite the cheerful surroundings, did not decrease,
but rather increased.   However the deep and boundless
love he had for his father was apparent, although he
did not make much show of it; but in every word and
gesture that concerned his father he expressed the gentlest
consideration and veneration, and the latter seemed to
observe this and to be grateful for it.   The evening passed
agreeably, for each of us was trying to avoid all the bitterness that had lately made life so hard for us, and to cheer,
not chill the other, and the very fact that each felt this
endeavor in the others made us happier.   It was late when
we broke up, and we separated cheerfully, indeed not without gaiety.   The pronounced and hearty way in which
Uncle Harre took leave of us all might have struck us,
if his fine and easy manner the whole evening had not
accustomed us to an elevated mood.   He accompanied us
to the front door, where he once more firmly clasped
Ezard's hand and smiled; Ezard's face remained as serious

as before and even seemed to me to express a painful lament, but I thought no more of it at the time.

Next day we received the news of Uncle Harre's death; he had taken his life with a revolver shot. All at once I saw the events of the past evening in another light. Above all I realized that this wonderful man had made his decision with open eyes and had wanted to part from us with equal assurance and composure. Nothing could have shaken me so unutterably as this behavior. He seemed to me a higher being, one of the noblest of men, and to this day I tell myself that he deserved to be so called in death. The manner in which he went to his death took all the bitterness and excessive pain from our grief, for he had succeeded in giving us the feeling that he was not to be pitied for what he lost in death, but that he was regaining something that his own conduct had lost him — inward peace and the respectful sympathy of the better class of men.

When I found myself alone with Ezard in the presence of the dead body, I distinctly recalled the previous evening, and yielding to a feeling that suddenly rose within me, I asked him whether he had been informed of his father's intention. He replied:

"I knew nothing but that it must be so and that he himself realized it. I knew he had felt it for weeks, and yesterday when I all at once saw him before me, so clear, so cheerful, and so proud, I felt: now he has made up his mind; now he will do it."

I could not repress a shudder, and asked, not without reproach: "You suspected or knew what was going on in your father's mind and did not restrain him? You talked oftener and more intimately with him than any of us, he hinted to you perhaps what he thought he must do; and you did not try to dissuade him, but looked on as he hastened to his death?"

"Yes," said Ezard, "I did, because it had to be. That part of his fortune that was in the water-works he left to the town, and thus paid his debt as far as was in his power. If he had gone on living he could never have made matters

good. For what would he have been for the remaining
years of his life? A decrepit, useless, weakened old man,
a diseased and injurious member of our family. That he
recognized that and shielded himself and us from it was
worthy of his finest years. Should I have hindered my
father whom I love, when he wanted to part from us as a
hero instead of living on in disgrace?''

Although there was much in these words that touched
and convinced me, yet because he spoke them so quietly,
though not without agitation, Ezard seemed to me incomprehensible and uncanny, and I remembered a similar
moment when we had stood beside the body of my unhappy
father and he had whispered those strange words: '' That
is the first.'' I was so horrified at the recollection that my
heart began to beat violently, and as I looked at Ezard I
felt that he read my thoughts — which was indeed possible
enough, for I had reached them through an association of
ideas which was perhaps more immediate with him than
with me. I felt a burning impulse to utter them, and yet
I trembled at the thought. Suddenly I heard myself jerk-
ing out the words in an over-loud voice, '' Ezard, is this
the second?''—at which I myself was so horrified that I
should not have understood his answer if he had replied.
But he said nothing, only I could see by his face and his
eyes, which rested on me at once so sadly and so fearfully,
that he had understood me. I regretted having uttered
the unspeakable; for now another question stirred in me,
though even to myself it seemed uncalled for and monstrous: who will be the third? And although I told myself
that I had no cause whatever to give Ezard's dream or
madness such a form, yet I could not prevent an answer
from constantly springing up in my mind which made me
giddy, as if I were standing on the edge of a precipitous
cliff, looking straight down before me into the depths. I
raced through the streets for I don't know how long, my
teeth chattering with inward chills; next day it seemed to
me like a wild dream, and I directed my thoughts to other
things; finally I forgot it again.

Chapter XXX

[People began to accuse Dr. Wittich of having hounded Uncle Harre to death. Ezard had become popular, and the new water-system turned out to be even better than had been expected — the opinion became current that the family had been sacrificed to the senate's egoism.

Galeide had finished her studies in Switzerland and was reported to have acquired rare skill in execution and to interpret with real genius. She wrote that she was coming home.]

So it came that one day I went to the station and stood there waiting for Galeide, thinking how long it was since I had accompanied her there when she seemed to be going away forever. I tried to imagine that I had not moved from the place since then, but had only closed my eyes and allowed a momentary dream to pass before my vision. This threw me into a strange state, so that I stood there as if drunk with sleep as the train rushed in, the passengers streamed out, and all at once Galeide stood before me with laughing eyes out of which quick tears streamed, kissed me on the mouth, and said: "Ludolf, let me look at you. Why, you are not a little boy any more!"

As soon as I heard her clear, ringing, childlike voice, which was unchanged, I no longer needed to imagine, but really felt that she had always been here, only that everything about us had changed in the meantime. She asked for a carriage, for she was trembling with eagerness to see Grandfather. As she was too agitated to talk much during the drive, I observed her at my leisure and found that she had grown older, but only in so far as age, up to a certain point, means an increase in strength. Her childlike soul, full of innocence and frankness, still radiated from brow and cheeks; there was a contented expression about her mouth, as if during all these years she had laughed much and never wept, which was almost amazing in view of the troubled time, full of heart-breaking experiences, that lay behind her. When we came to the part of town from which our old house could be seen, she turned away her head but did not say a word, and so I too remained silent, for each knew without speaking how the other felt. Finally in her excitement she kept asking every minute, "Are we there now? Now?"—for she didn't hear my answer. When the carriage stopped all the color left her face. "Where?" she asked. "One flight," I answered. At that she rushed up ahead of me with her light step; at the top stood Grandfather with his arms outstretched, and with a loud cry she threw herself so violently on his breast that he might easily have fallen. Beside her tall figure it was very clear how his body had shrunk, though but little bent.

Now she drew us with her into the room and said to me as she threw off her hat and cloak: "Ludolf, make Grandfather sit down;" then she began to run through all the rooms, looked out of every window, glanced over the pictures on the walls, celebrated a reunion with every object that she remembered from former times, and accompanied everything with hearty exclamations. In all this she reminded me of our mother, although she did not possess the latter's faultless beauty; but in compensation one could see how strong and well she felt, and that delights the eye almost as much as perfect regularity of feature.

I was inwardly full of agitation, for every moment I thought I must hear Ezard's step; he did not come, however, and in the evening I learned that he was away for a day or two. The suspicion immediately arose in my mind that he had met Galeide on the way, so as to be the first to greet her. I did not ask her about this, however, my real reason being that I was afraid to touch on these unhappy matters. Lucile had declared that she would not leave the city, that it was not for her to retreat before Galeide. But she did not want to see her and would manage to avoid it; likewise she would take care that the

children should not see her. I told Galeide this, and she
listened to me calmly and said that Lucile was right and
that she would not interfere with Lucile's wishes, in spite
of her great longing to see little Harre again. She added
of her own accord that she would not stay long, as she
knew well that it would not do for her and Ezard to be
in the same town. What my great-grandfather would say
to this was another question, to be sure, and one with which
we did not occupy ourselves at that time.

For as everything seemed to be well arranged for the
time being, I was glad of Galeide's presence; she was so
even, quiet, cheerful, and confident that it seemed easier
to live when she was there to soothe and refresh one at
the same time. Frequently I accompanied her violin-play-
ing, which was really beautiful, so that when you looked at
her graceful, proud pose it was easy to believe that she would
yet achieve greatness, even the highest eminence in her
art. At first my great-grandfather had had some difficulty
in reconciling her real appearance with his remembrance
of her, but after that his contentment grew from day to
day, and assumed gigantic proportions when he saw the
admiration of those outside the family. For old and new
acquaintances soon came to see what had come of the
returning stranger. She was also invited to play at a
public concert; for amusements and festivities were to
begin again, now that the cholera had at last completely
succumbed to winter. The long terrified people, who could
fitly regard themselves as miraculously saved, rushed with
thirsty senses into the enjoyments that were given back
to them, and Galeide, who as a child of the town, but tried
and recognized abroad, had their hearts with her in
advance, could have been sure of unusual success even without significant achievement. I must say, however, that
she deserved the tremendous applause that was given her.

Ezard was in the audience, which was considered right
and proper, as public opinion was now for us once for all;
I think other people looked on Ezard and Galeide as those

Permission Theo. Stroefer, Nürnberg

MAX KLINGER

ZEUS AND EROS

who had indeed gone astray but who had fully and gloriously repaired their errors by forceful, brilliant deeds.
It seemed just as natural, too, that Ezard should go home
with us after the concert, and now, for the first time since
my father's death, I saw the two together again.   The
unaffected gladness with which they greeted each other
strengthened my suspicion that they must have already
seen each other somewhere, while my great-grandfather,
on the contrary, saw in it the corroboration of his view
that their feeling for each other had become clarified into
a good brotherly and sisterly friendship.   The blissful
happiness that radiated from them whenever they were
together ought to have shown him that it was otherwise.

There were several other acquaintances with us, among
them Wendelin, who was still unmarried and for the sole
reason that he could not forget Galeide.   With his singed
wings the unhappy fellow had at once dragged himself to
the light that flamed up again, and renewed his old sufferings, which he sought to sweeten with blind hopes.   Galeide
met him as unconcernedly as if nothing had happened, and
this was not forced on her part, but the pain of a rejected
suitor made so little impression on her that she did not
even need to forget it in order to be able to talk to him
as indifferently as to any other man.   Moreover her passion was so whole-souled and powerful that she had no real
consciousness of any one but Ezard and yielded with all
her strength to the rapture of knowing him to be near her.
Several times, on one pretext or another, they managed to
see each other alone for a few moments apart from the
assembled company; they did this with the glad artless-
ness of an engaged couple, so fully did the triumphant feeling of their unity and love exclude all thought of the wrong
that they thus committed.   Although by no means assumed
for the purpose, it was just this frankness that made their
intimacy appear quite unsuspicious to others; for the
onlooker, who from the vantage-point of an unaffected
spectator can clearly perceive what is wrong, seldom grasps

the fact that the criminal by no means needs to be conscious of it to the same extent.

After the other guests had left us, Ezard still remained. And now it was as when fire or water, an element hard to subdue, is released and bursts forth. Not that their passion betrayed itself in tactless expressions of love, but it announced its indefinable presence with mysterious strength, like the perfume that a night flower begins to exhale as soon as it grows dark. Homage had been paid to Galeide in the form of a wreath of flowers; out of it some one had taken the roses and put red and white ones in her hair. Thus adorned she sat there, quiet but glowing like life itself, representing something legitimate and unsubvertible, which no opposition seems able to destroy. That, I feel certain, was the result of the inward composure which she really possessed, but which I should by no means like to hear called self-satisfaction or self-complacency; for if she was ever satisfied with herself, it was with the innocent gratitude one feels for a present, or it was even more that she regarded her nature and disposition as something unalterable, on which it would be foolish to waste time; she was much too thoughtless and too little inclined to introspection to be vain.

If at first I had allowed myself to be carried away by Ezard's and Galeide's tremendous assurance, so that I overlooked the outrageousness of their relation and accepted their close intimacy as something permanently unsubvertible, yet now that we were alone my judgment returned, and I felt the unconcern with which they dropped all restraint before our eyes to be an insulting slight or else the madness of an animal that runs amuck, and without wishing to do so, blindly knocks down everything in its way. My behavior may have brought the two to their senses, for Ezard suddenly rose to leave; nevertheless, when Galeide declared that she would go with him to the front door, I felt unable to interfere, but remained inactive where I was as if chained. I think both my great-grandfather and I trembled as we counted the short, seemingly eternal moments that she was absent. When she came back, she was very pale under her red roses, and seemed to expect a reproach or an attack from us. But as we remained silent, she knelt down beside Grandfather and said good-night to him with passionate tenderness. He must suddenly have realized that all the hopes which he had persuaded himself into believing were nothing but foam, and that his darling was unescapably menaced by the fate she had brought on herself; for he pressed her vehemently to him several times, and, taking her head between his hands, regarded her with a long, earnest glance.

It seemed as if the time were now to come again when one constantly trembles in fear of an annihilating thunderbolt, and yet at the same time wishes for it, so as to be freed one way or the other from the strain of a dreadful depression.

CHAPTER XXXI

WHEN it did come, however, it came as a surprise. It was the worst of all, the thing that I shudder to have experienced. Galeide wanted to go away, and a good opportunity happened to offer. In Geneva, where she had well-disposed friends, she was offered a place as violinist in the orchestra, which as a beginning would be an honorable position, if not a glorious one. It would allow her time to continue perfecting herself, so that she need by no means give up for this the higher career for which, according to the general opinion, she was created. She accepted at once, as she had grown fond of Geneva and its inhabitants, and understood how to combine whatever ambition she might have with much patience; on the other hand, it gave her the pretext she sought for leaving our great-grandfather and all that she called home. Grandfather agreed more readily than we had expected, but on condition that Galeide should not go until the time came for her to take the position, at Easter. Thus it was settled.

Immediately, however, Ezard and Galeide were again possessed by the feeling that this respite was a reprieve to be enjoyed to the full, just as a man condemned to death makes merry all through his last night, in which the hangman must gratify his every wish.

One day Lucile called me to her by letter. I went with the most uncomfortable premonitions, which proved to be justified; for she received me in a state of great excitement and informed me that Ezard had made known to her his relations to Galeide and had asked her to consent to a divorce. I felt almost relieved to think that Ezard had at last rent the web of deception and treason, especially as I had full confidence that he would be able to bring this course to a conclusion without injuring his prestige and that of our family. But I at once had to recognize that there was no hope of Lucile's doing her part toward an amicable solution. She said she had seen through Ezard's game much longer than he had suspected or desired (which she probably said only to avoid appearing as a wretched, deceived woman). He had worked, saved, and drudged to acquire enough money to buy his freedom from her. Meanwhile he had kept her in suspense and had tried to deceive her as to the actual state of things, so that matters should not come to a head until he could divorce her and still preserve his outward honor (by giving her in compensation as much happiness as wealth could procure). And now this time had come. But he had miscalculated her. She was not disposed to sacrifice herself so that two perfidious hearts might reap undeserved happiness. She had ceased to respect Ezard, or indeed any man, he was nothing to her. But she wanted her children to keep their father. Besides, it was against her principles to aid in the dissolution of a marriage that had been ordained by God and was holy. The fetters chafed her as much as him, but she would bear them because she had sworn before God to do so.

All these things were, indeed, quite in accord with her

character; but I saw something more behind them which was also entirely consistent with her nature, namely, that she would not give up Ezard because she still loved him in spite of everything as ardently or more so than before, and that she simulated all these other reasons for refusing him his liberty so that she need not make the humiliating confession of this weakness (for as such she regarded it) to herself, to say nothing of others. But just this convinced me of the hopelessness of Ezard's cause; for reasons might, on a pinch, have been refuted or at least silenced, but against her blind will simply to have and to hold him nothing could be done, unless she herself were miraculously freed from it. Nevertheless I did try to discuss the matter with her, not indeed excusing Ezard and Galeide, but still taking their part to the extent of pointing out that the mischief was done and could not be changed, and that it was after all better to have two happy than three unhappy; moreover, it might be safely assumed that she herself would feel more contented after she had voluntarily given up such a painful and undignified position as her present one.

But as I talked to her thus, the feeling that I was trying to snatch Ezard from her agitated her more and more, and she began to confuse her reasons and her principles with her love; and now she said that she must protect Ezard from Galeide, who would only make him unhappy after all, as she lacked all the truly womanly qualities, on which Ezard laid particular importance, and more things of the same sort. In the greatest excitement she finally cried, let Ezard do what he would, she would never give him up, except perhaps by leaving him forever, that is, by seeking death herself; if he and Galeide would then dare to clasp guilty hand, across her corpse, let them; their punishment would come. I grew alarmed, for I believed her capable of raising her hand against herself, contrary to all her principles, somewhat as a defiant child, too severely punished by its parents pretends sickness to frighten them.

At the same time I keenly felt her deserted state and her unhappiness, but more with my reason than with my heart, so that, gladly. as I would have been just to her, I may have seemed rather antagonist than friend; in reality I was neither.

Galeide, to whom I told all this, with my opinions and fears, seemed to have the most affection left for Lucile of us all, perhaps because she remembered how Lucile had been before cruel experience had embittered her soul and sharpened her features. She did not look at all aged or ugly, by the way; on the contrary, owing to the daintiness of her figure, she had retained something childlike, to which her large and very fiery eyes formed a charming contrast. What she lacked was the harmony of a finished and complete personality; Galeide had it, and hence she could inspire such peace and content, as if there were nothing more to desire on earth but to be always near her.

Galeide and Ezard and I had never talked about these relations and what we might do and hope. One evening we were out in a rowboat on the river on which our town is situated; it was warm and dark and we rowed slowly. Once we stopped altogether, so that the boat only rocked gently· from side to side and we gazed into the dark green depths, each pursuing his own thoughts. Galeide said:

"Soon I shall again be looking into blue Lake Geneva. Oh, if I were only there already, so that it would be over" ·(meaning the pain of parting).

"This time we shall not be separated for so long," said Ezard. "I feel as if our happiness and our love were something holy, for which I am responsible. Our star will conquer, I know it for sure."

Galeide, whose white face I could see from where I sat, made no reply, but slowly and sadly shook her head, smiling, however, at the same time, as if she were thinking of the happiness she had enjoyed, which, even though it had been sinfully wrested from fate, had still been happiness like any other. I said sorrowfully: "When I think that it seems to me as if it were only yesterday that Galeide and I secretly rowed on this river for the first time (for father would not hear of our going, fearing something might happen to us), and that now that beautiful time of hope, called youth, will soon lie wholly behind me, I cannot understand why we yearn, strive, and suffer for any real or supposed good; for everything passes like a dream, one way or another."

"Yes," answered Ezard in a firm voice, "life passes all too quickly. Therefore a man should spend as little time as possible in waiting, and should be his own destiny. We have only a single, short life, hence its course is no trifling matter. The happiness that I might have is mine by right, and I may fight for it." These words must have sounded uncanny to all of us, for none of us said anything more; we reached for the oars in silence and rowed back to the landing without stopping.

During these days a few cases of cholera had been observed, but this time they did not find us unprepared, for the physicians had pointed out from the beginning that the scourge might appear again in the spring. We now had enough experience not to be so quickly disconcerted, every one was at once in his place again and Ezard too resumed his former activity. It was less talked of than in the previous year, and at bottom no one was personally afraid; but now it happened that Lucile's little girl was taken violently ill. Eva and Galeide were at once ready to help, but Galeide was sharply repulsed, as might have been expected. Everything developed more rapidly than I can describe it. Lucile was completely beside herself; she would accept comfort and encouragement from no one. She refused to let the child leave her and so it remained at home without a doctor being consulted, which indeed was not necessary, as Ezard knew exactly all that could be done to alleviate and combat the disease. The child died that same evening. Eva came to our house, as she had given up trying to make headway against Lucile's passionate lamentation. She was not a little worried, for the pitiable mother refused to release the dead child from her arms and could not be persuaded to take the customary precautions to protect her own health. Lost in thought, I asked where Ezard was and what he was doing.

"Yes, Ezard! He should not let her alone, he ought to force her to control herself. But you know how they stand. I can do nothing."

Galeide, who was present, grew deathly pale and I imagined I could see her tremble.

When Eva was gone I said: "Galeide, what are you thinking?"

She looked at me wide-eyed and said: "I am thinking: what if she should be taken sick and die! You know that would be happiness and salvation for us. So, if I should listen to my heart I should have to desire it. That is a horrible thing to tell yourself."

I shuddered. Not long after Ezard sent for me, as Lucile was ill and asking for me. I looked at Galeide.

"Go to grandfather," I said, her appearance frightened me so.

She shook her head. "Come back soon," she begged in an expressionless voice.

Lucile lay in bed; her large eyes turned to me the moment I entered; at that instant she did not look much disfigured. She wanted to prevent my coming near to her, but in spite of that I sat down on a chair close beside her bed, which cost me not the slightest effort, for in my excitement I had no thought of caution or danger. She signed to Ezard that she wanted to speak to me alone, whereupon he left the room.

"Ludolf," she said, "will you see to it that my mother and my brother never learn that I renounced the Catholic faith?"

I had expected that she would speak to me about much more painful things, and because I felt relieved my liking for her increased at once (so selfish is man), and I said as heartily as I could: "I will take care that they never learn it. But the fact that you did so does not trouble you, does it? You acted in good faith, and God will understand that, if there is a God."

I now saw how much the unhappy woman must have missed affectionate sympathy, for the cordial tone of my words at once moved her to tears. "Do you know, Ludolf," she said sobbing, "that my child is dead? The only being on earth that loved me and needed me! If I had only stayed at home! Oh, if I had only stayed at home!"

This simple lament pierced my heart, and a great anguish came over me because of our harshness and lovelessness toward this stranger, which we should perhaps never be able to make good again. As I bent over her to speak soothingly to her, a convulsive twitching in her face showed me that the disease was about to seize her again. Full of terror, I started up to call Ezard, but she restrained me with a beseeching glance and amid evident torments said with difficulty, "When I am dead, Ludolf, take me home. I do not want to lie in your earth, I want to go home."

I nodded, but as I saw that she wanted a stronger confirmation I said aloud, "Yes, Lucile, I will take you home, if you die, you and your little girl. But you shall not die! I will call Ezard."

Ezard came into the room at that moment and quickly arranged several things intended to help Lucile, or at least to relieve her condition. But now my composure was suddenly at an end; the sight of this horrible suffering turned me sick. To that was added a strange notion: Ezard happened to be standing at the foot of Lucile's bed, and as he looked very pale and tall in the darkened room, there came into my mind the story of how Death showed himself at the foot of the sickbed when he wished to indicate that the sufferer was his victim. I could not drive away this thought and it increased my horror, which probably showed in my face; for Ezard whispered to me to leave the room, for I could not help and it would be better for me. I went, feeling altogether incapable of standing it in that chamber any longer, and sat down in a chair in the adjoining room; I shook all over and could not control myself. In my state of nausea I thought I could already feel the disease, whereby I grew steadily worse, so that finally I decided to leave the house and try the effect of fresh air. And really, after I had traversed a few streets, I felt better, and in about half an hour I brought myself to go back to Ezard's house.

In the meantime Lucile had died. I was so horrified that Ezard, who himself was perfectly calm, had to support me. When I had composed myself somewhat and observed him, his calm seemed to have something unnaturally rigid in it. I could not take my eyes from his terrible beauty. There had never been, and was not now, any trace of hardness, still less cruelty, in his face; on the contrary, the most sincere kindness always seemed to light it. I cannot say what I was really thinking, and besides I was only half conscious of my thoughts. As I looked at Lucile lying there so cold in death, my senses became more and more confused: suddenly it seemed as if everything grew silent in me and in this silence I heard distinctly, as if a strange voice were speaking within me: "That is the third." These words were repeated in my ears more and more frequently and rapidly, until at last the whole room seemed to resound with them. I looked over at Ezard to see whether he heard it, and thought I could tell by his face that he was listening, which of course was due only to my excited imagination. It was not impossible, however, that he was thinking of these words. It would have been impossible for me to utter them. As far as I can remember we did not exchange a word the whole time.

When I started to go Ezard said, "I will go with you, I must go to Galeide."

On the way I could no longer resist the abominable feeling that we were bringing home good news and hope for a better future. Galeide was standing upright in the room when we entered.

" Galeide," said Ezard in a suppressed voice, while still in the doorway, " she is dead."

Immediately they rushed into each other's arms and both broke into tears. Ezard wept so violently that it seemed as if he must wash away rocks from his heart with his streaming tears, and his countenance really grew suddenly brighter, and his bearing changed like that of a man who has had to drag an unendurable burden to the top of a mountain and now casts it down, having reached his goal. Nevertheless they were both serious and not because it was suitable for the occasion but because they felt so. As long as I was with Ezard and Galeide, my heart also grew lighter and I forgot my terrifying imaginings; but as soon as I was alone and tried to sleep they came again, and my agitation increased when the notion came into my head that I must keep on inwardly repeating to the rhythm of my heart-beats the words: the third, the third, the third. I saw Ezard before me as Death in the story, pale and mysterious and imperturbable.— I wonder whether on that day he really was Death's confederate? I know that he did not murder; but would not a just judge call it murder not to prevent death? It is over and no one thinks of it any more. Ezard and Galeide are dust like her who died and was ruined for their sake; instead of Happiness, on whose warm breast they violently sought to throw themselves, they embraced Death. I will tell this strange story in the following pages.

Chapter XXXII

No one thought it remarkable that Lucile and her child had died on two successive days, for of course during the cholera epidemic single deaths in any house were uncommon. Perhaps no one except myself entertained torturing thoughts about the exact course of the misfortune. It seems wonderful to me now that, in spite of that, I could associate with Ezard as usual, that I never for a moment ceased to love him, that it even did me good to be near him. The soul that looked at me out of his dark eyes had some trait of conscious innocence, which cast a triumphant spell over all who knew him. Perhaps, too, it was the irresistible force of the passion that was in him that imparted itself to others, so that no one asked how he could do this or that, but felt that he must.

I had not for a moment forgotten what I had promised Lucile, and in order to be more faithful to the dead than, unfortunately, I had been to the living, I resolved that I myself would take back to her home the coffin in which she and her child rested.

My great-grandfather proposed that Galeide should accompany me. I at once saw through his ulterior motive. It was taken for granted in our family that after a decent interval Ezard and Galeide would marry; but my great-grandfather feared they might make this interval too short and thus cause a scandal, and as he was very anxious that custom should not be disregarded, he wanted to send Galeide away for the present, thinking that the rest would take care of itself. She agreed, the more so because I supported my great-grandfather's request; for I looked forward with pleasure to wandering about with her in the Swiss mountains. Nor did Ezard object, but rather seemed to approve the plan, perhaps simply because he hoped Galeide would enjoy her stay in that beautiful country; besides, they were both so full of confidence and happy assurance in regard to their future that the word separation no longer had any meaning for them; so indissolubly did they feel themselves united.

So, as soon as the most necessary preparations were made, we went away together; Ezard accompanied us for a short distance. They said good-by to each other firmly and happily; Ezard stood beside the train till it left, and Galeide and I looked out of our compartment window.

They smiled at each other as long as Ezard was in sight;
not until we turned away from the window did I see that
she had tears in her eyes and had grown very pale. Meeting my astonished glance, she said!

" I thought I was not sad, and now I am after all. All
at once I felt so timid. How easily he might be taken ill!
I ought to have stayed at home."

I tried to dispel this alarming mood, and in order to
divert and at the same time prepare her I told her about
the people and conditions in Lucile's home, as I had seen
them years before. My description of young Gaspard,
whom I had secretly called Punch by way of disparagement,
especially amused her, and as I noticed that I went on to
tell in detail everything I still remembered about him,
whereby I really did achieve my end and restored her
cheerful humor. Lucile's mother met us at the station; she
did not look changed. A certain likeness between her face
and Lucile's probably affected Galeide, for she was pale
and silent as she walked beside the vigorous woman; the
latter, on her part, seemed at once pleased with my sister
and said pleasantly that Galeide's manner reminded her of
our mother whom she had liked so much.

She excused her son for not having also come to meet us:
it had been an inconvenient time for him. He had studied
the natural sciences and agriculture at different universities, as she told us, and had then relieved his mother of a
part of her work, and gradually acquired and cultivated
new lands, but at the same time continued his scientific
activity. Though we ourselves willingly avoided speaking
of Lucile, yet it struck me how seldom even her mother did
so. After the manner of country-dwellers, she was sparing with the expression of her feelings, and indeed with
the feelings themselves. Lucile was dead; what more was
there to say about her? She now no longer entered into the
matters of this earth, and the rest was God's affair, who
ruled over things in the other world. Our apprehension
as to how she would take the fact that Ezard himself had

not brought his wife's body home had also been entirely
unnecessary, for she understood at once that his profession
would not permit him to undertake a not insignificant
journey so unexpectedly; indeed, on the strength of that
she really seemed to respect him more than us, who could
fly up and away like butterflies if we chose, without leaving
any gap or doing any harm.

We did not see Gaspard till supper-time, when he offered
brief and rather insufficient excuses for not having greeted
us before. He at once reminded me of how little agreeable
we had found each other's society at our first meeting,
which, good-natured and humorous though it sounded, I
took at the same time to be a warning that if my conduct
were not different this time he was still the same as ever,
and would thrust his fist through the window-pane in just
the same way, if he could not otherwise carry out his will.
Galeide threw me an amused glance, in which I could read
that she thought him abominable, and this afforded me
uncommon gratification. I must admit that he was not
really ugly, but at the first glance his face almost startled
one, because it expressed such pleasure and power in
willing as is commonly seen in savage races who have no
consideration for the restrictions of society or even know
nothing of their existence. What chiefly irritated me and
spoiled even the most courteous words that fell from his
lips was that I imagined, or he really intended, them to be
a reward for my so far irreproachable conduct. He
observed Galeide closely and with unabashed openness,
which also annoyed me a little. She, however, did not seem
to notice it, and for the most part chatted with Madame
Leroy, displaying a modest amiability and grace which
were thoroughly natural to her, although they formed by
no means the most prominent feature of her character.
When she spoke to Gaspard, she did so with a certain feeling of superiority, probably due in part to the consciousness of her greater years, partly to the prejudice that I
had instilled into her mind; in general she was wont to

treat young men with condescending indifference. I could
not quite decide what impression this made on him, and
whether he might not feel offended, which I thought probable, from my knowledge of him. His behavior was imperturbable and correct, he ate with a hearty appetite, which
displeased me, as my health no longer allowed me such a
display of the alimentary instinct, but on the other hand
drank very little, which I thought discourteous and narrow,
particularly as he answered my request to make an exception on this evening with a dry, plain " no," to which he
also adhered. When Galeide and I exchanged impressions,
she was in very good spirits and full of comical ideas concerning Gaspard. The following day, however, was a
solemn one, for Lucile's interment in her native earth took
place.

The day before, Gaspard had had the coffin brought to
the house without any one's noticing it. It was now placed
in the hall and surrounded by tall yellow wax candles,
whose pale red light looked sad in the cold brightness of
day. The coffin was entirely covered with loose cut roses,
which was probably Gaspard's arrangement or doing.
Once as I was passing, while no one happened to be present, I thoughtfully regarded this most beautiful, rich-
colored summer-life upon the threshold of death, and as
the delicate but strong perfume from the many blossoms
rose about me, I was irresistibly reminded of the roses
that this same girl had once worn on her wedding-day,
probably the happiest and at the same time the most fateful of her life. How easily I could think away the years
that lay between, and take these roses to be the same that
at that time, yesterday let us say, had bloomed before the
altar and were today accompanying the daughter of the
house into the earth. I was absorbed in such strange
imaginings when Gaspard entered the hall. It was in my
mind to ask him whether these were roses from the bush
ˈer his window; but I was uncertain whether the expres-
ˈⁱs face promised a good-humored reply, and as I

did not care to lay myself open to any other I turned shortly away and went to fetch Galeide, for the coffin was now to be carried to the church, where we must attend a solemn burial service.

When I entered Galeide's room, in the middle of which she stood awaiting me, I started at her appearance, and suddenly there again stirred within me those execrable fantasies of Lucile's death-day, which I had had such difficulty in silencing, for my sister looked as if the trumpets of the day of doom were calling her to judgment, and she were now to appear before an omniscient God. In her usual manner, however, which I knew well enough, she still carried her head high and proudly, not like one who desires to defend himself, but like one who has expected and desires his condemnation, in order to throw himself voluntarily and without complaint into the abyss of hell. Nevertheless I tried to persuade myself that it was the memory of her once loved friend and of what the latter had suffered on her account, as well as the happiness that should bloom for her out of the misfortune of the dead woman, that had caused the sudden shock which now appeared in her face. I asked her whether she too would rather stay at home, but she only shook her head and together we went down the stairs leading to the hall. There stood Gaspard beside the coffin, and suddenly it seemed to me that he had been waiting for us, perhaps to see what impression the sight of the flower-covered coffin, which Galeide had not yet seen, would make on her. For it was by no means impossible that Lucile had written, if not to her mother, then to her brother about the unendurable circumstances in which she lived, and that he had conceived not only a dislike of us but even perhaps a suspicion that Galeide might at least have desired his sister's end. This idea tortured me and I observed him constantly, but could see nothing exactly hostile or distrustful in the way he regarded her; on the contrary, at times there seemed to be something like admiration and a gentle kindness in it. I could not help noticing

at the same time that the soulful expression shone from
his velvety black eyes like a planet from the bluish depths
of the night.

We now went to the church, where the coffin was again
set down and a row of candles lighted; Galeide and I stood
on one side of it, Gaspard and his mother on the other,
opposite us, so that we constantly had to see each other.
I heard nothing of what the French priest said, for the
voice of memory spoke unceasingly within me, and many
scenes passed before my eyes, of which the rose-covered
coffin in the village church was the last. Especially I
recalled that just about where the coffin now was Lucile had
once stood on Ezard's arm, I probably where I was now,
while Galeide occupied my mother's place. At intervals I
noticed Gaspard's eyes directed unceasingly at my sister,
which agitated me every time I observed it; but then when
I looked at her she seemed to have no suspicion of it, but
stared off into space as if she were in the midst of a dream.
I always felt that I could see her most impartially when I
put myself in the place of some one else who was looking
at her; and so in imagining what Gaspard might perhaps
think while he regarded her, her white face, with the eyes
that were almost never wide open, seemed to me to exhale
a wonderful sweetness, like the scent of a summer flower,
something that, ringing softly, encircles the soul like silver
strings. As I felt this, it seemed to me that it would not
be unnatural if Gaspard should fall in love with a nature
so unlike his own, whatever prejudices or suspicion of her
he might previously have had, and this idea quieted and
even pleased me immensely, as I wished him the humili-
ation to which he would infallibly subject himself. But in
his iron reserve there was something so difficult to decipher
that every moment I doubted what I had just thought of
him; in this way he constantly preoccupied me without
his intending it, which filled me more and more with a
hostile feeling toward him. Galeide certainly suspected
nothing of my thoughts in this direction, and I on the

other hand did not know the nature of the inward torment that she seemed to suffer during the service.

When it was over and the coffin was lifted to be carried to the churchyard, one of the roses which covered it fell to the ground, and Galeide, probably without any particular intention, perhaps without even being conscious of her action, stooped for it and kept it in her hand, which I noticed did not escape Gaspard's observant eye; my imagination, already active, interpreted the expression of his face to mean that he considered it a good sign that she should pick up and take with her a flower which he had cultivated and plucked (which, however, she perhaps did not even know). As is customary there, we now followed the coffin on foot to the churchyard, which was by no means beautiful nothing but a stiffly arranged garden, over-ornamented, gaudily resplendent with gay flowers, but which on account of its site might be called a truly heavenly spot. It covered the hills near the church and above the village, and one had a clear view in all directions and could see the white ribbon of the snowy mountains glistening on the horizon. The fact that the eye could thus penetrate the distance unchecked gave one a keen consciousness of the boundlessness of the world, and that, combined with the sight of the narrow graves among which we stood, oppressed the heart with premonitory sadness like a hangman. I seemed to be incarcerating here this wretched young being, before she had looked even once more at these pleasant green fields and radiant mountains, among which her happy childhood had passed. I could not repress the thought that Galeide too must feel this, and even be ashamed of the life that adorned her as she stood so young and strong beside the sad grave that had been prepared for this unfortunate. I could also perceive, for she had taken my arm, that at times a fleeting shudder ran through her and her eyes clung anxiously to the coffin; yet with her peculiar nature it might be that she was not thinking of Lucile at all but of death in general, which she did not so much fear as fairly hate, and, if one may say so, make war upon.

Now for the first time I saw some emotion in Lucile's mother, but nothing of the sort in Gaspard, who, however, made up for it by praying absorbedly and with endurance. As I myself had no faith or piety in me, I did not easily presuppose it in others, but was inclined to look on every performance of religious exercises as not much better than hypocrisy, particularly when by men whom I had to regard as educated and thinking people. Hence it irritated me to see Gaspard praying thus, although at bottom I knew well that he was thoroughly and deliberately in earnest. When I gave Galeide, who had been entirely sunk in her own thoughts, a sign to look at him, she opened her eyes wide in the most boundless amazement; for whereas in religious matters I was more what is commonly called sceptical, there was something positively heathen about her, and a natural impulse to rebel against Christian doctrines, such as the old Saxons at the time of Charlemagne may have felt. She looked at me to see what kind of an impression Gaspard's fanatical behavior made on me, and when our glances met, a bewitching, kind smile glided over her face, which all at once plunged into wholly innocent radiance the countenance that a few hours before had seemed to me frightfully Medusa-like and fateful. I never saw her smile again like that. It reminded me of the sun shining on the just and the unjust; however foolish or mistaken she might consider anything, she had less censure and ridicule for it than pity or modest amazement.

When the day was over, it seemed as if a stone had been lifted from Galeide's heart; laughter issued from her breast as one who has been buried alive, and whose coffin has been opened in time to save him, returns from his dark cage into the light; without cause it constantly gurgled about us, as if it never tired of hearing itself and rejoicing in its salvation. When we were alone she laughed at Gaspard, and had so many delightfully funny things to say about him that I wondered how she could have seen all that in so short a time, and without having observed him at all. Sometimes she boldly laughed in his face, and I think he saw very well that she was by no means much taken with him. But that was far from disturbing his calm and assurance; he continued to look at her whenever he could, so that I often thought it must annoy her.

Now that our duty was fulfilled, we might properly have continued our journey, for we intended to go to Geneva, where Galeide was to cancel her engagements with the orchestra, and at the same time take leave of old friends. Madame Leroy, however, unexpectedly pressed us so urgently to prolong our visit, that we could not but concede a few days. For my part, I was content to remain as long as possible near the mountains, the friends of my youth, and only feared that Galeide, who had after all not left home gladly, might desire a speedy return. But she agreed to stay without ado, and did not even betray especial longing for home, so that, as often before, she seemed to me a very soulless Undine. Whether it was the familiar voice of divine nature that lured and held her in that privileged country, or whether something else had already thrown its fateful chain about her soul, I do not know. So we remained, to our ruin.

SUMMARY OF CHAPTER XXXIII

[ALL at once Galeide noticed Gaspard's eyes, and from this time on he seemed to exercise a strange fascination over her, although she protested that she found him as detestable as before.]

CHAPTER XXXIV

NOTHING but a slight inward uneasiness, which I could scarcely call a suspicion, clouded these glorious days for me. But suddenly everything changed, just as sometimes in nature, after days of the bluest sky and without warn-

ing, we wake one morning to find the landscape all around
dull and gray.   Galeide laughed no longer, her eyes no
longer shone with inward happiness and she no longer
danced, although there was no visible reason for a change
in her demeanor.   Nor was it that she had exhausted herself in pleasure, and was now resting in the winter sleep of
everyday life.   No, from somewhere a shadow or a frost
must have fallen on her soul; and that was really the case,
as I was soon to learn.

One evening at a late hour I had been walking up and
down in the garden, thinking every one else in the house
had gone to rest.   As I noticed a light in Galeide's room,
however, I knocked at her door to say good night to her
before I went to bed myself.   As I entered, she was walking restlessly up and down in the rather large room, as if
pursued by some evil spirit, whose suspected nearness
frightened her into motion whenever she tried to stand
still.   My entrance did not stop her, and my impression
was the stranger because she wore soft shoes in which
she trod noiselessly back and forth, and which she had
perhaps put on so as not to disturb any one, or more probably because she was all ready to go to bed, for her hair
hung loose down her back.   I waited for her to explain her
incomprehensible behavior, which she suddenly did entirely of her own accord, standing at one end of the room
and saying with a horrified glance at me:

"I am glad you have come, Ludolf, for I can't bear it
any longer.   I must tell you everything now, or I shall
come to grief.   I cannot go on any longer."

After this introduction I was prepared for something
important and my heart began to beat anxiously; it was
curious that while I was exceedingly astonished by what
came then, I can declare that I had expected nothing else.

"You know," she said, "how I was going to fall in
love with Gaspard for fun?   Well, now I love him in
earnest."   But as soon as she had said it she took back
her words and said: "No, I don't love him at all.   You

know yourself that I love Ezard and can never, never, never love another. I swear to you that I love Ezard, that I feel toward him just as I have always felt since I first loved him. This is something different; Gaspard has fascinated me. I don't know how, nor how such a thing can be possible at all, but it is so, he has bewitched and enchanted me, it can't be anything else. I can't help myself any more."

She had now come quite close to me and sat down opposite me, looking urgently into my eyes; I had never before seen her so pathetically helpless. I had no other feeling but that a terrible bolt had fallen from the hand of fate; for, although I could not explain the fact that Galeide loved Punch, yet I saw clearly the havoc it had already accomplished. Nevertheless I tried to pull myself together and betrayed no fright, but began to talk to her with good-humored ridicule, because she seemed to need that most of all. She chimed in at once, smiling humbly and hopefully, like a sick person who swallows a bitter medicine which he expects to cure him, and then went on talking more quietly and confidentially, as if a stone had been taken from her heart and a seal from her lips.

"Yes, I know all that. What is he beside Ezard? I should never have noticed him if his eyes had not fascinated me with their persistent mysterious gaze. And you must say they are beautiful, such burning stars of eyes! He is self-willed and capricious and domineering, just like a woman; you see, I know all that, I am not blinded. But as he is, he is unique and incomparable. And the main thing is, that there is something in him that bewitches me. I have to watch him continually when he is present, and to think of him when he is not; that was his design, and I should like to spoil it for him, but I cannot."

Thus she went on talking, her face deathly pale, her eyes wide open and dreaming, like a somnambulist, and I could not disguise to myself the fact that she was caught hand and foot in the madness of love, even though she would

not admit it to herself.   At the same time I thought it
could not be anything but an aberration of her imagination, which must pass, and so I told her.   She seemed to
be highly delighted at that; she corroborated my opinion
and even said that she herself knew it must be so and was
obliged to laugh aloud sometimes when she thought with
what amused feelings she would later look back on this
misfortune.   At that moment we heard several lingering
tones of a flute, a fragment of a folksong with a very striking melody that had something excessively sad and yearning about it.   It could only be Gaspard, for he played the
flute, with no particular skill, it is true, but with great
feeling and grace, and he felt free to do so at any hour;
he must now be sitting with his instrument at an open
window, we could hear it so plainly.   Scarcely had we
heard these sounds when the confident expression vanished
from Galeide's face; she listened with her whole soul and
shrank within herself as if in fear.

"Do you hear?" she said.   "Now he knows that I am
still awake and is playing for me.   All day long he wouldn't
for the world say a kind word to me, and at night he takes
his flute and sings at my heart so that I can't defend
myself at all.   He has never told me so, but I know that
every tone is for me, and know what it means.   Why does
he do that?   Why does he not speak, like any other man?
Then I should laugh at him, but with his flute he fasci-
nates me."

I could hardly master my wrath any longer and said:
"Every tone means something to me too, namely, that he
is an unpolished, extremely disagreeable fellow, who would
show you much more attention by putting his head on his
pillow at midnight and going to sleep, instead of bothering
you with his wretched playing."

As in the meantime the flute had done its song, Galeide
was amused at my remark, agreed entirely, and said that
the flute really was to blame for everything.   She felt much
better now, she would go to sleep, and I must do the same

and not be cross with her for having troubled me with this foolish affair.

[Soon Galeide realized that her love for Ezard was gone, and was beside herself. Ludolf was powerless to aid her, and Galeide resolved to take refuge with Ezard, feeling that he could help her.]

Chapter XXXV

Now when we told our hosts of our intention to leave, without giving any sufficient reason, it must inevitably seem to Gaspard that it was due to some caprice of Galeide's, and that she thus wanted to show him that she did not love him, or wished to have nothing to do with him otherwise. Her brilliant and distinctive personality, her reputation as a musician, and his love may well have made him think of her as on a tremendously high and inaccessible plane, so that he would not find it unnatural for her to show a certain haughtiness in her treatment of a young Swiss agriculturist. This he had to be sure determined to overcome, which bore witness to his liking for the rare and unusual and to his invincible will, and this had perhaps pleased Galeide more than anything else about him. But now, with all his presumption, he could not disguise from himself the fact that he had suffered a serious defeat, and his manner on the last evening showed this in perhaps a very charming but quite unmanly and undignified way. He sat at the table, very pale and gloomy, ate nothing, merely gulping down a few morsels, did not speak unless directly addressed (from which Galeide could not refrain), in short he sulked like a coquette that is slowly torturing her unhappy lover to death by a method of her own devising. It was perhaps rendered pardonable by the fact that he himself suffered so visibly that his lips twitched with inward weeping when he spoke to Galeide, and his eyes resembled two beautiful, mournful stars, which are alone in immeasurable space and full of yearning. I saw clearly how his appearance tortured and delighted Galeide, and therefore hurried our separation, glad that we were not to see Gaspard again the following morning; for in his irritation he had announced that he would be busy at the time of our departure. Then we began to speak of seeing one another again,— of which to be sure I did not think seriously for a moment,— of the Leroys returning our visit, and in this connection we described exactly where we lived. Here Gaspard suddenly turned to Galeide and said with special emphasis:

"It is not necessary to tell me that; I shall find you wherever you are."

I tried to obliterate the impression these words made by giving them a humorous turn, but was myself not a little startled, particularly when I noticed how Galeide stared at the monster half malevolently, half anxiously, as if the conclusion of the whole matter depended on him, and she must wait like a tethered sheep at pasture to see whether the lightning struck her or not.

Between night and dawn I was awakened by Gaspard's flute, and at once recognized that melancholy melody that I had once heard him play. That was his farewell which he would not have been able to express unlike any one else with his lips and at a time when it would have been opportune. It sounded sweet, I will not deny, as if the night herself were singing, before she turns from the beautiful sun-youth whose warm heart she would much rather be going to meet. The music broke off abruptly, and immediately after I heard Gaspard leave the house; he was probably going out to the fields, as he had said. I could not go to sleep again, tossed about in unpleasant thought, and began the journey in a gloomy mood, as I was in despair in any case at the prospect of leaving behind me the mountains, the lake, and everything I loved. I could see that Galeide had been crying, for which the awful lamentation of the flute was of course responsible, about which, by the way, we did not exchange a word. As she sat opposite me in the train, so quiet and sad, I could not refrain from asking whether she were perhaps thinking of Punch, whereas she had far better begin at once to forget him.

She smiled at me and said: " It is so hard, it is so hard," convulsively clasping her hands several times, as if she were trying with body and soul to begin the good work. From time to time she apologized for not being more entertaining, and declared that she wanted to make up for everything just as soon as she was quite herself; after she had once seen Ezard again.

" Do you know," she said, with a roving, groping glance into space, " I can't remember how he looks. But I think that as soon as I see him, something like a bolt or a tempest will come and completely wipe out the miserable chaos of my imagination, so that everything can be again as it was before."

The nearer we came to our goal, the more excited did she become; it seemed as if she were afraid of the moment that should bring her either release or eternal damnation. When we expect something very great and definite of an event, it usually slips by without making any impression, which may be partly because the mind, overwrought by its anxious hope, relaxes its tension and collapses when what it has hoped for really comes and touches it. This seemed to be Galeide's case, when we came into the station, got out, and saw Ezard awaiting us. He, of course, felt nothing but high confidence and the certainty of happiness, and seemed glad and radiant, but simple and not in the least prepared for the fateful and mighty part that my sister expected of him. I read in her face that she did not feel anything, and that this lack of sensation frightened her. Ezard, however, was so entirely without suspicion that at first he saw absolutely no lack of love in her strikingly peculiar manner, while she longed for nothing so much as to pour out her heart to him. Although she had written him about the affair, yet at first he could not reconcile himself to the fact that she was in earnest, which had not

CHAPTER XXXVI

GRADUALLY a very satisfactory, trustful relationship did grow up again between Ezard and Galeide, differing from the former one only in that tempestuous passion was lacking; for Ezard suppressed his, more from tenderness than from pride, and Galeide no longer felt it, or, as it sometimes seemed to me, dared not feel it when it came over her. But their unalterable, convinced affection and the boundless esteem with which they looked up to each other, although not as ecstatic as before, were yet fully as comforting, and, above all, inspired confidence that these were permanent and indestructible, after all. Of her own accord Galeide suggested that the marriage should take place sooner than had originally been intended. Under the existing circumstances they dispensed with a religious ceremony, and our great-grandfather was to hear nothing of their plans until everything was ready and settled.

This prospect seemed to make Ezard younger and stronger. It by no means escaped him that in making this proposal Galeide had been moved less by her own longing than by the desire to anticipate his wish, and that she hoped especially that their old relation might be most rapidly and completely reëstablished when once they were man and wife. Ezard too was confident of this; he was firmly convinced that when once he had Galeide entirely to himself his love would be able to destroy and obliterate everything alien and morbid. He no longer repressed his feelings and his smothered passion flamed up joyously and so filled him with light that in radiant beauty he again resembled what he had formerly been, when, wanton but enraptured, he snatched the blossoms of his happiness from the abyss. This influenced Galeide too; for although she had understood and admired the considerate magnanimity with which he had renounced and restrained his feeling, yet she had perhaps needed a wilder, less considerate way that would have carried her away like a hurricane without

asking whether it was agreeable to her.   With hope he
regained the desire and the strength to do this.   He even
began to speak frequently of Gaspard: he should be glad
to see him again and had never been angry with him, for
it was only natural that every one who knew Galeide should
love her; as a boy Gaspard had pleased him very much,
and it was possible that Gaspard even deserved Galeide
more than he himself, if it were not that the superior power
of his love gave him the greatest claim to her.   He had
really considered whether he should renounce Galeide, so
that she might follow her imagination, caprice, love, or
whatever it was; for she might have been happy after all,
there was so much strength, originality, and soundness in
her nature.   (The soundness has gone to the devil, I
thought.)   But, much as he had wrestled with himself, he
had not been able to bring himself to do it; he was still
too young, after all, to be able to live and to see her if she
were not his, and the thought that some one else was to
her what he had once been would make not only living
but also dying impossible to him; unless he could take her
down with him into the earth, and that was probably what
he would do in such a case.

Galeide gazed at him with her very happiest and most
innocent expression and said: "Yes, yes, that is what you
would have to do!   If I should love some one else, then
you would have to kill me, so that I should not become
detestable to myself and that nothing might harm our love.
But it would be too dreadful if I should have to love some
one else."

She shuddered as she spoke these words, at which, however, Ezard, in his wonderful feeling of security, took no
offense, but drew her to him and said merrily: "Yes,
then I will kill you and you shall kill me.   But I shall not
let it come to that.   I will show you whom you must love —
me, me, me, to the end of your days!"

"Yes, you, you, you to the end of my days," repeated
Galeide radiantly, and now they again stood together like

two whom not chance but the selecting hand of all-wise Nature has placed inseparable side by side.

About this time Galeide played in a charity concert, for which she had prepared very thoroughly, as she was now more active again; the undivided success which she achieved was well deserved. The concert was given in the church, a circumstance which forbade all theatrical features, finery, and loud applause. Childishly as my sister enjoyed any demonstration of appreciation, yet she could entirely dispense with it at those moments when her soul was fully absorbed in her art. She had no idea how raptly the audience listened to her playing; moreover, all eyes were fixed with pleasure on the softly ingratiating lines of her charming figure. Ezard, Grandfather, and I were in the church; it struck me that people greeted us and made room for us with marked respect, and it filled me with gratification that we had regained that esteem. Though this was due to Ezard above all, yet Galeide too had her share in it, who had formerly brought on herself the criticism and love of scandal of the very people whose hearts she was now stirring with her lovely art.

[Galeide received a letter from Gaspard, and realized at once that she could not shake off his power over her. Ludolf went to fetch Ezard.]

Ezard was far more frightened than I had expected. All the color left his face, and I was now all at once convinced, like Galeide, that everything was really lost. We walked together the short distance to our house in silence. When we entered the music room, which was still dark as I had left it, Galeide picked herself up from the rug where she must have been lying, flew to Ezard, drew him to a chair, knelt beside him, and pressed close to him. She said nothing, except that she rapidly repeated his name several times, like an exorcism.

After awhile Ezard said: "Galeide, I cannot give you up to some one else. I cannot. Don't ask me, I cannot."

She replied, "I don't want you to! That is why I sent for you, so that you should not leave me. Hold me tight! Don't let me go! I am so afraid!"

"Oh, Galeide," he said in a voice that seemed to be heavy with tears, "can you really love another? It can't be possible! You are forgetting your Ezard! It is not possible."

At that Galeide groaned aloud and cried, "I don't know whether it is love, or what it is, but I cannot do anything to hurt him. Oh, kill me, Ezard, help me and kill me!"

He took hold of her by the shoulders and looked long into her face, then he let his arms drop and said: "Wretch that I am, I can't do that either. I cannot kill you!"

Galeide pressed closer to him and said in a low voice, "But if you saw me beside him, could you then? Yes, then you could!"

While he kept horrified silence, I went up to them, for I shuddered at this conversation, and said: "You always think only of yourselves. Consider us too. Galeide, you must control your madness." "Yes," she said humbly, "that is what I ought to do, but feel that I cannot. I know myself too well; it might come to pass that I should marry him. Do you want to live to see such a shameful ending? Look, Ezard, and even if I loved some one else ever so much, you would still be to me the noblest of all, and you shall not have to suffer anything low through me. If I should die, you could bear that, and you, Ludolf. I am less concerned for you than for Grandfather. He ought not to have lived to see this."

We sat together dumbly for a time in the dark. Midnight had passed when I went, leaving the two still in the room. Much later I heard Galeide go to her room. I felt relieved when I saw her again next morning, for all night fear had lain on my breast that I should never again see her alive.

CHAPTER XXXVII

In regard to Gaspard, I thought the wisest thing was to do nothing; his letter was not answered, from which he might have concluded that he was not exactly welcome; if we had asked him not to come, that would perhaps have caused him — contrary and headstrong as he was — to hasten his visit all the more. A change took place in Ezard's behavior: after that evening he did not come to our house any more; he could not bear to see Galeide in her present state. Galeide, who was in constant anxiety about him, urged me to visit him as much as possible, so that he should not be alone, which I did willingly, the more so as he seemed to be glad of my society. Frequently I stayed the night with him, for the nights were the most unendurable time, when he could not sleep or had a dream, night after night the same, which I will now relate. He dreamt that two spirits, my father's and his, came in white robes through the closed door into his room, and that although frozen with horror he sat up and asked: "Whom are you seeking?" Whereupon they both answered at once, softly but distinctly and audibly: "The third!"

When Ezard told me this, an icy terror took hold of me, and I said with an effort, "And then Lucile comes?"

But Ezard shook his head and looked at me with burning, black eyes. "No," he said, "Lucile does not come. She was not the right one." It was clear to me what thoughts had given rise to this dream; but at that moment I felt as if Fate herself had stepped between us, invisible as a spirit, and was looking down on us with a gaze from which we could not escape.

Several days passed, during which I was in hourly expectation that Gaspard would appear accompanied by some unnerving omens. But reality can dispense with the lightning-flash and the crash of thunder without which our imagination cannot picture any significant event, for it is always certain of its impression, just because it is real.

Gaspard came on a day when for the first time I had entirely
forgotten him, on a day when Galeide was again to play
in a concert. The first concert had been so much enjoyed
that a repetition of it was desired, which took the more
that a charitable purpose could again be combined with it.
Galeide had consented. When the appointed afternoon
arrived, a carriage was sent for her early: just as I was
about to set out for the church on foot, Gaspard came.
Surprise almost overcame my annoyance; I welcomed him
none too pleasantly nevertheless, but could not do otherwise than tell him whither I was bound and ask him whether
he cared to accompany me. So we walked together and
while Gaspard irritated me both with his French and his
superior wisdom, I was anxiously trying to think what
course I must adopt to make him as harmless as possible
to Galeide.

In the church I at once saw Ezard, who wanted to hear
Galeide, although he could no longer bear to look at her.
I should gladly have avoided him, but as he had recognized
me, he made his way to me through the crowd, and did not
catch sight of Gaspard until he stood directly in front of us.
They greeted each other, while each doubtless had feelings
of hatred to master, Ezard on Galeide's and Gaspard on
his sister's account. But I thought I noticed that they
were pleased with each other in spite of that, and when I
tried to see Gaspard with Ezard's eyes he appeared less
obnoxious to me too. His behavior was as peculiar as
ever; at every moment he presented a finished picture
of his own personality. We could see Galeide from where
we sat by turning round in an uncomfortable position.
Gaspard found this attitude at once, assumed it, and
regarded my sister uninterruptedly — through two pairs
of glasses. He did not utter a word about the music, and
paid not the slightest attention to Ezard and me, but, judg-
ing by the emotional play of his features, was occupied
with fantastic dreams and plans; it struck me how entertaining and even charming it was to watch his face, and

suddenly I could understand how one might be steadily moved by the desire and the impulse to take possession of this capricious soul, so as to be able constantly to enjoy its odd ways.   When he smiled, such an unexpected charm appeared in his dark face that one was easily led to do this or that so that this sunrise-spectacle might be repeated, especially any one who had such an insatiable, childishly avaricious heart as Galeide, who would have liked best to carry away in her pocket any mountain or lake that pleased her.   I felt as if I positively must hide Gaspard, cover him up, in short make him invisible in some way, so that Galeide should not see him.

When the concert was over I hoped to take him out a side door unnoticed in the crowd, without knowing, to be sure, what I should do with him afterward.   But Galeide happened down into the nave, perhaps to look for Ezard, and suddenly she came toward us.   She did not sink down as if struck by lightning, neither did she sway nor change color, for she was always best able to control herself when she was unexpectedly very violently agitated.   She nodded to us and shook hands with Gaspard; they smiled at each other like two people who have an innocent secret and are giving each other some sign in regard to it.   Then, however, Galeide turned quickly to Ezard, asked him to take her to her carriage, and left us with a bow.   Thus Gaspard was left to me, and he seemed to take it as a matter of course that I should offer him our hospitality, which, indeed, I could not well have avoided without giving him a formal explanation.   It did seem to have struck him that Galeide had turned from us so abruptly and asked Ezard's escort; his face had changed in an instant, like a valley after the sun has sunk behind the mountains.   Distress was so abundantly stamped upon it that he looked not only sad but ill, and again I could imagine how any one who had the power to do so must be tempted to coax the golden laughter out again from behind the clouds.   As soon as we got home I went at once to Galeide, who was alone in her room, and asked her what was to be done now, and whether I should frankly tell Gaspard everything, so that he should leave us. But she vehemently made me promise not to do anything like that.

"If you should tell him everything," she said, "he would hate me, and I cannot bear that. Tell him after I am dead." But directly afterward she changed her mind and said: "I should gladly tell him everything and ask him whether he hated me or whether he still loved me in spite of it. Yes, that is what I should like to do, tell him how much I love him and then die. But how could I treat Ezard so? Don't leave me alone with him for a moment, do you hear, so that my heart cannot forget itself."

I asked whether it would not be better for her not to see him at all; for that evening at any rate she could easily pretend a slight indisposition, so that she would not have to come to supper. She said yes, she would do that; but I could see how hard it was for her to hurt her darling so, and I doubted whether she would stand it.

While Gaspard, in spite of his increasing sadness, talked very charmingly to my great-grandfather, so that the latter was captivated with him, I was listening full of disquietude to every sound; for I had a suspicion that Galeide would appear after all, and did not know how I should manage to get Gaspard out of the way first. He made no move to withdraw, but listened as I did, to hear whether a light step would not announce Galeide. And as I had thought, Geleide finally yielded to the urgings of her wayward heart. Suddenly she stood bright and glowing in the doorway, looking at us as if to say: "Here I am after all; I couldn't help it." When she came nearer, we saw that she had a black and white spotted kitten on her arm; she said it must have crept into the house, she had found it in her room and meant to keep it now. She held the soft creature pressed to her breast, so that it could nestle its little head against her throat; she sat down in a chair at some distance from us and began to play with the animal, admiring and

THE ABDUCTION OF PROMETHEUS

THE ABDUCTION OF PROMETHEUS

From an Etching by Max Klinger

PERMISSION AMSLER & RUTHARDT BERLIN

praising its big, round eyes, its delicate paws, and everything about it.

Gaspard had not moved nor said a word when Galeide came into the room, but he watched her incessantly in his own peculiar manner with steady ardor, which, by the way, I well understood, for Galeide, conscious perhaps that she had succumbed in the struggle with her love, looked more humble, lovely, and childishly helpless than I had ever seen her, but at the same time full of human warmth and strength, just because it was the passion in her that had conquered her. She did not once look over at Gaspard, yet she felt the power of his glance so strongly that her hands suddenly ceased their play and the cat was able to escape. Gaspard picked her up and handled her rather clumsily with his childlike fists, which was droll and not unattractive, especially as his dark head contrasted so splendidly with the cat's white fur. Galeide had had to look at him now, and a heartily amused laugh immediately transfigured her whole face. And now she could not much longer refrain from addressing him and said: "You mustn't torment my cat, Monsieur Leroy!" He answered Galeide in an extremely graceful and touching way: "I am not tormenting it; I want to ask it what it does to make you so fond of it."

He said these words in German, and as his voice always took on a hesitating, particularly soft tone when he spoke this unaccustomed language, which he secretly loved on Galeide's account, their own charming effect was heightened. I could not help feeling kindly toward him at that moment, and Galeide — she was so bewitched by the pleading music of his little lament, that I should not have been surprised to see her suddenly at his feet. At any rate her soul knelt there, and one could almost see it flying bodily over to him from her eyes and her half open, trembling lips. Without the slightest connection with the previous conversation she suddenly said:

"What shall I do for you? Shall I tell you a fairy story? Shall I accompany your flute? Shall I play the violin?"

Gaspard nodded; the kitten slipped away again and made off through the open window.

"Then I will play, if you like," said Galeide rising.

We went up to the music room on the floor above, only our great-grandfather stayed downstairs to listen from there. Gaspard had scarcely become conscious again of his power over Galeide, when he made use of it like a capricious girl to torment her and at the same time punish her, as it were, for having resisted it so long. Secretly he was trembling at once with happiness and with fear that the crown of life might yet escape him; but distinctly as one could see the most yearning love vibrating in his black eyes, yet full of defiance and vanity he assumed an entirely different appearance, and grumbled to Galeide that he hated this or that piece, and that he had heard enough violin music that day any way and was tired of it.

"But what shall I do then?" asked Galeide patiently.

"Sing something," said the wretch, as if it were a matter of course that she would eat spiders if he should so command; and when she modestly objected that she was not a singer, he said in the same softly domineering voice: "Please sing."

While I was deliberating whether I might not take him by the collar and throttle him on the spot, Galeide hunted among her music until she had found something to sing, and sat down at the piano to accompany herself. But her voice broke at the first notes, probably because she was inwardly much too excited, and she stopped and said: "I cannot."

"Then why do you say that you will do anything I want?" insisted the monster.

"Try me," answered Galeide. "Tell me what you want! Shall I jump out of the window?" She had turned the piano stool so that she sat directly opposite him and was looking full into his face. He sat there motionless like a sluggard on whom a horn of plenty is showering the sweetest things, and who keeps perfectly still so as not to dispel the beautiful miracle. "Shall I?" asked Galeide once more, softly.

He nodded and said his half sung: "Oui, Mademoiselle."

She rose immediately and went toward the nearest window; all were open, as it was a very warm night. Gaspard watched her with a quiet smile, and may have thought: "How will she get out of her noose now? I'll let her dangle a little first." I, on the contrary, felt my senses leaving me, I saw everything and still did not see it, knew what was coming and still did not grasp it.

In a moment she had swung herself up onto the window-sill and stood there tall and free in the high frame. Then she laughed softly and lightly, a kind, ringing little laugh such as she often gave when she had some roguery in mind. Yes, she was laughing at him, at Punch; but what was it costing her? All her splendid young life, never to be recalled! For the pleasant, silvery peal of her voice had not died away when she lay dead among the lily blossoms in the bed before our house.

I have never been able to realize that she is actually wholly gone from the earth, that she is not to be found somewhere deep in the mountain or in a desert on the heights. Even now when I take a solitary walk along the slope of the mountain at the edge of the woods it often seems to me that she must suddenly step out from among the trees with her radiant face and hold out her soft, strong hands to me. Or at least her voice must answer from somewhere if I called her by name: Galeide! Good little Galeide!

CHAPTER XXXVIII (CONDENSED)

EZARD had been wandering about in our garden that evening; love and jealousy had probably driven him thither, where he was near her without disturbing or in any way influencing her decisions. And now she was his again; cold and pale and soulless, she had yet faithfully come back to him. He now sat beside her for hours, his head nestling against her breast, and no one thought of trying to take him away. At times he raised himself, looked at her long, and sadly shook his head as if he still could not grasp it. And there was surely reason for one who had seen and lived through everything with her from the beginning to lapse into forgetfulness of all other things and only keep one question on his lips: is it possible? is it possible?

My great-grandfather, who on that evening had waited for the tones of the violin, which he was never again to hear in his life, had been surprised by the event wholly without preparation or defense. Although he was already about ninety-five, yet his nature had retained its peculiar tenacity so completely that his bearing on this unnerving occasion was point for point exactly as one would have had to determine it from his conduct in earlier days. His blind love triumphed altogether over all his principles and his firm convictions. He would not have endured the most sparing censure of Galeide; he soon fitted her out as a saint, to which title she certainly would have made no claim and scarcely might have rightly or justly done so. But still he had pitched too suddenly from the height of his extravagant hopes. All at once his forces gave way like the man in the fairy tale, who without knowing it had wandered about for a hundred years in the world and then on seeing the graves of his loved ones suddenly crumbled into a little heap of ashes. A few months after Galeide's death he died, conscious and composed, compelling to the last the admiration we so gladly pay to a fully developed, individual character.

After my great-grandfather's death Ezard and Harreken moved into our house. Eva had left our town with her child, so as to be near her family, not so much because she longed to go away from us to them, as because she thought she ought to remove herself from the Ursleu sphere of influence. Anna Elisabeth in particular had advised her to do this. " Once and for all," she had said, " the Olethurms and the Ursleus are a bad combination." And did

Eva want to see her child and Harreken make a couple?
Eva went; I believe partly because she did not wish to
remain near Ezard, now that both he and she were free.
We continued to correspond, but I never saw her again,
neither her nor her child, fair Heileke.

Our position in our native city was all that we could have
desired. People treated us with respect, and did not take
it amiss that we kept as remote as possible from intercourse
with other people. Following his father's example, Ezard
had presented the city with that part of his fortune that
was in the water-works, so that only their indebtedness
to the Norwegian remained to be paid. The rest of Ezard's
fortune was not large at the time of Galeide's and grandfather's death; but his untiring activity as an attorney,
which he did not give up, although an honorable municipal
post was offered him, made it possible for him to save considerable sums every year. That was the only thing in life
for which he still showed interest. He often said that it
was his fixed endeavor to leave his son an ample fortune.
Not that he wished thus to provide him with the opportunity to be idle, on the contrary, he hoped by force of
example to keep the boy's energy and love of work active.
It was his opinion, however, that lasting and genuine happiness can only be developed on the basis of assured property. It would be best if this property consisted of land,
from which the owner himself would have to wrest profit
with exertion and labor. He always regretted that he could
not live as a farmer among his fields. He knew well, however, that much money often proved a misfortune to men
and dragged them down, but he could not provide for his
son against the incalculable: he would give him what he
could: the training of the fine and useful qualities that
nature had bestowed upon him, and the means of making
good use of them in life.

In conformity with this Harre grew up. He had a
gentle disposition and was inclined to dream; but it was
well for him that he had a drop of alien blood in him, as

I have often said, for it was due to this that he had more sense of order, moderation, and self-limitation in his demands on life than the nature of his ancestors on the paternal side had given him. We took particular care to develop these qualities, and the older he grew the more did the two sides of his nature fuse in beneficial harmony, so that he inspired confidence that he would never let himself be diverted from any path he had once entered, and would never choose any but one which, though not often traversed, would certainly lead to an honorable goal.

Ezard was fifty years old when he died of the evil complications of a cold, which his love of wandering about in all kinds of wind and weather had brought upon him.

As he lay dead before me he seemed to have grown younger; his beauty was more exalted than in life, when the warm human soul had animated it. What was it in him that had attracted all people and bound them to him? Beside his good and splendid deeds there were others which one would have to censure wholly, indeed, to call criminal. But that does not determine what we feel for a man. Some mystery remains in the fact that one man is loved so much and another, who seems to resemble him in all qualities, so little. A man is a favorite with men if he is nature's favorite, created by her under a fortunate constellation. Nature had offered Ezard, like all her favorites, happiness and unhappiness, distributing them equally, and early took him from the earth; for she desires that what has once existed in perfection shall never decay but, like the heroes of the antique world, be set among the stars while still young, where they can enjoy their immortality in beauty and strength; thus she lets her noblest creation die, so that earthly transitoriness may not affect it. Ezard lay on the bier like a triumphant conqueror, whom the immortals call to their side because his work on earth is done. To think of him does not soften but strengthens and invigorates me. That is the man I should like to have been! Even to have known him is good; to have loved him I consider my most precious remembrance.

Chapter XXXIX (Condensed)

Before I close the book of my life I wish to speak once more of the unfortunate destroyer Gaspard. From the evening when Galeide died, my anger against him had cooled. For what he had to suffer until he had learned all the causes of this calamity would have been enough to disarm the bitterest enemy of his hate. His reticence and habit of living entirely to himself like an oyster in its shell, which no one can open except by force, threw him altogether on his own resources and no one could help or comfort him. Sometimes the lonely soul in his black eyes seemed to wail for loving sympathy; but no one knew how to reach him and he could not teach us.

For a long time we heard nothing of him. Then, several years afterward, I learned that he had entered a monastery at home. I thought that a venerable old cloister with echoing arches and mysterious passages was the proper lair for such a misanthropic marmot, for there it could live and whistle and hibernate as long as it liked, amid the most indescribable criss-cross dreams, and yielding to my old affection for the Swiss mountains, I set out to visit him. I had expected to speak to him of Galeide, but her name refused to cross my lips when he sat facing me in his cowl, looking like a monk of the Middle Ages with his gloomy, visionary eyes. So we talked of other things relating to religion and monastic life, and he expressed himself by no means fanatically, but simply and sensibly. What I had not dared to do, that is to speak of Galeide, he finally did without embarrassment, asking me into whose possession her violin had come and whether he could not obtain it.

I said that it was hanging on the wall in my room and was dear to me, but that I would give it to him; for I believed that if I could ask Galeide she would assent.

I sent him the violin as soon as I reached home again, and added a handful of roses from Galeide's grave. He never answered me; but I have always imagined that the violin hangs beside the window at which we sat when I visited him, and where the breeze that blows in from the garden can play with it; that sometimes, when he knows that no one can hear him, he takes it timidly and firmly in his arms and draws the oddest sounds from the strings with his clumsy, brown fingers, and that finally, some still night, he will seize and break it (at which he will be more successful), so that no one else can sing with it when he is dead.

Many have taken me for a pious or else a foolish man for having accepted the Catholic faith and entered a monastery. In reality, however, neither that confession nor religion in general had a jot to do with it. The system and the peace within these walls, where the glimmer of my beloved Alps falls, attracted me and suit me. The most important thing is that I am buried in this isolation like a dead man in his grave; if once the madness to live should seize me, whose glory smiles upon the patient sufferer even amid the pains it causes him, I should be held by the fetter with which I have chained myself. And thus I desire it to be. For what is man's life? Like the raindrops that fall from heaven to the earth we traverse our span of time, driven hither and thither by the wind of fate. Wind and fate have their unalterable laws, according to which they move; but what does the raindrop that they sweep before them know of these laws? It rushes through the air with the others until it can filter through the sand. But heaven gathers them all to her again and pours them out once more; and gathers and pours them again and again, always the same and yet different.

But I, Ludolf Ursleu, have enough of life. If I might last, I should like to look down on the hosts of men with a friendly eye, like a star, seeing and knowing, unattainably distant. I do not long for human eternities. And yet — if as a little boy I could run once more through our blooming garden hand in hand with Galeide to meet our laughing mother — would I not live through a hundred years of sorrow for the sake of that one moment? Oh hush, my soul; it is over.

MIDNIGHT *

By RICARDA HUCH.

To this grave of mine
Come not in the morning,
Come on ways of darkness,
Dearest, by the dim moonshine.

For when through the skies
Bells are tolling midnight,
From my earthly prison
To the lovely air I rise.

In my death-dress white
On my grave I linger,
Watch the stars and measure
Time's placid tread at night.

Come and have no fear!
Can you still give kisses?
I forgot them never
While I slept the winters drear.

Kiss me hard and long.
In the east already
Sings the morning sunlight
—Lack-a-day!—its joyful song.

You were mine again!
Go and taste life's sweetness!—
I in deep, deep darkness
Sleep once more with pain.

---

* Translator: Margarete Münsterberg.

[485]